THE BIRDWATCHER

○ SILVER LINK RAILWAY ANTHOLOGIES ○

THE BIRDWATCHER

and other tales from the footplate

○ Stan Wilson ○

• CHILLERS, THRILLERS AND ECCENTRICS •
from
The NOSTALGIA *Collection*

To the memory of two marvellous people whose capacity for
encouraging new talent was inexhaustible:
Herbert Smith, late producer of the North Region of the BBC
and
Brian Redhead, late Editor of the *Manchester Evening News*.

Also in celebration of my friendship since childhood with
Wallace Chamberlain, whose company is always golden.

A Silver Link book
from
The NOSTALGIA *Collection*

© Stan Wilson 1995 and 2002

First published as *Steaming Eccentrics* in August 1995
This edition first published 2002

British Library Cataloguing in Publication Data

A catalogue record for this book is available from the British Library.

ISBN 1 85794 153 5

Silver Link Publishing Ltd
The Trundle
Ringstead Road
Great Addington
Kettering
Northants NN14 4BW

Tel/Fax: 01536 330588
email: sales@nostalgiacollection.com
Website: www.nostalgiacollection.com

Printed and bound in Great Britain

Contents

Preface

No period of British industrial history has been quite so thoroughly documented as the railway Steam Age. In countless books and magazines published over the years, every railway line, locomotive and company livery, every gauge, gradient and goods wagon along with every station, siding and signal is listed somewhere. And yet, in this enormous catalogue of information, hardly any reference is made to the colourful characters who manned the locomotives. It is to rectify this omission that I offer the following stories.

This book deals not with the typical men of the Iron Road who put up with their erratic hours and demanding labour with a stoic resignation rarely equalled, but with the more outrageously bizarre members of the fraternity whose zany behaviour provoked gales of laughter in all who learned of their antics.

Clanky Junction is a composite representation of all the engine sheds on the system. All the characters and most of the locations are fictitious, but the germ of every episode is true. They are humorous, irreverent stories that I hope will appeal not only to steam enthusiasts, but to everyone blessed with a sense of humour.

Acknowledgement

My sincere thanks to Ian Hazelgrove, Alan Carr and all the members of the 8E Association at Northwich who encouraged me constantly to increase my efforts to get this book published.

1
The Grudge

*I*t is now well over half a century ago that I started work at Clanky Junction on the old London Midland & Scottish Railway at the height of the Steam Age. It was my father's idea. He was always saying, 'If you want a job with no unemployment, go an' be an engine driver.' One could understand him I suppose, for in those days, with millions on the dole, a regular job was rare as a Manx cat.

With five other youths of my own age I started as an engine cleaner, which was just about the filthiest job imaginable. On our first day we were led through the enormous engine shed by a one-armed foreman who had been an engine driver himself once, but had been crippled in a train smash years before. Leading us to a giant locomotive on a quiet road, he explained how two of our number were to climb on the framing of the engine to clean a side of the boiler each, while another pair would tackle the wheels. To the remaining two he allocated a side of the tender each.

After giving his instructions, he showed us where to obtain a bucketful of 'patch', a foul-smelling mixture of oil and paraffin, threw a bundle of rags at us and told us that we would be allowed in the tackhouse for our dinner only when the engine gleamed as it had done the day it left the works.

I remained a cleaner for six months and, wherever I went during that period, I stank like an oil-lamp. It seemed the foul-smelling 'patch' removed the grime from the locomotives by the simple process of transferring it to our clothes and hair. It penetrated our very pores and solidified under our finger nails. After a week on the job my boots began to rot.

Handing each of us a brand-new book containing the company's rules and regulations, the one-armed foreman started holding instruction classes in a dingy hut on one of the pits. He went to great lengths to explain how a fireman's job was more than just shovelling coal into an engine's firebox; he explained how we would have to keep an eye on the water level of the boiler. When he revealed that a locomotive could guzzle between three and four thousand gallons on a fifty-mile trip we saw the reason why. It was the fireman's job to keep a look-out for the signals that came up on the driver's blind side and to sweep the footplate free of coal dust so that it wouldn't get in his eyes. At the end of each class he always administered a strong dose of regulation brainwash.

'While you're running you must always be on your toes. Keep your eyes open! When you're running at speed watch for your driver shutting the regulator so you can open the blower to avoid a backlash from the firebox. If you get one of those it'll roast you alive!'

The way he went on it sounded terribly dramatic and, as he continued outlining our future responsibilities, we found ourselves squaring our shoulders to show that we were equal to anything. Finally, his voice rising in volume, he declared, 'And don't forget – the driver's the boss! He's like the captain of a ship. It doesn't matter what he tells you to do – do it and don't ask questions. If anything goes wrong he'll answer for it, not you!'

When the day of our fireman's test arrived we were nervous as a bunch of students taking their finals. At that time they were anxious to fill the lower rungs of the promotion ladder pending the retirement of a whole generation of drivers. Instead of sending us to the Inspector in ones and twos, as was usually the case, they sent us in droves to queue outside the office where he would put us through our paces individually. In our gang only one failed, but he was just plain backward.

Equipped in our new uniforms we grew in stature. Now we could swagger into the tackhouse to rub shoulders with men who had steamed to all parts of the land. Some of the lads screwed up their caps to give themselves a veteran look, but the experienced ones said that they could tell we were novices by the way we walked. They reckoned that when we had been on the shovel a few months we would get the lurch and roll of a loco in our legs and, falling for the bait, we attempted to anticipate this by exaggerated imitations.

And yet, passing our fireman's test seemed to make no difference to our prospects. Week after week went by without our being called for our first trips. As we leaned on the wall of the shed watching the trains go by we began to feel miserable, for those lines led to London, Leeds and Liverpool; to Carlisle, Coventry and Crewe; to Goole, Grimsby and Glasgow; and we wanted to go there too.

When time becomes laden with stagnant ambitions, young shoulders sag easily. Our pride at passing our fireman's test and the glamour of our new uniforms soon wore off. After three weeks without a sign of our being called for our first trip, we were slouching about the shed like a bunch of delinquents. We had more time on our hands now, for we had discovered that by tying two extra stales to a long mop we could reach the highest point of an engine's boiler without climbing on the framing. By this method, along with a few other dodges, we learned to get through our work in half the time. With time on our hands we drifted into mischief, with some of the foolhardy pranks we got up to ending close to disaster.

Climbing on board an express engine one day, we set it in motion. The engine was in reverse and, with hardly any steam in her, the brakes were ineffective. Setting the engine in motion we found we couldn't stop it. Panic-stricken, we abandoned it like frightened rabbits and, seconds later, it collided with a reverberating shudder into another engine a few yards along the pit. Another time we conceived the idea of knocking wedges under the wheels of an engine about to leave the shed. When the driver climbed on board and did everything he knew to set the engine in motion without success, he couldn't believe it! Every day for most of his life he had released the brakes, opened the regulator and glided smoothly off the pit. This time his engine wouldn't budge! Frantically winding the engine into reverse he tried again, but it still wouldn't move. Completely perplexed, he lifted his cap and scratched his head as he searched the controls for something he had missed. It took him several minutes to find the wedges and, as he kicked them violently from under the wheels, we contorted with stifled laughter on the footplate of another engine six pits away.

Another week confined to the engine shed and we would probably have been sent packing. Just in time the one-armed foreman told three of us to report to the shed boss for our first trips. As we dashed eagerly for our instructions I imagined myself on the footplate of a mighty express engine pounding along the main line heading for some distant city, but it turned out to be nothing like so adventurous. An hour later I found myself on a scruffy little saddle-tank, see-sawing up and down a coal sidings with only twenty minutes for dinner. At the end of the shift I was tired and weary and my hands were bruised and bleeding where I had knocked them up on the steel plates of the cramped cab.

At first it was one day on the footplate and five in the shed cleaning, but after three months I was on the main line every day. They kept us off the expresses until we perfected the knack of wielding the shovel as the engine lurched and leaned round curves at seventy. Then, with about two hundred firing turns to my credit and a few hundred tons of coal behind me, the day arrived when, as I signed off one day, my driver shouted to the foreman, 'This lad's ready for the big 'uns, Alf!'

Shortly after this the coast was the limit. The Calder, the Clyde, the Mersey, the Humber – there were drivers at the shed who had steamed over them all. Every day saw me pounding towards one coast or the other, and it was here that I left my youth behind to begin working and talking like a man. What more could a young stripling of eighteen wish for?

Although I was firing on the main line every day by this time, in official eyes I was still a cleaner. To become a regular fireman one had to wait until a surge in promotion allowed them to type one's name next to that of a regular driver on the roster sheets. When my time came, they put me with old Ned Thomas.

At first Ned's very appearance scared me to death. Over six feet tall and almost as broad, he glowered over a moustache that bristled like a yard brush. The forbidding aspect of his appearance was further enhanced by a great watch chain, which, thick enough to haul a train-load of steel ingots, dangled in two huge loops across his greasy waistcoat. On our first day together we prepared the engine for the journey without a word to each other, the first time he spoke being as we moved off the pit to commence the journey. As I wiped the oil from my hands I saw him step from the driver's platform and grasp the coal pick lying on top of the coal bunker. Approaching me, he looked me straight in the eyes as he brandished the coal pick.

'Tha see this?' he threatened. 'If tha doesn't do thi work to my liking tha'll get this on thi head!'

Quite clearly my first mate wasn't going to be an easy man to get along with. But then, when one was faced with the prospect of working with the same driver for a year or more, it paid to cultivate a friendly relationship. Life on the footplate could be hell on earth when a driver and fireman didn't see eye to eye. So, despite Ned's threat with the coal pick, I resolved to do all I could to make a success of my time with him.

One of the first obstacles I came up against had to do with the pipe Ned smoked, a gnarled monster with a bowl like a coal engine's blastpipe. Sometimes, usually when I turned from the firebox for my next shovelful of coal, he'd take his pipe from his mouth, take aim, then shoot a stream of tobacco-stained spittle at the firehole. Nine times out of ten his aim was accurate as a Bisley marksman's, but sometimes his face clouded with disappointment as the foul expectorate landed on the hot rim of the firehole to sizzle offensively. Whenever he did this I became alarmed, afraid that if I made my turn a little slower than usual or if he let go a little quicker, it would land on my arms. In an attempt to shame the old devil into stopping the habit, I started spitting over to his side of the cab the moment I saw him take aim. I kept this up for a week, but it was all to no avail. He appeared to approve of my behaviour, as though I was showing signs of maturity. Now and again he seemed on the point of giving me advice on how to be more accurate.

Another of his idiosyncrasies was his determination to take home a supply of firewood every day. Before Beeching the rails sat in steel chairs held firm by wooden keys hammered home by platelayers. The vibration of the ground as the trains pounded along the lines shook some of the keys loose and every morning the platelayers would be seen walking their lengths hammering home those that had fallen to the ballast. Before I had been with Ned a week he had me trained to collect four of these every day for him to take home at the end of the trip. He showed such pleasure when I clambered back on board with them that I half expected to be patted on the head, but when I forgot the task he would go home sulking.

Beyond horse-racing, beer and locomotives, Ned's life was a complete void. At first I experienced great difficulty in conversing with him at all, and it soon became apparent that if I was to establish a basis for further communication, I would have to become familiar with such terms as 'odds on', 'even money' and 'each-way treble'. My first attempts to engage him in conversation on the subject of horse-racing failed miserably. Mentioning a horse I selected at random from the list of runners as a likely winner, I hoped to render him animated, but each selection I mentioned had less chance of winning than a three-legged donkey. Furthermore Ned knew it. He received my offerings with such disdain that his threat with the coal pick surfaced in my thoughts again.

Then, with a bit of luck I came across the deliberations of 'Anthony Oracle', a tipster in one of the more popular newspapers. Bearing one of his selections in mind, I mentioned it to Ned as though I had selected it by my own intuition and asked to be included in the flutter to the extent of sixpence. The horse won at three to one and, from that day forth, he started discussing his own fancies with me as though I had finally proved worthy of sharing his most sacred deliberations.

Encouraged by my success, my hopes of establishing an amicable working relationship with the old devil improved, but, as the days went by, I experienced further pangs of despair. It wasn't that I was no good with a shovel, for he was never short of steam throughout our time together. It was the little things that got in the way of cultivating the harmony so necessary for the smooth handling of a locomotive on the many journeys ahead of us. I'm sure he saw me wince when, after pouring engine oil over his huge maulers, he wiped it off with a greasy rag, then proceeded to handle his sandwiches so that the oil stains left by his fingers went down with the rest. It was the same with his penknife; he used this to cut the thick twist he smoked in his pipe, trim the wick of his oil-lamp and shred the cheese he fried on the shovel. To give him his due, he cleaned the penknife before using it, but it was on the same oily rag he used to wipe his hands!

Despite everything, right up to our last day together the possibility of Ned and I parting company at loggerheads never entered my mind. To get as far as I did with him in cultivating a working partnership is proof of the tact and patience I employed. After all, the difference in our ages spanned four decades, two wars and four monarchs. Surely no one with a grain of understanding could believe that I'd wreck it deliberately?

Yet wreck it I did! Old Ned took it hard too. Afterwards, if he saw me approaching a hundred yards away or bumped into me turning a corner, he would disguise the fact that he had seen me by looking away. There was something despairing in his attitude, like a father meeting a son who had changed his religion or started supporting a football team other than the one he had taken him to watch as a child.

When we left the shed at two o'clock that morning, there was absolutely nothing to portend the incident that, a few hours later, would turn Ned into a raving maniac displaying downright malice to everything under the sun. We were exactly on time leaving the shed; we manned a locomotive that steamed freely; and our guard was as reliable as the best of them. Indeed, everything seemed set for an uneventful trip far over the Pennines with a full jag of empties and an equally uneventful return trip with a fully loaded coal train.

To disarm me even more, it turned out to be a night for the poets, wonderfully clear with wisps of delicate white cirrus reaching across a moonlit sky. As we rumbled through the jagged silhouettes of the houses and factories of the sleeping city, the roofs and gables appeared as glass and, with everything sharply etched in black and white, the soot and scars of the profit-grinding world were hidden in deep black shadows. Through the gaps in the buildings alongside the line I could see the deserted roads, jaundiced and eerie under the amber street lights. Leaving the city far behind we began to pound up the Lancashire side of the Pennines where the hilly horizon could be seen as clearly as in daylight and the river was a ribbon of silver on the floor of the valley.

Miles over the Pennines we exchanged trains for the return trip. We blasted harder now, for instead of a trainload of empty wagons we hauled a full load of Yorkshire best. For mile after mile I worked hard, perspiring freely with the task of heaving coal into the firebox as we blasted up the eastern slopes of the hills until, finally, we squealed off the main line into the loop of Edenroyd sidings. By this time I was ready for breakfast. After a shunter had uncoupled the engine we moved ahead to clear the points then ran back into the sidings to pick up six more wagons urgently needed at our destination, and, as the engine clanked past the Inspector's cabin, he came to the door and shouted up to us, 'Stand in No 3 road, driver, and get your scoff!'

As the buffers of the engine contacted those of the first of the stationary wagons in No 3 road, we came to rest, and, as I screwed on the handbrake, Ned closed the steam valve that supplied the brakes, and the hiss that came from it died, allowing the silence of the hills to enter the cab. I already knew that Ned intended to cook his breakfast on the shovel for I had noticed how carefully he had stowed the ingredients earlier that morning. When one had been on the footplate a few months one could read the signs. Without a word I took my parcel of sandwiches from my locker and Ned and I changed sides. This was part of the age-old ritual; for the next fifteen minutes he would be completely absorbed in cooking his breakfast while I acted as look-out.

Outside the cab there was a nip in the air, with the mist of a new day hanging low in the valley, and, faintly discernible on the eastern horizon, the first pale hint of daylight was poised to dispel the darkness. Oblivious to all this, Ned took hold of the shovel and held the blade in the hot coals of the firebox. A few seconds later he withdrew it with the blade glowing a dull red. Waiting until it cooled black, he took a rag out of his pocket and began polishing it, letting out an oath as his fingers touched the hot metal and holding out his hand until the pain subsided. Then, when the blade was polished to his satisfaction, he wedged the shovel across the cab and, taking several small packages from his locker, proceeded to open them. The first contained the bacon, and, with the same penknife that he used to slice his thick twist and trim the wick of his lamp, he stabbed two rashers and dropped them on the shovel. They started spluttering at once and a pool of fat began to accumulate. Taking an egg, he cracked it deftly on the raised flange of the blade, dropped the contents into the bacon fat, then inserted the shovel into the firebox to commence the cooking.

After a few moments he withdrew the shovel again. Then, gripping the shaft between his legs to free both hands, he wiped the blade of his penknife on his oily rag and shredded a small onion and a piece of cheese and added these to the bacon fat. This done, he inserted the shovel into the firebox for the last time and got down on his haunches to watch over the final cooking with intense concentration.

As the mouth-watering aroma of Ned's breakfast filled the cab, my cheese sandwiches turned to sawdust. Glancing at the one I had left, I became impatient for the moment when, as was my privilege on such an occasion, I would be allowed to dip it in the bacon fat when Ned withdrew the shovel for the last time.

That anything could have occurred to ruin the idyllic atmosphere of the engine cab at that moment as Ned poked about the contents of the shovel anticipating his first mouthful would have been sacrilegious to contemplate. And yet, in an instant, the comforting ambience of the scene was completely destroyed by a malevolent current of air, which, darting into the chimney of the locomotive, swept through the tubes of the boiler and invaded the firebox to cause a blowback that enveloped Ned in a pall of hot smoke. The moment the searing smoke burgeoned from the firehole, Ned leaned back on his haunches, shielding his formidable moustache with his right hand as he did so. Although alarmed at the occurrence, I knew what to do. Oh yes, I knew instantly just what the situation called for.

Leaping from my stool I swiped at the blower handle as the foreman cleaner had instructed me during my first days at the engine shed, but alas, in my enthusiastic desire to fill the breach, I swiped so hard, not only did the smoke pall turn back on itself to disappear into the firebox, but the tremendous draught of air it caused to rush in through the firehole whipped Ned's breakfast clean off the shovel to be consumed by the flames with the ferocity of a half-starved beast!

With his face briefly illuminated by the sudden glare from the firebox, I watched Ned remove his hand from his face after wiping the tears from his eyes, then make to resume his gastronomic ministrations. The moment he observed the empty blade of the shovel his face appeared to freeze. As though hypnotised, he remained quite motionless, unable to believe his eyes!

Like the calm before a storm, the silence of the engine cab intensified and, as I waited for him to react, a mouthful of bread and cheese stuck in my gullet. Still holding the shovel and staring in disbelief at the empty blade, he slowly got to his feet. For a moment I thought he was going to crush my skull with it. Instead, stretching himself to his full height, he raised the shovel above his head with both hands and, with a great explosion of energy, flung it with all his strength at the steel doors of the tender. With a loud clatter it fell to the footplate where it rocked several times on its rounded bulge then became quite still. In the ominous silence that followed, Ned returned to his own side of the cab as I smartly vacated it, turned his back on me and stared fiercely at the hills across the valley.

Like all those who work with their hands, I was no stranger to obscene language, but I have never heard curses so black or so varied as those that poured from Ned's lips in the dawn of that morning. As they poured from his mouth without pause, his fingers worked in a ceaseless spasm of frustration behind his back. Some of the curses seemed to get stuck in his throat and, from time to time, he had to jerk his head forward to eject them.

Old Ned was still cursing when the first glint of the sun illuminated the hilly horizon twenty minutes later. He cursed the day he was born, the day he started work on the railway, the government, his landlord, the eight-hour day and the Union; he cursed the engine, the man who designed it, the superintendent of Clanky Junction and all mothers who gave birth to brats like me. But, most of all, he cursed all my generation of firemen of whose utter uselessness I was the most stupid example. And, like I said earlier, things were never quite the same between us afterwards.

2
Tommy Lunch-bun

The 'Odd Fellows' at Clanky Junction, those who, at one time or another, had exposed an unusual trait or habit to the lightning wit of the nickname coiners, were as varied in character as the stones in a moorland wall. Tommy Toot-Toot was named simply for his habit of remarking 'I'll give a couple o' toots' whenever he was brought to a halt at a signal. Sweeney Todd was the name given to a driver who would cut your hair for fourpence as you sat on an upturned bucket. There was Ernie Up-'n'-Down, an engine driver with one leg shorter than the other, and Freddie Fairy Soap, a fireman who washed his hands a dozen times a day with scented soap instead of using the tallow-like substance issued by the railway company.

That's how it was on the Iron Road during the days of steam. It didn't matter how far from the engine shed they might be, if an engine driver or his stoker exposed some odd behaviour or said something out of the ordinary, there was always the other to tell the story and, the moment it travelled along the lines, someone would fix it in railway lore by slapping a nickname on the victim in less time than it takes to sneeze.

While some of the nicknames were awarded for a single, dramatic blunder that could befall any unsuspecting mortal, others took a long time to evolve. This was the case with Tommy Lunch-bun.

To see him walking to board his locomotive with the thumb of his left hand hooked in the armhole of his waistcoat and his right hand swinging a neat, brown paper parcel tied with string, the origin of his nickname was in no way obvious. It is undoubtedly true that the brown paper parcel had something to do with it, but it was only when the contents of the parcel were exposed that the connection became clear.

When I first worked with him on the same footplate, Tommy was almost at the end of his time on the Iron Road, whereas I, a raw youth of seventeen, was just commencing mine. Whenever I had passed him previously, he had never impressed me as a man with much character or charisma, but my acquaintance with him taught me that the more modest, inoffensive members of the species very often have more to give the world.

Tommy was so sparsely built and delicately featured that it was difficult to imagine him at the controls of a giant locomotive. On our first trip together he climbed on board the engine like a schoolboy on a picnic, the fingers of a tiny, pink hand gripping the string of his brown paper parcel and his twinkling blue eyes gently smiling under the neb of his cloth cap.

Looking back on the events of that day I realise now that my curiosity ought to have been aroused by the manner he stowed his brown paper food parcel in his locker, but it wasn't until much later that the relevance of his strange behaviour to his wider character became apparent. Opening the steel door of his locker, he placed the parcel inside with the utmost reverence. Then, pausing in the act of taking off his jacket, he turned about and re-opened the locker as though prompted by an afterthought. Placing a hand on each side of the parcel, he re-positioned it ever so slightly, then stood back to observe it with his head cocked to one side. But he still appeared dissatisfied. Stepping forward he made a further minute adjustment and appraised his handiwork once more. Then, finally satisfied with the way the parcel rested in the locker, he took off his jacket and proceeded to fill his oilcan to commence oiling the engine for the trip ahead.

The outward trip to Leeds with the parcel train revealed another surprising facet of Tommy's character. During my short experience as a fireman I was accustomed to working with drivers who drove their engines as ebullient huntsmen rode their horses – dominantly, masterfully. Men who lunged on the regulator, blasted on the whistle and swiped at the brake. Tommy's style was the antithesis of this. He coaxed; he eased; he petted the beast. It was as though the engine drove itself! The journey seemed effortless and, when we finally came to a standstill exactly on time at Leeds, it dawned on me that I had shovelled far less coal than I usually did on the trip. Knowing nothing of the agony to which he would submit me before the trip was over, this amazing discovery caused me to warm to the little man.

Four hours after we signed on duty, after we had turned the engine for the return journey from Leeds, the reason for Tommy's nickname slowly revealed itself. Our engine was stationary at the time, standing on a short spur of line just beyond the turntable. It was scoff-time. Opening the door of his food locker, he took out his food parcel with the same painstaking care with which he had stowed it earlier on boarding the engine at the shed. Placing it carefully on his stool, he glanced across the cab at me like a diminutive Houdini and started to untie the knots in the string.

There must have been half a dozen knots to untie. He picked and fumbled at them for so long that by the time the last of them was finally undone I had picked two cold lamb chops to the bone and got rid of two rounds of bread and butter! Taking the string from the parcel at last, he wound it round two fingers into a tidy skein, looped an end round the middle and, with the utmost care, tied a knot. This done, he finished it off with a neat little bow, placed the skein of string in the top pocket of his serge jacket and stood back in silent appraisal of the still-unopened parcel.

It was here that I was suddenly invaded by a powerful feeling of expectancy. Any other man of the Iron Road would have taken his food from his locker, unwrapped it and taken the first bite in less time than it had taken Tommy to undo the first knot! My curiosity increased; what could such a precious parcel contain? Did it conceal morsels from the table of the Gods?

Even when I swallowed my last mouthful of apple pie, Tommy still hadn't taken a single bite! With laborious care, he was still unfolding the brown paper wrapping of his parcel, laying each fold back with deliberate caution and smoothing it flat with the back of his hand. As the last fold was laid back to expose an inner wrapping of tissue paper, he slowly unfolded this until, with the expression of a child about to show a pal his lucky marble, he turned back the last fold to reveal the contents. There, in the clammy, coal-strewn engine cab shone six of the daintiest quarter sandwiches I have ever set eyes on! They were snow-white and crustless. But that wasn't all! As though by a magnet, my gaze was drawn to a gorgeous little bun reposing in the centre of the arrangement. Golden brown, it was dressed in a tiny skirt of crinkly pink paper, and in its centre was a disc of pure white icing on which was mounted a blushing red cherry. It was more like the repast of an ageing dowager than the meal of a man of the Iron Road! And yet, everything about the scene – Tommy's gentle manner, his miniature form and the dainty repast – were in perfect proportion.

Quietly picking the remains of the lamb chops from my teeth with a sharpened spent match, I watched silently as Tommy nibbled like a squirrel on the first of his dainty sandwiches. He nibbled so long on his first mouthful that I began to speculate as to when he would swallow. It entered my thoughts that perhaps he subscribed to the theory that all food should be chewed an exact number of times to extract every vestige of nourishment, and, with heightened interest, I actually started counting. His second bite took thirty-one nibbles to swallow, but, to my chagrin, the next mouthful he disposed of in twenty-nine. Throughout his meal he stood with his back to me looking through the cab window. There was something about his manner that was almost reverential, and, as I continued to watch him, ready to divert my gaze at once if he should turn to face me, my fascination increased.

With tantalising slowness the tiny white sandwiches diminished in number until only the bun remained, and, as I waited for him to tackle the golden confection still flaunting itself on its bed of tissue paper, my impatience mounted. Why couldn't he get rid of it? Hell, it was small enough! He could have put it into his mouth in one go, but no, instead of reaching for the bun he started brushing the crumbs from his overalls as though he had all day to eat his meal. I restrained a powerful urge to shout 'For goodness sake, Tommy – put it in your mouth!' Then, to inflame my impatience even more, after satisfying himself that his overalls were free of crumbs, he took a spotless white handkerchief from his pocket and began to wipe his mouth. It was like watching a full-blooded Italian tenor walk from the stage without singing the final note of a magnificent aria!

The tension I felt was becoming unbearable. Turning my face away from the scene, I began to look over the side of the engine. The spur on which it was standing was surrounded as far as the eye could see by a vast network of tracks. A few lines away a boisterous shunting engine blustered up and down some sidings intermittently ramming a raft of wagons to send them hurtling into the roads in ones and twos, while, on the up slow, a lumbering goods train threaded its way through a myriad tracks towards the West Coast. From every direction the cacophony of railway noises rose and fell incessantly, reaching a climax as the Pullman, twenty seconds out of Leeds, blasted its way round a curve in its urgent need to gain express momentum as it headed for King's Cross. Rapidly gaining speed with every thrust of its pistons, the engine whistled shrilly as it passed, and I continued to watch its majestic progress until it finally disappeared from sight round another curve further up the line.

As the sound of the Pullman subsided, I turned again to face my procrastinating little driver in the hope that he had finally disposed of the tantalising confection basking daintily on the tissue paper. My hopes proved futile, for the pretty little currant bun with the cherry on top still reposed in the centre of the wrapping exactly as before. My impatience turned to frustration. A wedge of apple pie or a round of bread and jam to round off a meal on a footplate was quite acceptable, but that virgin confection posing coyly in its crinkly pink skirt had no place in the cab of a locomotive! Then, as though reading my thoughts, and to my intense relief, Tommy took hold of the bun. But, instead of raising it to his mouth as I fully expected, he cupped it in his hands like a chalice, stepped across the footplate and, holding it out to me, said, 'Would you care for a bun, sonny?'

His gesture was so unexpected that it took me completely by surprise. With embarrassment and gratitude vying with each other for control of my feelings, I felt like someone trying to go in two directions at the same time. Then, as I shifted awkwardly on my stool, I noticed the expression on his face. It was almost saintly – the kindest and gentlest I had ever seen on a man. Thanking him with a grunt from my gaping mouth, I took hold of the bun and started to peel off the crinkly pink paper.

Without more ado, Tommy turned about, screwed up the flimsy tissue paper and threw it in the firebox. Then, taking hold of the brown paper wrapping, he shook the crumbs off it and began to fold it with painstaking care into a small package. This completed, he took the skein of string from the top pocket of his serge jacket and proceeded to wind it neatly round it. When this was accomplished, he tied several knots, finished it off with a perfect bow, then stepped to his locker and placed it reverently inside. With this, he stuck his head through the cab window, whistled quietly for the signal, and a few moments later we left to couple up to the train awaiting us at the station.

When I had been at Clanky Junction a little longer, I discovered that Tommy Lunch-bun had brought a bun with icing and a cherry on top every day to present to whoever happened to be his fireman. Even more remarkable, so painstaking was the care he lavished on his food parcel, he had been known to make the same piece of brown paper and the same length of string last for more than a year at a time.

3
The Count of
Clanky Junction

Of all the engine drivers on the old London Midland & Scottish Railway, there wasn't one with the stately bearing and dignified demeanour of Edward Arnold Bickerstaff. Six feet two inches in height with carefully tended clusters of iron-grey hair brushed back from his temples, Edward Arnold Bickerstaff stood out in a crowd like a Rolls-Royce in a car park. At fifty years of age he appeared nothing less than an aristocrat in overalls, whose very presence imbued those who met him for the first time with an impulse to step well to one side to allow him plenty of room to pass by.

To observe the treatment he received from the women in the station refreshment room when he called for a cup of tea and a snack between trains was to witness abject servility, as his approach to the counter set their hearts fluttering with a desire to serve him. Young or old, fat or thin, they all reacted the same. The moment they saw him enter, their movements would be charged with undignified urgency as they competed for the thrill of being the first available to serve him the moment he arrived at the counter. If he was dissatisfied with the fare they placed before him, he had only to raise an eyebrow in genteel disapproval and everything would be changed.

Without a doubt, Ted Bickerstaff was born in the mould of the distinguished: with a bit of luck he might have been a film star, a toastmaster or even a politician! If I close my eyes and picture him in his Sunday best I can see him making the budget speech without the slightest difficulty. As it was, however, Ted was an engine driver at Clanky Junction where, among those who knew him best, his standing was quite different. The world outside the confines of the great engine shed might have seen him as a man of striking appearance whose measured words of wisdom never failed to impress, but to the engine drivers and firemen with whom he worked he was an inveterate liar!

It always seemed to me that this was too harsh a judgement. After all, to call someone a liar implies either malice or cowardice, but Ted possessed neither of these traits. For me, 'The Count', as we called him, was the victim of a rampant imagination capable of conjuring startling visions of grandeur, an affliction no less terrible in its effect on a person's character than a 12-inch nose or a left-handed right leg. Of one thing I am absolutely certain – 'The Count' could prevent himself from relating his fantastic stories no more than he could prevent himself catching a cold.

And yet there were times when one couldn't help sympathising with those who displayed intolerance towards him. I recall only too clearly sitting right next to him in a porter's room miles from anywhere at the dead of night, surrounded by other locomen waiting to relieve westbound freight trains, when, to my astonishment, he declared:

'No, you can keep Devon and Cornwall for me! When my good lady and I decide to go on vacation we like nothing better than visiting the family estate. 'Course, I'm one of the Lincolnshire Bickerstaffs y'know, the potato people! Oh yes, we visit the family estate every summer!

'The chauffeur's there to meet us at the station with the Daimler! He won't allow us to carry a bag! 'Course, y'know, there's no need for me to work at all really. They pester me to return to the family estate every time we pay a visit, but as I keep tellin' 'em, I like railways! Allus 'ave done! An' anyway, as I keep tellin' 'em – it's a bit o' spendin' money!'

He said this with such earnestness accompanied by such grave gestures that a single word of ridicule from his gaping audience would have amounted to sacrilege. With a face that had never felt the tingling blush of guilt, he paused to allow the import of his words to register, cleared his throat, then continued garnishing the story as though he had all night to spare. The more unlikely the story became, the more his audience marvelled at the incredible guile of the man.

'Yes, my dear lady would go back tomorrow. I can understand her, mind you – it can't be easy puttin' up wi' the hours worked by an engine driver when you've seen how the better half live. I could pack up just like that! A line to the Colonel tellin' 'im to get our room ready an' that 'ud be it! 'Course, when your heart an' soul's in the railway, what can you do? I don't know what I'd do without the feel of a footplate under me feet!'

All this might have been entertaining or even convincing to those present who didn't know him from Adam. When their trains pulled into the station they'd be off into the night never to set eyes on him again, but when one knew him of old and faced the prospect of working with him for months on end, he made one feel like a poor relation! It was this feeling that roused many of his workmates to a state of murder, for unlike those he met by chance, they knew that he had been born not two miles from Clanky Junction to the wife of a lamplighter!

The inspiration for 'The Count's' many and varied fantasies remains a mystery. I sometimes imagined he had stored the tales he had read in the 'penny bloods' of his youth, graduating in his later years to the flowery fables of the women's magazines. The story of the house he was having built, a story kept alive by the endless malevolent enquiries of his workmates, went on for ever, but one could never pin him down to it's exact location.

'On the south side, y'know, out in the country!'

By even the wildest standards of working men it was going to be a palace. Set in several acres of woodland, 'The Count's' imaginary house was going to contain seven bedrooms, three bathrooms, a lounge as big as a ballroom and a wine cellar. Through the years he added every conceivable refinement and, when someone hinted at the enormous cost of such a domain, he replied, 'Yes, it'll cost me a fortune I dare say, but there's the legacy y'see. What's life without a bit o' comfort? Money isn't everything y'know!'

He explained the endless delay in the completion of the house by referring to countless alterations that varied according to his mood. He sacked architects nonchalantly as a bored millionaire discards his clothes, and, on one occasion, took legal action against the Council for erecting a bus stop near the entrance to the drive.

Intrigued no less than the others at 'The Count's' inventiveness, one morning as we shunted up and down Dankworth sidings I asked him about his imaginary house.

'Moving into your new house soon, Ted?'

Turning to face me, his face bearing the expression of a Judge, he replied, 'No son, it isn't quite to my liking yet – I'm not satisfied with the music room. My dear lady's getting impatient, d'y'know. I'll have to get a fresh architect if things don't improve.'

After one or two brief encounters with the engine driver obsessed by wild fantasies, I finally found myself marked on the rosters as his regular fireman. I worked with him for eighteen months and, when we eventually parted, I was so disorientated I experienced great difficulty re-adjusting myself to the real world. One of the stories I heard him relate during my time with him was so fantastic that it could have been taken from the Boy's Own Paper!

After ten hours on the footplate, 'The Count' and I were relieved from duty far over the Pennines and instructed to make our way back to our home depot on the first available passenger train. This happened to be an early morning train out of Leeds, which stopped at every station to Rochdale then ran non-stop to Manchester. Just before daybreak, as we swayed and lurched in a self-contained compartment of a rather ancient set of coaches behind a fussy, little side-tank of a locomotive, we were soon joined by more passengers.

They came in relays. The first to enter the compartment were the Yorkshire miners, huge thick-set men hunched in their overcoats to conserve the heat of their bodies in the chill dawn. When these alighted at various stations along the line they were replaced by the men making for the woollen mills, pale, wraith-like creatures, their clothes flecked with fleece. Finally, when the men destined for the woollen mills alighted just before we crossed the county border in the full spate of the morning, we were joined by the men who worked in the offices of Manchester armed with their briefcases and folded newspapers.

As the city gents settled themselves on their seats they immediately hid their faces behind their newspapers and we continued our journey in silence. Very soon, rocked by the swaying of the train, I fell asleep. Then, after a little while, I slowly became aware of 'The Count's' voice rising and falling in his best affectation and, as I sleepily gazed round the compartment, I noticed the city gents were no longer reading their newspapers, but leaning forward on the edge of their seats listening with rapt attention to every word coming from 'The Count's' lips! Rambling on like Henry Irving at the Garrick, he was having the time of his life!

'...six foot seven in his stockin' feet an' sixteen stone stripped is that boy of mine! A modern Hercules, that's what he is! A finer figure of a man you've never set eyes on!'

Noticing that I had opened my eyes and knowing full well I knew that he had no children of his own, my illustrious driver made a slight correction.

'Well, he's not really my boy, he's my nephew – my dear lady has never been able to give me a son of my own – her health, y'know. Mind you, the way he calls me Pop you'd think he was mine! What a specimen! He was tellin' me only the other day when he came home on leave – he's in the Black Watch y'know...'

Of course, it had to be the Black Watch; nothing as lowly as the Pay Corps or the Pioneers for anyone 'The Count' knew!

'...he was tellin' me how they dropped him by parachute in the wilds of Scotland miles from anywhere. There he was, no food an' only a single blanket to keep him warm! He was on one o' them survival things, y'know – had to find his way back to base by compass, livin' off the land as he went. Eh, what a fine figure of a man that boy is! D'y'know, for three days not a morsel of food passed his lips! Not the tiniest morsel!'

One of the city gents shook his head in wonder, allowing a faint gasp to escape his half-open mouth. 'The Count' rambled on.

'He's like a young bullock! Great big limbs – tough as steel he is! As I was sayin', there he was miles from anywhere – nothin' to eat for three whole days when, all of a sudden, he saw a rabbit! There it was right in front of 'im – his only chance of survival! And d'y'know – he chased that rabbit for over an hour until it dropped to the grass exhausted!' Pausing, 'The Count' moved to the edge of his seat.

'I'll tell you summat else, an' all – d'y'know, he ate that rabbit alive!'

If any of the city gents doubted the truth of Ted's fantastic flight of fancy, they didn't show it. Indeed, when the train arrived at its destination, one of them raised his bowler to him as he left the compartment.

There was no cure for Ted Bickerstaff's embarrassing forays into his private world of make-believe, with those who tried to put him down continually being made to look quite shabby. At a time when one could purchase a perfectly good suit for not much more than a tenner, one driver tried to turn the tables on him only to be checkmated by his inimitable panache.

'It's funny I should bump into you like this, Ted, but I was just thinking – the next time I buy a suit I think I'll get one o' them hundred guinea jobs you keep tellin' us about!'

Pausing only to assume his customary attitude of aristocratic deliberation, 'The Count' replied, 'Now that's a very sound idea, very sound indeed. But while you're at it, don't leave it at one – get three! You can't have enough things of quality, y'know! You just can't have enough!'

Needless to say, 'The Count' never moved into the new house he was for ever having built, nor did he retire to the family estate of the Lincolnshire Bickerstaffs, the potato people. The last time I set eyes on him more than fifty years ago was in the shunter's cabin at Dankworth sidings. Confronted by an attentive audience of shunters during their meal break, he was telling them of the racehorse he was planning to buy and, as always, he related the story with such ardent conviction that it would have been sacrilegious to interrupt him.

The destabilisation of the way I viewed the world inflicted on me during my time with Ted, I thought I had conquered completely after a few months with another driver, but it is disturbingly evident that this hasn't been the case, for whenever the memory of the man steals into my thoughts, he always appears with his little finger daintily extended as he sips his tea from the lid of a gold-plated brewcan.

4
The Folly of
Little Tommy Trot

Greatly envied by most of the men who laboured at Clanky Junction engine shed, engine driver Thomas Trot had the cushiest job on the London, Midland & Scottish Railway. Not for him the marrow-chilling traipse to the engine shed an hour before dawn on a raw winter's morning to lug an eastbound freight over the Pennines; no pounding up tortuous gradients on the midnight Mail with a fireman who didn't know the right end of a shovel. None of this for Tommy. Indeed, he had been confined to shed limits for so long he had almost forgotten what a main-line signal looked like!

Tommy's remarkable good fortune could be traced back to a fateful event that occurred many years before when he had collapsed at the controls of his stationary locomotive in Central station. When they carried him to the ambulance he was observed clutching his abdomen and writhing in agony, a sight that evoked a sense of ill-omen to all those who witnessed it. And yet, as though to prove the truth of the old adage that every cloud has a silver lining, when Tommy resumed duty at the engine shed a month later, he was brought off main-line duties on doctor's orders and appointed to the most coveted job at the Junction as the permanent driver of the shed pilot.

On this job all was peace and tranquillity. There was one shift – eight in the morning until four in the afternoon – one speed – five miles an hour – and just one locomotive – a Lancashire & Yorkshire relic tall in the smokestack and high in the cab – which Tommy wouldn't allow anyone to approach even with a silk duster.

Despite its ancient origin, the shed pilot engine, scoured and polished every morning with concoctions formulated by Tommy himself, possessed the sheen of a proud, old cat. So many layers of tallow had been applied to the boiler casing over the years that it appeared to be coated with varnish. The steampipes glistened like polished silver and the brasses, Tommy's pride and joy, gleamed like virgin gold.

The cab of the engine boasted many refinements lovingly designed to enhance its comfort. Instead of sitting on the bare steel of the rear sandboxes, Tommy and Charlie Harper, his loyal stoker, enjoyed the luxury of upholstered boards. To avoid getting to his feet to operate the controls, the resourceful little engine driver had fitted a crafty extension to the regulator, and, to sound the whistle, he simply pulled on a lavatory chain attached to the lever situated under the roof of the cab.

Just before eight o'clock every morning, little Tommy Trot and Charlie Harper climbed aboard their ancient relic and scoured and polished for almost an hour. Then, when the interior of the cab gleamed like a jeweller's shop window, they leisurely washed their hands in hot water drawn from the boiler and proceeded to wedge two Spanish onions and several potatoes behind the steampipes. Tommy was partial to onions cooked in this fashion. He refused to turn a wheel until this ritual was performed with due reverence.

At the first sign of rain, the two enginemen would, with a silent spontaneity cultivated over many years, unroll a carefully stowed tarpaulin sheet and proceed to fasten it over the open cab. Then, when all was ready, Tommy would sound a subdued crow on the whistle and he and his loyal stoker would glide in a leisurely fashion up and down the shed roads aboard their ancient relic shunting a wagon here and a disabled engine there, contented as two cats on a hearth rug.

If one continued to observe this fortunate pair it would soon become apparent that fate had bestowed one more blessing on their idyllic partnership, it's crowning glory, for just as Tommy possessed a fine tenor voice, his fireman was endowed with an equally fine baritone. Never a day passed without their giving voice to several of their favourite duets, their repertoire ranging from snatches of Italian opera to such heart-rending ballads as 'Come into the garden, Maud' and 'Who is Sylvia?'. Finally, every evening when the shift was over and they brought their engine to rest behind the platelayer's hut, they ended the day with a blissful rendering of their favourite song of all – 'Beautiful Dreamer'. To hear this, their grand finale, floating over the coal stacks on an autumn evening was to experience a rare interlude of exquisite joy.

And so, day after day throughout countless seasons, this superb partnership flourished as though ordained by heaven, their sublime contentment reinforcing one's faith in human nature. Furthermore, although acutely envied by the other 'glassbacks' at the Junction, those who, because of genuine or faked disabilities, were barred from duty on the main line, the intrepid pair on the shed pilot projected an air of such supreme confidence that they convinced all contenders their occupancy of the most coveted job at the engine shed was completely impregnable.

And yet, despite the blissful harmony with which this remarkable partnership was blessed, the old hands at the Junction could recall a time when, just three years after they came together on the same footplate, the idyllic relationship of Little Tommy Trot and Charlie Harper had been threatened by a terrible schism because of a shameful breach of faith on the part of Tommy. With their sublime partnership trembling on the edge of the abyss for three interminable weeks in full view of their workmates, it had been touch and go. Indeed there were some amongst the latter whose most ardent desire was to push it over the brink to satisfy their own selfish ambitions, and for three long weeks the threatening catastrophe became the sole topic of conversation, with rumour and speculation running rampant throughout the confines of the engine shed and beyond.

There was absolutely no doubt that had Tommy been mad enough to pursue to the end the crazy obsession that gripped him he would have lost his highly coveted job on the shed pilot for good. It was a very near thing! Only a last-minute return to sanity on his part prevented him from being reinstated on main-line expresses to endure the turmoil of fast running and the disjointed sleeping regime that such a terrible fate held in store, and, although time healed the wound inflicted by his waywardness, the scar remained. Tommy suffered a wave of nausea whenever the memory of his narrow escape stole into his mind, and he would frown uneasily and give an extra rub to his beloved brasses to dispel the agony of it.

It all happened in the days before the whine of jet engines desecrated the skies of the British countryside and eight-wheeled lorries bullied the bicycles off the roads; a time when one could identify North, South, East and West by the colour of a train standing in a station. Then, everything from the mail that dropped through the letters boxes, the fish on the fishmonger's slab or a day at the seaside depended on the powerful monsters of steel that clanked from under the soot-grimed roofs of countless engine sheds throughout the land enveloped in clouds of swirling steam.

Unlike those who toiled in the mills and factories, the men who worked at the loco yards didn't arrive in a crowd at the sound of a hooter to queue at a clock they hated the sight of. Locomen arrived in ones and twos throughout the twenty-four hours of the day and night, for the wheels of the railway never stopped turning twice round the clock. They said that if you could stick it a year you'd be there for a lifetime, but to those who rebelled at the thought of being imprisoned in a factory, the Iron Road appealed like the sea to men with salt in their veins.

To be a locoman for a lifetime one needed the constitution of an alpine goat, the dedication of a monk and a wife who could tolerate loneliness on the frequent occasions one left home on a double trip. The shifts were cruel, often calling for the men to vacate their beds at any minute between two, three, four and five o'clock in the morning whatever the weather; and the irregular meals and disjointed sleeping patterns imposed on those who worked them played havoc with the health of the men. Every engine shed therefore had its contingent of 'glassbacks', drivers and firemen who, because of a dicky heart or a bellyful of ulcers, along with those who shamelessly shammed such maladies, were barred from the demanding duties on the main line.

This was how Little Tommy Trot and Charlie Harper came to be on the shed pilot in the first place. The difference was, however, that Charlie's disability was plain for all to see: crushed between two buffers years before, his left hand was three fingers missing and, despite being greatly envied in being appointed to the most coveted job at the Junction, not a man there begrudged him his remarkable good fortune.

Tommy's claim to 'glassback' status, however, was wide open to suspicion right from the start. For one thing his disability lacked the conspicuousness of three missing fingers. Indeed, Tommy possessed no visible symptoms whatsoever. There was no limp, no missing members, no squint – not even a cough! Tommy's claim to the most sought-after job at the Junction rested on nothing more tangible than a rather mysterious condition he vaguely referred to as 'a weeping bladder'! It is undoubtedly true that some of the men claimed he wore waterproof underpants, but none of them was prepared to vouchsafe that he had seen them with his own eyes.

That he convinced the company doctor of the validity of his condition goes without saying, but it was generally felt by the men at the Junction that with this condition, what he lacked in symptoms could easily be made up by a bit of good acting. With such doubt, mystery and suspicion surrounding Tommy's claim to 'glassback' status, his occupancy of the cushiest job at the Junction was, to say the least, tenuous, and when Charlie Harper repeatedly warned him of the risk he was taking in the foolhardy way he was behaving, he knew what he was doing.

If Charlie Harper's annual medical check-up (a cross borne bravely by every 'glassback' at the engine shed) had taken place on any other day of the week, the pristine relationship enjoyed by the two enginemen would have remained unsullied throughout. As it turned out, however, that Tuesday the fireman they allocated to Tommy in

Charlie's brief absence was no other than young Butch Johnson, a nineteen-year-old physical training fanatic possessing the persuasive power of an evangelist!

From the day he started work at the Junction, Butch Johnson had championed the cause of the body beautiful like a crusader. Completely obsessed by the cult, he displayed proudly in the lapel of his serge jacket a badge showing the nude figure of Atlas bearing the world on his shoulder. Underneath the figure of Atlas was a small scroll declaring: 'SACRED THY BODY EVEN AS THY SOUL'.

The men of the Junction were set in their ways as miners and trawlermen. Nothing like the craze for physical fitness inspired by young Butch had ever been known before. Within a few weeks of his arrival at the place he persuaded the football committee to allow him the use of a dressing room for the energetic devotions of his newly launched physical training club, and, in next to no time, with young cleaners and firemen joining in droves, it began to flourish beyond his wildest dreams. Blinded by the promise of a second youth, some of the older men joined.

The normally quiet atmosphere of the tackhouse was transformed by gangs of eager young cleaners and firemen comparing muscles or avidly reading magazines on how to build the physique of a Greek god. The cult of the body beautiful got such a hold of them that they started neglecting their work and, with increasing frequency, engine drivers came storming into the tackhouse to drag their reluctant firemen back to the pits where their engines waited, minutes overdue for the start of a trip.

There had always been the odd strong man at the Junction – men like Joe Bennet who could throw a set of steel couplings over the boiler of a 'Scot', and Pat Kelly who, legend had it, could push a saddle-tank the distance of its own length with his shoulder. But these men had strength in their nature; they never did any training or book-reading. To maintain their Herculean powers they simply wolfed enormous meals and drank a barrel of beer between weekends. The cult championed by young Butch, however, claimed that it could make short men tall, weak men strong and bow-legged men straight-limbed. He enrolled one middle-aged recruit with the promise that with persistence and the right regimen, his bald head would sprout again!

At fifty years of age with a physique as impressive as that of a stray pigeon, Little Tommy Trot fell for Butch Johnson's promises as a virgin falls for the sugared words of her first lover. It was the books that clinched his conversion, books with glossy covers showing magnificent specimens of manhood in their birthday suits. One was entitled *Man be Big*, another *How to Get a Body like Mine*.

When Charlie Harper boarded the old relic the day after his check-up he was totally unprepared for the sight that met his eyes. He himself couldn't have been more contented with his lot. The doctor had confirmed his disability that barred him from duty on the main line and he knew for certain that his job on the shed pilot was secure for another twelve months. Of course, having three fingers missing on one hand was almost a twenty-four carat guarantee of keeping the cushiest job at the engine shed. Nevertheless, he could never quite find it within himself to be over-confident. A few days before he was due to appear before the doctor he always experienced a nagging doubt, unable to dismiss the possibility of the scientists inventing an artificial substitute for his missing fingers that would enable them to send him back on the main line shovelling coal by the ton. Now, his confidence fully restored, he climbed on board the engine singing 'You Are My Heart's Delight'.

Tommy was already there, but, to Charlie's astonishment, instead of joining in the song with his sweet tenor as he always did he suddenly exploded into a flurry of Swedish drill! With legs apart and arms spreadeagled he was bending to touch the toes of his boots with alternate hands! Right hand, left toe, left hand, right toe, groaning and puffing like a derelict 'Pug' engine with the effort. Stunned to silence in mid-song, Charlie stood completely still staring at the strange antics of his little mate in utter disbelief. Then, as Tommy switched to a mad spasm of knee bends, the astonished fireman's mouth fell agape.

The change in Tommy was total. In twenty-four hours he had become an entirely different personality leaving Charlie completely at a loss as to how to deal with the situation. From that day forth Tommy's blind, enthusiastic chase after Adonis led him into taking risks that no 'glassback' would ever dream of taking. The close proximity of the football ground didn't help matters. All he had to do to get there was to cross the branch line, scramble over the low wall and in five minutes flat his five-foot-three of skin and bone was twisting and twirling on the parallel bars. Sadly, from the day of his fatal conversion, the idyllic partnership of the two men of the Iron Road lost all its enchantment.

Rumours were circulating throughout the engine shed in no time at all. When another driver observed Tommy legging it round the football pitch like an alcoholic a minute before closing time, he tackled Charlie about it.

He came to the point at once. 'Has that mate o' yours gone completely off his head, Charlie? I mean, who does he think he is, the Mighty Atom? I'll tell you this, lad, if he's gorra weepin' bladder it must be cryin' its eyes out the way he's carryin' on! Doesn't the stupid little sod realise he's tempting fate?'

Alas, there was no counselling Tommy. The more Charlie lectured him on his stupidity, the more enthusiastic he appeared to become. He not only refused to join in the songs whenever Charlie tried to tempt him by launching into one of their favourite duets, but he began to refuse the Spanish onion he offered him at dinnertime, declaring that the only food the body required was bananas, brown bread and orange juice!

By a strange paradox, the more Tommy gained in health and strength, the more his once proud locomotive deteriorated. The old relic seemed as disgusted as Charlie at its driver's behaviour. As the estrangement of the once happy pair on the shed pilot deepened, Tommy began to leave the scouring and polishing entirely to Charlie, who, in an attempt to shame his recalcitrant driver, continued to do it alone. When this failed to do the trick, he abandoned the chores altogether as a lesson to him and, before long, the steampipes started to rust and the brasses became as tarnished as neglected souvenirs. From every joint in the steampipes and cylinders steam began to escape in such volume there were times when the ancient locomotive was completely enveloped.

It was only too obvious that things couldn't go on much longer as they were. Before many days had passed every driver and fireman at the Junction was commenting on Tommy's mad behaviour, saying quite openly that he had obtained the cushiest job at the engine shed by false pretences: 'I ask yer, could a man wi' a weepin' bladder carry on as he's doin'? Why, it doesn't stand to reason!'

And then, with brutal suddenness and just as Charlie had expected, fate struck the fatal blow. A full three months before it was due, Tommy received notice to appear before the company doctor for a medical examination. During all his time on the shed pilot he had always been called to attend for his annual check-up on the first Friday in August. Yet there it was in black and white, clutched tremulously in his hand before May was out!

DRIVER TROT: No 248
You will sign on duty at 9.15am on Tuesday May 25th to present yourself for a medical examination by the Company Doctor.
                                                          W. C. Philpot. Sup't.

As the realisation that his remarkable return to health and fitness had surfaced to the attention of higher powers smote him with stark suddenness, Tommy's cockiness abandoned him with miraculous haste. He knew the signs were ominous.

Utterly crestfallen, he held out the official note towards Charlie who stood with his back to him in the cab of the old relic. Unable to disguise the anxiety in his voice, he addressed him.

'Hey Charlie, wha'd'y'make o' this? They want me to see the doctor three months before I'm due! What am I gonna do?'

Ignoring him completely his fireman didn't even turn to face him. His instinct told him what Tommy was complaining about, for he had noticed the fateful chitty from the corner of his eye. After all, it was only what he had been expecting. With a distinct whine in his voice, Tommy appealed to him again.

'Charlie! Why don't yer turn round? I say they want me to see the doctor three months before I'm due! What am I gonna do, Charlie? Eh? What am I gonna do?'

Completely unmoved, Charlie remained standing with his back to his driver, his disgust at his foolhardy behaviour reinforcing his resolve to have nothing whatever to do with the matter. Meanwhile, the whine in Tommy's voice increased.

'Oh aye, it's all right for you, isn't it? It's not you whose got to see 'im! You're all right, aren't yer – he's already passed you unfit for main-line trains! Aye, you're all right! You've nowt to worry about! But what about me, eh, Charlie? What about me?'

Still unmoved, Charlie continued to stare over the side of the cab with his back to his driver.

'Why don't yer turn round Charlie? Why don't yer turn round an' talk to me? They're gonna take me off the pilot! That's what they're gonna do! You know that, don't yer ,Charlie?'

When his fireman still refused to respond to his pleading, Tommy's desperation increased.

'Say summat, Charlie! Why don't yer speak to me? D'yer wanna see me go or summat? Eh? D'yer wanna get rid o' me?'

At last, unable to stand more of Tommy's whining, Charlie turned on him.

'It serves you right, you an' your bloody physical jerks! Everyone knew you wouldn't get away with it! God's truth, they give you the cushiest job in the kingdom because of physical disability, an' you go throwin' yourself about as though you're trainin' for the Olympics! It's your brains that want exercisin', not your bloody arms an' legs! Haven't I been tellin' yer fer weeks, you stupid little sod? 'Course, you wouldn't listen, would yer? You were so set on makin' y'self a pint-sized Tarzan of the Apes you wouldn't listen! Well, you've gone an' done it this time all right, an' I hope you're satisfied wi' yourself!'

Charlie's onslaught reduced Tommy to a state of hopelessness, but the angry fireman hadn't finished.

'Y'know what's gonna happen now, don't yer? You'll be gettin' up at two o'clock in the mornin' next week to work the milk train! That's what's gonna happen, you silly little bugger! Oh aye, you've gone an' done it this time all right!'

Although Tommy moaned and whined about his fate throughout the rest of the morning, it was all to no avail, for his disgusted fireman remained silent and aloof. During their long, idyllic partnership the two enginemen had always dined together in the pleasant ambience of their well-appointed engine cab, but for several days past Charlie had taken to leaving the engine at dinnertime to dine alone in the tackhouse. He did this now. Taking his roasted onion and potatoes from behind the steampipes, he wrapped them in a small parcel containing a ready-cooked lamb chop and, grabbing his brewcan, descended from the engine leaving the distraught Tommy to ponder alone on the disconcerting uncertainty of his future.

And how he pondered! Unseen by anyone he probed the intricacies of his dilemma with such concentration that he spent the whole of his dinnertime talking to himself. Examining the catastrophe from every angle he found little cause for hope, but, when considering his fireman's refusal to co-operate, he discovered a chink of light in the darkness of his misery. Clutching at this in desperation, he worked on it with all his cunning during Charlie's absence so that when his fireman returned to the engine his plan was ready.

With Charlie continuing to shun him, Tommy chose later in the day to make his final attempt to pacify him. Waiting slyly until the atmosphere seemed favourable, he made his move.

'Y'know, Charlie, it's all right you pretendin' it's nowt to do wi' you, but if they take me off the pilot it won't be only me as'll suffer, y'know. It strikes me y'aven't thought about it, Charlie. In fact, I don't think you've thought about it at all!

Hoping the veiled warning in his statement would induce Charlie to turn and face him, he paused, but he was disappointed. Undaunted, he waited a few moments longer, then, moving closer, played his trump.

'Who d'yer think's next in line for this job if they get rid o' me? Go on Charlie, tell me that!'

When again Charlie failed to respond he paused again, then, 'Aye, you're sayin' nowt, are yer, Charlie, eh? I say y'sayin' nowt! Well, I'll tell yer who'll get this job if they take me off the pilot – you'll 'ave Asthmatical Jimmy fer a mate, that's who you'll 'ave! Asthmatical bloody Jimmy, coughin' an' splutterin' all over the footplate from signin' on to signin' off! A man who couldn't giver yer a song if his life depended on it! Now then, how yer gonna like that, eh, Charlie? Eh? How yer gonna like it?'

As the morbid image of Asthmatical Jimmy entered his thoughts,

Charlie felt all his resolve drain from him and, completely undermined, he turned to face the triumphant driver. Recognising his victory at once, Tommy sidled up to his fireman and placed an arm round his shoulders.

'Come on, Charlie, tell us what I'm gonna do. You don't really want to see me go, do yer? I mean, we've allus gorron well together, 'aven't we? You could get a worse mate, y'know.'

And so, for the for the first time in many days the two men remained close to each other as Charlie proceeded to advise his wayward driver on the steps he would have to take to extricate himself from the mess in which he had landed himself. It was a long, earnest counselling, with Tommy absorbing every tactic Charlie proffered with eager bouts of nodding.

The day before he was due to present himself for a medical examination, the whole of Clanky Junction blazed with the news of how Little Tommy Trot had collapsed at the controls of his locomotive, and throughout the rest of the day a constant stream of enquirers visited the old relic to glean the finer details from Charlie Harper. With appropriate solemnity and inexhaustible patience, Charlie related how the rigorous course of physical training undertaken by Tommy to cure his disability had finally proven too much for his delicate constitution, and how, that very morning, while performing a particularly intricate shunt, he had suddenly collapsed at the controls clutching that part of his anatomy where his bladder was situated.

The way Charlie told it, the situation was relieved by the appearance of an Angel of Mercy in the person of Driver Harry Spinks, Tommy's brother-in-law, who by the merest chance just happened to be passing the engine on his bicycle after signing off duty. With great effort the two of them succeeded in sitting the helpless Tommy on the crossbar of the bicycle and, pedalling as hard as he could, Harry had set off to convey the stricken driver home with the assurance that he would call at the family doctor afterwards to arrange an emergency visit.

When Little Tommy Trot resumed duty after a week at home and a week convalescing by the sea, a benefit to which he was fully entitled by virtue of a weekly subscription, he found the old relic resplendent in its former glory. It was only too clear that his loyal fireman had been very busy during his absence, for the brasses and steampipes gleamed as in happier times and, even as he stepped aboard, the mouth-watering aroma of roasting Spanish onions and potatoes was pervading the cab.

And yet, for a brief interlude, an air of awkwardness prevailed with the perfect understanding that they had known previously taking a few hours to blossom again. Like a pair of estranged lovers newly reconciled, they found themselves starting to speak at the same time, and it was only at the end of the shift, as they put away their engine for the night behind the platelayer's hut, that they fully restored the harmony they had known before Tommy's breach of faith.

It was Tommy who made the first gesture of reconciliation by commencing to sing their most favourite song in his sweet tenor voice, which, as befitted the occasion, was unusually subtle and enticing.

'Beautiful dreamer, wake unto me,
Starlight and dewdrops are waiting for thee.
Sounds of the rude world heard in the day,
Lulled by the moonlight have all passed away.'

Charlie couldn't resist the temptation. As Tommy launched into the chorus his fireman's rich baritone embraced his sweet tenor to reverberate the air over the Junction in perfect harmony. It was a deeply poignant moment. Indeed, there was a point during the rendering when, in a sudden surge of emotion, Tommy found himself struggling to avoid a break in his voice as he realised with vivid clarity just how close he had come to destroying his idyllic existence, but, pulling himself together just in time, he proceeded to sing bravely in a pronounced mood of thanksgiving.

If, for the reconciled pair on the shed pilot, the song was in the nature of a celebration, for others at the engine shed it was a dirge. The agonising rift between the intrepid pair had disturbed the working fraternity of Clanky Junction to its very foundations. For a brief, turbulent interlude, bitter jealousies and rampant ambitions had been unleashed to threaten the usual equanimity of the place. There were many contenders for the cushiest job on the Iron Road, but now the hopes of Asthmatical Jimmy, Palpitating Albert and many other 'glassbacks' both fake and genuine were completely shattered. When they had dashed off their applications for the expected vacancy in secret the moment they heard of Tommy's premature medical examination, their expectations had soared to dizzy heights. Now, alas, all was lost.

As the song of the two locomen floated over the coal stacks with a perfection they had never achieved before, the aspiring contenders for the job and everyone else at the Junction knew for certain that Little Tommy Trot and Charlie Harper, his fireman, would spend the rest of their days together on their Lancashire & Yorkshire relic, shunting a wagon here and a disabled engine there, contented as two cats on a hearth rug.

5
Almost a Hero

B etween the wars a job on the railway wasn't to be sniffed at. Above all other considerations it possessed the very desirable feature of being regular. In those days the mines and cotton mills, engineering and the building trades limped along in fits and starts so one never knew for certain if one would be in work three weeks together. The railways were different. There, such terms as 'short time' or 'laid off' were rarely heard. It helped matters if one happened to live in the same street as an engine driver. If one happened to be around when he dropped the hint that they were taking on more lads at the Junction, one's prospects glowed like a dying ember in a newly sprung breeze.

But it wasn't just the prospect of a regular pay packet that made a job on the Iron Road desirable. The myriad tracks of those days wound their way through the prettiest vales and valleys of England, Scotland and Wales. With every curve holding the promise of a new vision, a young fireman fresh on the footplate felt something akin to an explorer's joy.

That's how it was with young Jamie. At eighteen years of age and after barely a year at the Junction, he wore the grime of the engine shed like a badge of honour. He could hardly believe his luck! The very thought that he could board any one of over two hundred locomotives without hindrance filled him with awe. Furthermore, if a driver asked him to 'Take her back a bit' he was quite capable of doing so. His two pals, one a bricklayer's apprentice, the other a clerk at the Town Hall, listened enviously as he related his experiences. It seemed to them that if he had to choose between a night at the local dance hall and a shift at the Junction, he'd be sure to choose the latter.

In the manner of the fledgling, Jamie exaggerated the accounts of his experiences. If his driver asked him to move the engine a few feet along the line to enable him to oil an ill-set bearing, he would relate the incident as though he had driven the engine on a five-mile trip. On one occasion, when his driver rammed a wagon with slightly more than the usual force, he inflated the incident to the proportions of a disaster. When his pals ask him why it hadn't appeared in the newspapers, he stammered a little then explained how it had been 'hushed up'.

The night he was called to work his first trip on the main line his enthusiasm soared to new heights. When the foreman told him to report to a Driver Pratt impatiently waiting on a locomotive in the darkness of the shed yard to work a special freight to Bingley Dale, the name of the driver meant nothing to him. He was so elated at the prospect of venturing on to the main line for the first time, he was completely unaware that he was about to suffer the misfortune of working with one of the most notorious characters at the engine shed. But then, how was a raw, eager youth to know that when lifted to the crest of a wave, a wise man always looks for the trough? It was all very well viewing the world through the eyes of the bold characters in the 'twopenny bloods' of his youth, but the world has more than enough Albert Pratts and the sooner one makes their acquaintance the better.

Engine driver Albert Pratt was renowned not only for his enormous appetite but also for his manic taste in seasonings and flavours. Whereas most engine drivers contented themselves with a shovel-fry, say, once or twice a month, Albert indulged daily. The usual ingredients for this time-honoured ritual were eggs and bacon, with sausages, shredded cheese and onion as variants when a change was desired. With Albert it was nothing but red meat. Sometimes a slab of steak; sometimes three lamb chops cleaved at three-inch intervals; sometimes a pound of liver. After treating the meat to lethal doses of salt and pepper, he would hold the shovel just inside the firebox and proceed to observe every splutter and spit of the cooking meat until it was done to a turn. Finally, like an obscene maniac defiling a Van Gogh, he'd drown the lot with half a bottle of ketchup and attack it ravenously.

Not surprisingly, Albert was afflicted by the twin vice of gluttony – bone idleness. Once he settled his fat rump on the driver's seat he would get to his feet only to fry his meat on the shovel. An unwary fireman became his slave, fetching and carrying for him from the start of a trip to arrival back on the shed. So bone idle was he that he resented having to get to his feet to blow the whistle. When this was required he simply bellowed across the cab, 'Come on lad, give us a crow!'

Although Albert exploited Jamie's innocence to the full, the young fireman found the trip to Bingley Dale nothing short of rapturous. The snowstorm that sprang up at the start of the journey intensified his excitement, the sight of the lonely Derbyshire hills covered in snow in the moonlight elevating his spirits to a silent song. He was completely unruffled by Albert's incessant demands to heave more coal on the fire, to sweep the footplate, to pull on the whistle and a dozen other duties. The story he would relate to his pals on his return would make them envious.

Arriving at Bingley Dale three hours later, Albert raised himself laboriously from his seat and opened his food locker to start his shovel-fry. By this time the snowstorm had increased to a blizzard. Sliding shut the window to keep out the driving snow, Jamie huddled in his corner and watched wide-eyed as the rotund engine driver slapped a huge steak on the blade of the shovel. Crowning it with a chunk of dripping, he rested the blade on the lip of the firehole just inside the firebox, withdrawing it every few minutes to poke the contents with his penknife. After about ten minutes he withdrew it altogether and sprinkled the steak with lethal doses of pepper and salt that he took from a battered Oxo tin divided into two compartments. He then re-inserted the blade in the firebox until the steak was done to a turn. Withdrawing the shovel for the last time, he drenched the meal with dollops of tomato ketchup from a bottle that he took from his locker, wedged the shovel across the cab and, while Jamie chewed on his frugal sandwiches, wolfed down the steak as though he hadn't eaten for a week.

Fifteen minutes later, as the gluttonous carnivore leaned back on his seat with his belly cradled in his hands, snaking out his tongue for the remains of the tomato ketchup lingering round his nose and mouth as his meal entered the first, comforting stages of digestion, the voice of the Inspector pierced the howling wind.

'There's nothing for you to take back, driver! You'll be going back light!'

This suited Albert down to the ground. A leisurely fifty-mile return trip without any wagons after turning the engine on the fork and, with a bit of luck, he'd be in bed before daylight.

With Bingley Dale no more than five miles behind them after commencing the return trip, Albert's optimism began to wane. As the engine clanked homewards up the southern slopes of the Derbyshire hills in the raging blizzard it was brought to a stand at every signal. At first it was just a few minutes' delay at each, but the higher they climbed the longer they had to wait. Near the summit, as Albert braked to a standstill at Gowpoles's home signal, the engine lurched through a three-foot snowdrift. He had Jamie jumping about at once.

'Come on lad, get on the phone to the signalman! Tell 'im we're here!'

Peering down at the snowdrift in the light of his handlamp, Jamie protested, 'I can't go down there, Albert! I'll be buried alive!'

His driver was adamant. 'Take your shovel an' dig your way to the signal!'

So, while Albert remained glued to his seat still probing with his tongue for the last traces of ketchup, Jamie made to comply.

Soaked to the waist, he returned ten minutes later with the news that the line ahead was blocked. Albert stared at him as though it was all his fault. Then, lifting his feet from the footplate with a tremendous effort, he instructed his fireman again, 'Just sweep the coal dust from under me feet.'

Once more, Jamie complied without a murmur and Albert lowered his feet to settle himself more comfortably on his stool. Here, he addressed Jamie again.

'Y'know the rule, lad? You get on that phone every five minutes to remind the signalman we're here!'

Jamie replied eagerly, 'Of course I know the rule – Rule 55!'

'Well, don't forget to carry it out then – every five minutes – an' if we're still here after you've rung twice, go to the signal box an' sign the book, y'understand?'

As Jamie nodded, Albert cradled his belly in his hands, closed his eyes and went to sleep.

When they arrived at the signal it was three o'clock on Sunday morning. Telephoning the signalman twice at five-minute intervals, Jamie was informed that the line ahead was still blocked, and, after waiting a further five minutes, he set off in the blizzard towards the signal box faintly visible through the driving snow, and, soaked to the waist, wearily climbed the steps. The signalman informed him that the line was blocked by deep snowdrifts both in front and behind them and, if there was no let-up, there was no knowing how long they would be stranded.

After signing the book, Jamie left the signal box and returned to the engine. Back on the footplate he began to feel abandoned. Approaching his snoring driver to convey the signalman's verdict, he suddenly stopped his hand as, faintly, between Albert's snores, he thought he heard strange noises coming from his driver's bulging waistcoat. Sure enough, when he placed an ear to it he heard his gastric juices bubbling and squeaking like a mouse trapped in a drum. Oddly, he found the noises reassuring. Going back to his own side of the cab, he donned his overcoat, lay full length close to the firebox and joined his mate in slumber.

Long after daybreak Jamie awakened with a start. The first thing he noticed was the quietness. The wind had dropped. Jumping to his feet he saw with alarm that the snow nearly covered the boiler! Shaking his driver frantically he shouted, 'Albert! Albert! We're buried!'

Coughing and spluttering, Albert shook himself awake and, peering through his snow-covered eye-glass, sized up the situation at once.

'Hey, this is serious, lad! We'll be here for days! We'll be lucky if we don't starve to death! It's up to you, lad – only you can save the situation! Get your deggin' pipe!'

Taking hold of the degging pipe, Jamie passed it to him.

'Come on, lad, turn the water on!'

As Jamie turned the valve to release the scalding water, Albert played it on the snow outside the steps of the engine until, in a matter of seconds, a large black pit appeared. He shouted again. 'Come on lad, get your shovel!'

Jamie obeyed.

'Now, here's what I want you to do. Climb down the steps and dig your way across three sets of lines! D'yer foller? Three yards past the third set you'll have to watch y'self – if you don't, you'll fall down the embankment! Are yer with me?'

Jamie nodded excitedly.

'When you get to the top of the embankment you'll see Gowpoles a mile across the valley!'

Here he grabbed Jamie by the shoulders and looked him straight in the eyes. 'Now, here's what I want you to do lad! Fight your way there an' tell 'em we're starvin'!'

With youthful gallantry Jamie descended the steps and was shovelling like mad before Albert finished his instructions.

'Try an' get a bit of lamb – half-a-dozen chops!'

Sure enough, over the third set of tracks Jamie's shovel entered thin air. There, through the gap he had made in the snowdrift, he saw Gowpoles, a tiny village nestling at the foot of the hills across the valley. The cluster of tiny cottages and the simple church were almost engulfed. Although it was no more than a mile distant, it looked more like ten to Jamie. Stepping as high as he could, he found himself somersaulting down unexpected slopes, tearing his clothes on invisible barbed wire and crashing through the ice of concealed streams. Staggering like a wounded deer, he fell countless times before he reached the lane that led to the village, but, picking himself up each time, he struggled bravely forward towards the goal of his desperate errand.

At last, panting clouds of steam and on the point of exhaustion, he stopped outside a row of simple cottages. From one a spiral of blue smoke curled. Choosing this one, he dug his way through a snowdrift barring the path and knocked on the door. A grey-haired woman appeared in a cheerful pinafore. Shivering in his sodden boots and clothes, he started to explain the purpose of his mission – telling how he and his driver were stranded on their snowbound engine with no chance of getting through. The old woman, a member of a railway community all her life, learned more with her eyes than from Jamie's words, and, in no time at all, had him sitting before a blazing fire clasping a mug of steaming tea.

Thickly buttering four home-made muffins, she placed a thick slice of cheese between each of them and wrapped them in brown paper. Then, filling a pop bottle with the rest of the tea in the teapot, she added four teaspoons of sugar, corked it, and placed it next to the parcel of sandwiches. As Jamie got up to leave, he felt for the shilling he knew he had in his pocket and offered it to the woman. Taking it, she gazed at it for a moment then slipped it back into his pocket. With this, she hugged him, kissed his cheek then ushered him to the front door.

As he waved goodbye to the old woman, the church bells rang out and, with fresh hope, Jamie set off back to the stranded engine with the determination of a Yukon prospector. Retracing his footprints still visible in the snow, he plodded his way back to the stranded engine with the food parcel stuffed under his pullover, the tea-bottle protruding from his jacket pocket and his shovel over his shoulder. On the less hazardous stretches of the terrain his mind began to conjure visions of greatness as his thoughts soared to the realms of heroism. The next time he saw his pals he would turn them green with envy as he related the experience. With his imagination in full flight he began to see mention of his exploit in the newspapers, telling how he had saved the day by sheer determination.

And what about Albert, his driver? Why, he'd be eating his heart out with anxiety awaiting his return. And so, his spirits rekindled by thoughts of his imminent fame and the welcome he would receive when, mission accomplished, he finally climbed back on board the engine, he strode out boldly and immediately went somersaulting in the snow as his boot slipped on a hidden boulder. An hour later, after losing the food parcel many times and sodden from the toes of his boots to his armpits, Jamie pulled himself up to the footplate utterly spent.

Albert grabbed the food parcel the moment the weary youth staggered through the handrails, his eyes glinting with gluttony as he commenced feverishly to unwrap it. Taking one of the muffins he offered it to Jamie, then retreated quickly to his own side of the cab bearing the other three like a beast with its prey. Then, as Jamie slumped wearily on his stool, the greedy engine driver parted one of his muffins to examine the filling. Suddenly, his face distorted with disappointment, he bellowed, 'Bloody cheese? Is this the best y'could do?' Then, probing with a fat finger, he screeched, 'No bloody pickles neither!'

It was here that a dark cloud of bitter disillusionment passed over the sun of Jamie's youth, and, as he gave a great sigh, the invisible mantle of heroism slipped from his shoulders like a leaf in autumn.

6
The Cock
That Got Away

*E*ngine driver Jacob Purdy was a confirmed bachelor who lived with a spinster sister in a tiny, terraced railway house adjacent to the engine shed. Fifty-five years of age, tough as nails but easy to get on with providing that one didn't challenge his knowledge of war statistics or belittle the glory of the British soldier, he stood about five foot six, had a nose like Punch and was as bald as a monk. British to his very marrow, when he discoursed on world events he made it plain that he believed the rest of the world was populated by hordes of 'natives', a few million sex-mad Froggies and a few more square-headed Germans, all of whom owed everything they knew or were going to know to the British Empire and its superlative fighting man, the British soldier.

That was Jacob Purdy, an engine driver since the day he passed his driving examination four years after his demobilisation in 1918, and these were some of the things everyone at the Junction knew about him.

Among the thousand or so drivers, firemen and fitters at the engine shed, Jacob hadn't a single enemy. The knowledge that he had been mentioned in dispatches for bravery in the face of the enemy on the field of battle and had once driven the Royal Train, gave him a head start in any company. Even Wally Philpot, the District Locomotive Superintendent, afforded him the greatest respect whenever Jacob entered his office.

I worked with Jacob for so long that I got to know him better than any driver I worked with. Promotion was so slow at the time that the senior fireman was moaning every day at not being called for his driving examination: 'The way things are goin' I'll retire wi' a bleedin' shovel in me hands!'

There were rumours every week that the tedious climb up the rosters was going to get moving again, but still nothing happened. Month after month saw Jacob and me on the same footplate pounding over countless sleepers to all parts of the system in a partnership that blossomed into a strong, mutual loyalty that discouraged any outside interference. If another driver poked his head into the cab of our engine intent on offering me advice, Jacob didn't hesitate to tell him to mind his own business: 'You bugger off – if my fireman wants to know anythin' about railways, I'll tell 'im, not you!'

I became similarly smitten, finding myself making threatening gestures whenever I overheard any of my mates making doubtful remarks about Jacob.

It was only when old Charlie Wilkes, a driver on the Scotch run, dropped dead as he climbed from his engine at midnight after returning from a Glasgow trip, that the overdue spurt in promotion occurred.

By the time Jacob and I parted company as everyone moved up a rung on the ladder of promotion, we were like father and son. I knew him so well that I could tell he was in a crowd by recognising the noise his nose made when he blew it into his large red handkerchief. When he raised his arm to scratch his head, I could predict with perfect accuracy the exact spot just above his right ear where his fingers would touch first. Whenever he lit a fag he used the spent match to poke his ears. I saw him do this so often that I almost shared the pleasure he seemed to derive from the habit.

Had I worked with him for the usual span, say nine months or a year, his relationship with Elsie might have appeared nothing more than a platonic friendship with a close neighbour. Elsie was a married woman who lived on the opposite side of the same street, and whose husband worked alternate day and night shifts at the carriage works. From time to time Jacob praised her warm, friendly manner, but it was only after I had been his fireman for eighteen months that I realised he extolled her virtues only when we were on days and her husband was on nights.

This realisation dawned slowly, beginning when he revealed that he occasionally went across to Elsie's to have his tealeaves read. He claimed she was very good at this and had predicted many events in his life. There was also the question of the chocolates. Whenever we found ourselves wandering the thoroughfares of a distant city when lodging away on a double trip, he'd send me into a sweet shop to purchase a small box for him. Somehow Jacob and chocolates didn't go together and, when I handed them to him, he'd look slightly embarrassed, looking about furtively as he stuffed them under his jacket as though concealing ill-gotten gains. The first time he asked me to get them I enquired if they were for his sister, and I remember how he shook his head in a slightly guilty manner, saying, 'No son, they're for Elsie. She's very good to me y'know, lad. She's very fond of a few chocolates.'

As he enlightened me as to the recipient of the chocolates I thought that I detected the faintest sign of embarrassment on his face as we continued looking at each other in silence. Then, searching my features for signs of rebuke and finding none there, his left eye flickered in a wink and he hugged the chocolates already concealed under his jacket.

After eighteen months together I was convinced that there was nothing more I could learn about him. His habits and gestures I could predict with perfect accuracy. I even knew the shop he preferred when buying his socks, and how, no matter what time of the day or night he got out of his bed, he couldn't get going until he had drunk three cups of strong tea and smoked two fags.

At this stage in our relationship he appeared an open book, then, almost at the end of our time together, I discovered something quite unexpected. It came to light that Jacob was the most hated man I had ever encountered. I know I said earlier that he hadn't an enemy at the shed, but it wasn't any of his mates that hated him, nor any human for that matter – it was the magnificent Rhode Island red cockerel that ruled the roost only six yards from his own back door!

I knew only too well that he kept hens. Of all the topics I heard him discuss during our time together, not one aroused his interest as much as probing the mysteries of the feathered species favoured by the members of the poultry club that thrived at the Junction. With Jacob, all other pursuits and pastimes, be they football, cricket or politics, horse-racing, bowls or darts, gardening or old-tyme dancing, paled into insignificance when compared to husbanding the common backyard fowl. He was completely obsessed by the creatures. On every other subject he would comment with complete lack of commitment, but mention the virtues of backyard poultry and one would inflame his interest at once. There were also visible signs of his obsession. Whenever he made an incursion into his henpen immediately before leaving for the Junction, he would arrive with his jacket covered in feathers and his boots caked with hen droppings.

Jacob's interest in poultry germinated during his years in the trenches in the First World War, where he learned what it was to go hungry. He told me how, on being demobilised, his mother welcomed him home by cooking him three fried eggs with a slice of ham and the memory of it glowed in his mind even as he described it to me more than twenty years later. As though to commemorate the event he frequently treated me to a special fry-up announced the day before as we signed off duty: 'By the way, lad, don't bring any grub tomorrer. Just a few rounds o' bread. I'll be bringing the old ham an' eggs.'

The next day, usually at dawn when the engine was tucked away in some remote sidings, he would asked me to share a delicious meal cooked on the shovel with a devotion that would have shamed a head chef. He often declared that whether fried, boiled, scrambled or swallowed raw, an egg was a meal in itself that could be produced for next to nothing in the backyard.

With such faith in 'The meal in a shell', as he called it, it wasn't surprising that when Jacob got settled in his job on the railway he quickly knocked together a rickety henpen from old boards filched from the carriage works and sent off for half-a-dozen laying pullets. From that day hens became his main passion, with Elsie appearing later as a good second.

Unlike the roads, railways left the city by the backyard where rusty tin baths and derelict bicycles ended their days, a languid world of decay brightened only by the lines of washing that appeared like bunting on washdays. The women who appeared from time to time wore headscarves over their curlers, their careworn faces set grimly impatient for the day to pass so that they could accompany their husbands to the local pub as night fell. Here and there the blistered body of an ancient tramcar or omnibus gave its last ounce of usefulness sheltering a brood of chickens and, late on a summer evening, one would see the older men, part-time poultry-keepers, scattering corn or just sitting there drawing on their pipes in silence as the hens scratched around them.

Jacob liked nothing more than being stopped at a signal on a line that climbed higher than the backyards, where, gazing down on the makeshift shanties of his fellow poultry-keepers, he could issue praise or criticism according to his assessment of their efforts. I couldn't tell the difference between a white leghorn and a wyandotte, but the devotion that showed on his face was so pleasant to observe that I pretended to be interested and plied him with questions.

On the subject of poultry his patience was inexhaustible. He answered all my questions as though I intended to build a pen of my own the very next day.

'No lad, don't do that. What you want to do is gerrem about eight weeks old. It's no use botherin' wi' day-olds – they'll all die on yer unless you know how to rear 'em. No, you do as I say an' get half-a-dozen eight-week-old white leghorns – they won't start layin' till they're five months old, but it'll give 'em a chance to get to know yer, if yer see what I mean.'

From what he told me, Jacob obtained more eggs from his hens than anyone else in the poultry club. As far as I observed, this was his only vanity, for, as with his fierce belief in the supremacy of the British soldier, on the subject of producing eggs he deferred to no man. With a knowing wink he would explain, 'Oh aye, one a day lad, reg'lar as clockwork! Aye, they're no good to anyone if they don't give one a day – not worth their corn! I don't mind a miss now an' again, but if they're not doin' their stuff reg'lar – one a day – there's only one thing for it an' that's to pull their necks. I mean, you don't keep 'em for fun, do yer? They're not bloody canaries! Aye, one a day or in the pot – that's what I say. If I don't do my job properly I get a Form 1, don't I? Well, you can't send a bloody hen a Form 1 to make her buck her ideas up, can yer?'

Whenever Jacob went on like this I used to wonder if there was any way of letting the birds know the alternative to 'one a day'. It occurred to me that if the warning could have been got across to them, perhaps they would have slipped in one or two double-yoked ones as a kind of insurance. But, as Jacob continued it became apparent that it wasn't just the prospect of having their necks pulled that kept them regular.

'Y'see, lad, some of them as keeps poultry don't know how to do it. The important thing's to keep 'em scratchin'. A lazy bird's no good to anyone. Oh aye, you've got to keep 'em scratchin', that's what I say.'

Then, with his customary nod and a wink of one who knew a thing or two, 'An' don't forget the cabbage – not much, mind you, else you'll taint the eggs – just a few leaves now and again – about once a week. That's what does the trick.'

He imparted this advice like a share dealer on to a hot tip.

It was during one of these conversations that I learned of the Rhode Island red cockerel for the first time. It was a sweltering day in midsummer when the pungent smell of the creosoted sleepers was at its strongest. To make matters worse, the engine that we manned was notorious for the discomfort of its footplate. Built for the old London & North Western Railway at the end of the last century, the class to which it belonged had one great fault – the man who designed it forgot to take into account the indisputable phenomenon that when a man's blood boils he drops dead. Every other engine I ever worked on had a sandwich of asbestos between the firebox plates and the outer casing; on this monstrosity the firebox plates were completely exposed. In the depth of winter they were just about tolerable but, on a sweltering day in mid-summer, the driver and fireman melted like two slabs of lard in a chip-pan.

After shunting our train at Daunton sidings, our ancient 'Super D' was turned into No 1 road to allow Jacob and me to take our meal break of twenty minutes. To escape the lethal heat of the cab, we climbed from the engine and, with our backs to the wheels, sat side by side on the ballast overlooking a cluster of dilapidated henpens.

Pausing now and again to mop his glistening bald head as we commenced on our sandwiches, Jacob was rambling on about the best way of dealing with a broody hen. From what he told me, the cure for this malady, an abberation in a laying bird that could stop her laying for weeks, was almost as drastic as pulling a bird's neck when she refused to give one a day. In the case of a broody hen, however, there appeared to be hope. According to Jacob, the only recourse was to immerse the stricken bird completely under water just short of drowning her, then pull her out quickly.

'It's the only thing, son. It works like a charm. Never known it fail.'

Tied to a fence in the henpen below us, a wretch of a mongrel snarled at us like a half-starved wolf. My attention was fixed so intently on the dog that most of what Jacob was saying droned into oblivion. Then, realising that he had stopped talking altogether, and thinking he might have lost patience at my inattention, I said the first thing that came into my head – just to show there was no ill-feeling.

'I wouldn't care to meet that on a dark night, eh, Jacob?'

Looking disdainfully at the snarling mongrel, he appraised it's thin body, then, in a very matter-of-fact manner, said, 'That? Why, I've gorra cock at home as 'ud lick that poor brute to a frazzle!'

His remark didn't seem to call for an answer, and I turned away, taking out my handkerchief to mop my forehead. As I pocketed the handkerchief I felt him staring at me as though awaiting a reply, and, turning to face him, I attempted to change the subject.

'If this keeps up we'll be a couple o' grease spots before the day's out, Jacob!'

Completely ignoring my remark, he returned to the subject of the cockerel.

'Don't you believe me?'

There was no doubting his seriousness. The challenge in his eyes demanded a reply.

'Believe what, Jacob?'

'Don't you believe I've gorra cock at home as 'ud lick that poor brute to a frazzle?'

A little overwhelmed by his enthusiasm I looked at him without replying, a response he apparently interpreted as doubt.

'Look, I tell you what, we're on afternoons this week – come an' see for yourself in the mornin'. Why, he'd see 'im off in no time! He's had two cats an' a dog already! I tell yer, he'd see 'im off in next to no time. He'll go for anythin' – he has a go at me!'

So, partly to satisfy Jacob and partly to dispel the vision of a bird as big as an ostrich with the head of a dragon, the very next morning I arrived at the house of Jacob. He was waiting for me. Glistening like a freshly hung carcase of pork in bib and brace overalls, he opened the door the moment I knocked and ushered me inside. Over the fireplace hung a faded sepia photograph of a grinning youth in khaki with his cap at a rakish angle. On another wall was a picture of the King and, below this on the sideboard, two highly polished shell cases of brass, relics of Jacob's past glory.

Plump and friendly, his sister threw me a smile through the door to the kitchen where she was pouring steaming water into a teapot and, ignoring my blushes, Jacob started telling her what a marvel I was with a shovel. There was no escape; that's how it was with engine drivers in the Steam Age when a fireman who took their fancy paid them a visit.

After we had drunk the tea and Jacob had exhausted my virtues in the direction of keeping a good head of steam, he got up from the table and made for the back door.

'Well, son, come on, I'll show you th' owd cock.'

As I got to my feet to follow him out, his sister shouted a warning. 'You watch that there cockerel, Jacob! Don't let him get behind you!'

As I closed the door behind me I felt my flesh tingling with excitement. Resting against the henhouse door was a brake-stick, a four-foot length of stout ash used for pinning down wagon brakes. Grasping this firmly in his right hand, Jacob took hold of the latch with his left and crouched low. As I crouched behind him he whispered loudly over his shoulder.

'When I open the door follow me inside and shut it quickly behind yer. Are y'ready? Right, come on!'

Releasing the latch, the door jarred open and we rushed inside to the accompaniment of the hens erupting into a frenzied cacophony of squawking as they retreated to the far wall of the henhouse. Half flying, half running, they tumbled over each other in their vain bid to escape, leaving in proud isolation the most magnificent guardian of the feathered world I have ever set eyes on!

The specimen I beheld was surely no ordinary backyard cockerel. To start the strain from which that creature came, an ostrich must have taken a fancy to a golden eagle! Unless my memory is playing tricks on me, from its wicked claws to the crest of it's blood-red comb it stood almost a yard high!

Standing first on one foot then the other, it appeared to be sizing us up! Its feathers had the sheen of vitreous enamel, with gold, red, green and purple hues alternating in the sunlight from the grimy henhouse window. It possessed the proud bearing of a fearless warrior, and the glint in its eyes was cold and lethal.

As Jacob and the cockerel faced each other waiting to see who would make the first move, the giant bird started clawing the floor, its piercing eyes fixed on its adversary in a wicked gleam. Jacob shouted a warning.

'Watch him! He'll come for us any second!'

How right he was! Taking three rapid strides forward, the cockerel suddenly shot to the roof of the henhouse and came at Jacob like a Stuka bomber! As I closed my eyes and crouched so low behind Jacob – I was almost lying on the floor – I heard the thud of the brake-stick as he took a swipe at the clawing bird. Then, standing up, I saw it land amongst the terrified hens. Quick as a flash it came again. It was screeching venom. Again the brake-stick struck home, and again the cockerel landed amongst the squawking hens. Once more it tried, but this time it finished up lying prostrated with exhaustion in a circle of terrified hens.

In a gentle shower of feathers, Jacob stood over the defeated bird like a reluctant conqueror. His voice full of remorse, he shouted at it, 'When are yer gonna learn, you silly old cock? Can't y'see I wanna be your pal? What d'yer want me to do – stand here an' let you scratch me eyes out?'

Continuing to stare at the cockerel a few moments longer, Jacob finally relaxed and, turning to me, said, 'What did I tell yer? Didn't I tell yer he'd go for anyone?'

Back in the house I tried to get to the bottom of the feud between Jacob and the giant cockerel.

'Well, it's the first time I've seen a creature bite the hand that feeds it, Jacob. We have a dog at home that'll go for anyone approaching the house, but he's like a lamb with the family.'

Jacob flapped his arms in a gesture of helplessness.

'Well, you saw it with your own eyes, didn't yer, son? You wouldn't believe it, would you? If you hadn't seen it with your own eyes you wouldn't' 'ave believed it, now would you?'

Here, he gave a great sigh.

'I wouldn't mind so much but, d'yer know, when that there cock was twelve month old I went in there to pull it's flamin' neck! Didn't I, Alice?'

His sister nodded sadly as Jacob continued.

'I had the bloody money for 'im – promised 'im to Jackie Smethurst for Christmas! Didn't I, Alice?'

As though recalling a very painful episode in her life, Alice nodded again.

'D'yer know, son, I tried all ways to see 'im off! I held 'im under me arm an' pulled, I held 'im between me legs an' pulled. I even wedged 'im in the door and pulled – an' he still wouldn't give in! D'yer know, son, I pulled that bloody cock's neck till I was too tired to pull any more! I mean, it's not as though I'm a novice at pullin' bird's necks! We have 'em regular – I've pulled hundreds in me time!'

As he said all this, he looked at me as though appealing for sympathy. Then, 'Well I can tell yer, I came in for the axe at the finish, didn't I, Alice?'

Again his sister nodded.

'An' d'yer know, son, when I went in to finish 'im off wi' the axe an' saw 'im lyin' there gaspin', I said to meself – I said, well if he's that fond o' life he can 'ave it – an' I came back in wi' the axe without finishin' 'im off! Didn't I, Alice?'

When Alice confirmed in her usual manner that what Jacob said was the bitter truth, he turned to face me with a deeply puzzled expression on his face. Then, with a final despairing shrug of his shoulders, he pointed vexedly at the henhouse door and exclaimed, 'An' that's the bloody thanks you get!'

It just goes to show how easily a man can be misunderstood, I suppose.

7
Shove Potion

*I*magine a drop of thick black engine oil as it leaves the spout of an oilcan, enlarge it to the proportions of a short man and picture how it would appear if a shaft of sunlight shone on its glistening skin near the top; do this and you will have a good impression of engine driver Daniel Lockett at thirty yards distance.

Dan stood about five foot five. Side-on, his outline broadened downwards into two huge curves, one round his tremendous belly, the other, not quite so big, encompassing his generous backside. Dan's belly commenced its alarming expansion the day he abandoned the fireman's shovel to take the controls on the driver's side of the cab, when, to celebrate his promotion, he regaled himself with a brand new English lever watch and chain, which, with periodical adjustments, he had worn ever since across his straining waistcoat.

As though by some adjusting mechanism of his anatomy, the further his belly protruded the more his head went backwards, so that, by adding its weight to that of his behind, he was better able to support the enormous load of his paunch.

Despite his unwieldy shape, Dan waddled along at a surprising pace. With his belly jerking from side to side with each movement of his short, stumpy legs, he appeared for all the world like the big drummer in a Whit Week procession.

Dan was fifty-seven years of age. In his railway uniform he appeared the kind of man who would be as bald as a plucked chicken, but, whenever he raised his cap to scratch his head, an unsuspecting onlooker would be startled by his rich sward of rebellious red hair. His face was fresh as a country girl's, and under his sand-coloured eyebrows were two closely set pale blue eyes. They were small like a pig's and a little offset in a disconcerting squint. At close quarters the permanent blush on each side of his face was seen to be delicate patterns of lace-like veins in pink, red and purple centred on his cheekbones.

To everyone at Clanky Junction, engine driver Daniel Lockett was known simply as 'Dirty Dan'. I never discovered whether this was due to the black obscenity of his language or his practice of wearing his overalls until they disintegrated with oil rot. Whatever the reason, there was absolutely no doubt but that the name suited him perfectly. It never appeared to bother him that his workmates walked round him rather than past him, nor that whenever he approached a group of them he caused an instant dispersal to occur. Although Dan's tendency was to insult everything and everyone in sight, he himself was encased in a hide so thick that such abuse bounced off him without having the slightest effect.

Even to this day, more than fifty years after I had the misfortune to make his acquaintance, I still have my doubts as to whether Dan was born in the usual manner. I am still inclined to the view that one dark and dismal night he was blasted from the chimney of a saddle-tank labouring up Tichworth colliery bank grasping an oilcan in his hand, swathed in the overalls he had worn ever since and cursing fit to shame a Sergeant Major drilling a squad of new recruits. Pursuing my fantasy further, after being blasted into the night sky I see him landing in the tender of a coal engine heading for Clanky Junction where, despite all they did to get rid of him, he remained to torment all who laboured on the Iron Road to the end of his days.

Filed away in the Superintendent's office, Dan's service record card listed some of the highlights of his rebellious career on the railway. It showed forty-one years' service; timekeeping, good; general acumen, average. Then, in red capitals, there followed a long list of reprimands and suspensions. There was one for threatening his driver with the shovel in his early days as a fireman, another for transporting a harmonium he had salvaged in some distant city on the back of the tender of his locomotive, and another for buckling the smokebox doors of several locomotives through persistently wedging a jemmy in their blastpipes to increase the blast of the exhaust.

One of his more awkward escapades was marked by a suspension of two days for being discovered playing crib in the porter's room at Central station while his train stood in the platform three minutes after the guard had waved his green flag and the signal had been lowered to the clear position. In the remarks column, with uncompromising brevity, it stated, 'Stubborn – requires firm discipline'.

As a guide to his notoriety, however, Dan's service record card was entirely inadequate. To understand fully the putrid richness of the man, one had to work with him on the same locomotive.

Dan was a scourge; something that challenged all forms of discipline, ignored all manifestations of authority and blasphemed its way through all arguments no matter how well-informed the opposition. He was so cross-grained and unpredictable by nature that from the lowliest fireman to the most richly gold-braided official he received only the most respectful deference.

When it became known that Dan was at the controls of a locomotive one might have thought that he was coupled to a train loaded with dynamite. Nobody seemed to want him to linger in their domain. When a signalman learned that he was at the controls of a train about to enter his section of line, he would leap to his levers as though he was dealing with the Royal Train. Instead of simply informing the next signal box along the line of its approach, he would telephone every box four miles ahead. The signals would change to clear with magical rapidity and, as the train rumbled past his box he would lean from a window to make sure all went well. Only when the guard's van squealed past would he slide the window shut and replace his signals to danger. Then, darting to the telephone, he would call his colleague higher up the line.

'That you, Jud? He's all yours now, mate. What's it like ahead? Good – keep the swine movin'.'

When his train arrived at a siding at which another train was already waiting to be shunted, he would be given preference. Dealing with the train with frantic haste, as the last wagons flew into the sidings the Inspector would dispatch him to the shed, exclaiming as his tail-lamp receded down the line, 'Thank God for that!'

I consider myself exceedingly fortunate to have found myself working on the same footplate as Dirty Dan only once during my time on the Iron Road. Nevertheless, it was an experience I shall remember to the end of my days. Our encounter came about because of a long spell of freak weather. After raining without let-up for days on end, the line through the Royt valley was inundated, causing the cancellation of all trains running that way, including mine. My regular driver had been fixed up on another journey, leaving me standing in the signing-on hall awaiting instructions. After hanging about for almost half an hour, I saw the foreman answer the telephone and, immediately afterwards, he came to the window and instructed me to report to 2766 to work the 1.55 Dankworth to Shawcross goods.

Having been drenched by a deluge on my way to the engine shed, I was anxious to get to the locomotive and, instead of lingering to enquire as to the name of the driver, I hastened to the stores to collect my tools and shovel completely unaware of what the night held in store for me.

Throwing the shovel between the handrails of the engine, I climbed on board to find the footplate deserted. Whoever the driver was, it was obvious that he hadn't arrived. Hanging my raincoat and jacket on the side of the cab, I rolled up my sleeves and, with more than customary force, opened the firehole door to survey the state of the fire. The entire grate area was covered by a substantial layer of smouldering, dark red coals on which, here and there, formations of red, yellow and purple flames lazily licked each other in a slow, sensuous dance. When the time arrived for leaving the shed, a pull on the damper and a turn on the blower would soon put life in it.

Although the shift had just begun I felt drowsy. It was always the same between midnight and six in the morning; no matter how much sleep one might have had before setting out for the shed, the heat from the firebox seemed always to put back the tiredness in one's bones.

Satisfied that the fire would require no further attention until we left the shed to start our journey, I turned my thoughts to obtaining a supply of oil from the stores to allow the driver, whoever he was, to lubricate the bearings. This was a task every conscientious fireman saw to at once to set the tone for the rest of the trip. It pleased the engine drivers of the Steam Age more than can be imagined to board their locomotives to find two large tin bottles, one containing engine oil and the other cylinder oil, resting on the warming plate just above the firehole to render the oil free-flowing.

So, with this in mind, I reached down to the locker on the driver's side of the cab to locate the oil bottles when, wheezing like a punctured organ pipe, Dirty Dan pulled himself between the handrails and stepped on to the footplate. The very sight of him was enough to depress a saint, but, to make matters worse, he was accompanied by an odour like the stench of a thousand rotting bones! Standing in the centre of the footplate like a moth-eaten washerwoman in a pantomime, he clasped to his belly a tattered bundle of hessian as big as a week's washing! He stood there hesitating, staring at me as though challenging me to say something. In the light from the firebox his face bore an expression of complete indifference as, to my utter astonishment, I realised the stench emanating from the ghastly bundle had not the slightest effect on him!

My spirits plummeted. This surely was destined to be the most miserable night of my life! Discovering that Dan was my driver made the night's prospects bad enough without further tribulations. Had my regular train been running I would have been coasting along a line as flat as the Pendine sands by this time with a driver as genial as a favourite uncle. Now, not only had I a seven-mile gradient that demanded a pint of sweat for every mile to contend with, but a driver whose reputation would have barred him from a job cleaning the sewers and a mysterious bundle of heaven knew what that stank like a month-old corpse! And all this before we had hardly got started!

With Dan's gaze following me, inviting comment, I put my hand to my nose and retreated to the furthest corner of the cab away from the odious hessian sack he clasped to his belly. For a few moments we stared at each other without speaking, but it was impossible to remain silent.

'What the Devil have you got there?'

Ignoring my question completely, with a great heave and a grunt he tossed the disgusting bundle to the back of the cab, where it landed with a sickening squelch.

Desperate to escape from the foul atmosphere of the cab if only for a short respite, I hurriedly grabbed the oil bottles and left for the stores. Re-entering the cab on my return, the smell was so overwhelming that I had to protest again.

'You don't expect me to work near that stink all night, do you?'

Waddling towards me with a confiding air, he replied in the grunt language he always used, 'You'll be glad o' that afore t'night's out!'

With this, he turned about and waddled to his own side of the cab. As he proceeded to fill his oilcan with engine oil from one of the bottles, I tried again.

'What do you mean, I'll be glad of it? What possible use can we have for an evil-smelling bundle like that?'

Shrugging my question aside, he replied, 'You'll see!'

It was time to leave for the shed outlet signal tender-first to allow another engine to couple up to us. Sounding a loud crow on the whistle, Dan pointed to the handbrake which I unscrewed viciously and, as he opened the regulator, we began to move slowly off the pit. Thrusting my head through the cab window, I filled my lungs with the night air, but no matter how I gulped, the foul odour of Dan's abominable bundle lingered persistently in every crevice of my nose and throat.

The 1.55 Dankworth to Shawcross freight had run for more than fifty years, shattering the nocturnal silence six nights of the week just when the unfortunate people who occupied the houses alongside the line ought to have been cocooned in deep folds of slumber. Vibrating the earth and everything on it for three miles each side of the railway, the monster train blasted from Dankworth sidings until, three miles down the line, it stopped to allow a bank engine to come behind to assist it up a seven-mile gradient. To get the six-hundred-ton load up the incline took the power of three locomotives, the skill of three drivers and the sweat of three firemen. Two of the engines pulled at the front while the other pushed behind.

Every night except Sunday, the poor wretches occupying the dreary terraced houses alongside the line tossed in their beds in nervous anticipation waiting for the dreaded moment when the very foundations of their houses would start trembling threateningly as the huge engines pounded past their back doors with the noise of a cannonade.

It always took longer for the ear-splitting sound to subside than it did for it to increase on the train's approach and, when the wind was from the east, they would continue to hear it as the engines blasted up the stiff gradient several miles away. I often wondered how the inhabitants of the houses fared on Sundays when they forgot what day it was, poised on the brink of sleep in agonising suspense, waiting for the monster train that wouldn't pass until Monday.

Twenty minutes later the two engines ran into Dankworth sidings and coupled up to the awaiting train. All that remained was for the guard to give Dan and the driver of the engine in front details of the load. By this time the heat from the firebox was having a telling effect on the bundle lying at the foot of the tender. The smell coming from it was stronger than ever. It was beginning hum like a putrescent haggis. On the way to the sidings I had toyed with the idea of pitching it over the side of the engine when Dan had his back turned, but, strangely, as the smell intensified so did my curiosity. Before the night was over I was determined to solve the mystery of that disgusting bundle.

Dan got up to the anti-social pranks for which he was renowned the moment the guard shouted up to him from the foot of the engine steps, 'What name is it, driver?' The guard's question was perfectly in order. At the beginning of every trip it was part of the guard's duty to obtain the name of the driver and the number of the locomotive and enter them in his journal. Like me, it must have been the first time he had worked the 1.55 Shawcross that week, for, by this time everybody else along the line knew that Dirty Dan was at the controls.

When Dan failed to reply, the guard tried again. 'Your name, driver!'

Taking his time, Dan waddled to the top of the steps and looked down at the guard. For an agonising moment I thought he was going to spit at him! Then, very slowly and with deliberate sarcasm, he replied: 'William… Henery…Charlie…Coughdrop!'

Realising instantly the identity of the driver he was dealing with, the guard scuttled off without another word to the driver of the leading engine, where he was given a friendlier reception.

At last, when the signal dropped and the guard displayed a green light, Dan and the driver on the leading engine lunged on their regulators. Straining at the heavy load, both locomotives roared into a mad dance as the wheels slipped on the wet rails, sending two streams of red-hot cinders shooting skywards to descend like molten rain on the sidings. Shutting off steam, they opened the sanders and opened up again. This time, slowly but surely, the wheels of the two locomotives gripped the sanded rails and they eased the long train from the sidings and crossed to the main line.

Three miles out of Dankworth we stopped at Eccleston to allow the bank engine to come behind. After a few minutes we heard the driver whistle in the distance to indicate that he was ready when, without warning, Dan started ranting and raving for all he was worth! I got the impression that his rotund figure was going to explode any second with the pent-up wrath he was trying to get rid of. He was beside himself! In the time it took for the bank engine to squeeze five wagons together, albeit to no avail, he hurled every threat, curse and blasphemy in its direction over the top of the tender. From what I could make of his outburst, it seemed that so far that week the bank engine hadn't been doing his share of getting the heavy train to the top of the gradient. Dan, in characteristic fashion, was simply letting him know he wasn't going to stand for it!

When the driver on the leading engine whistled to acknowledge the bank engine's readiness, the two drivers opened up again and the steel plates of the two locomotives shuddered as the great pistons began to move in the cylinders as we started our journey in earnest. With deafening blasts at the chimney-tops we set off to tackle the gradient ahead of us with Dan screaming a final burst of invective over the tender in the direction of the bank engine.

'You'll shove tonight, you lazy bastards, you see if you don't! If you think you're 'avin'…'

Here my youthful ears were spared more of his profanities as a cloud of warm, clammy steam gushed into the cab to stifle his words as we blasted under a bridge.

By now the rain had stopped. From the fireboxes of the two straining locomotives, two shafts of incandescent light pierced the night sky as I and my colleague on the engine in front got down to the task of heaving coal. Sweat began coursing down my arms and legs, causing my vest and trousers to stick to my skin. Before we hit the gradient we had to be rattling along at fifty. If we didn't take full advantage of a short level stretch of line that intervened, we would be struggling halfway up the incline.

It soon became apparent that we weren't achieving the necessary momentum when, once again, Dan commenced another tirade of curses in the direction of the bank engine. As we pounded along the track a vast trail of smoke traced our progress towards the gradient and cinders bounced from the cotton mills alongside the line, glowing red a second before they died. Again I leapt to the shovel. More coal, more sweat, and, as I shut the firehole door, a lethal gush of steam blasted from the safety valve.

Less than halfway up the gruelling gradient it became ominously clear that the bank engine at the rear of the train couldn't have been pushing more than three or four wagons. 'Crowing' on the whistle like a man possessed, Dan's curses were getting more vile with each painful revolution of the wheels. To make matters more frustrating, when I dived to the tender for each shovelful of coal my nose was no more than a foot from the disgusting bundle of mystery lying in the corner. By this time it was perspiring as freely as I was. To alleviate the torture I tried shovelling in quick bursts, but even this was to no avail, the relief I gained by removing my nose smartly from its overpowering odour being countered by having it there twice as often. Truly, my night trip with Dirty Dan was turning into a nightmare!

Entering Doddington Tunnel with the engine struggling for every yard of track, Dan was jumping up and down with rage and cursing incoherently. Even I knew what lay in store for us if we stopped now. If we failed to drag the train from the mile-long tunnel we would be stuck inside it for ages gasping for breath in a cloud of sulphur fumes. Glancing at the steam gauge to see the pointer hovering on the red mark and knowing only too well that Dan was applying all the power the engine was capable of producing, I was just about to plunge into a deep mood of pessimism when, suddenly, almost sending me flying in his eagerness, Dan leapt to the centre of the footplate. With the locomotive lurching from side to side with each laboured stroke of its pistons, I watched spellbound as he grabbed hold of the evil-smelling bundle lying in the corner and dumped it in front of the firehole. Frantically untying the knots he was muttering like a lunatic.

'I'll make the bastards shove, you see if I don't!'

Holding my nose, I watched incredulously as he threw back the folds of the hessian to reveal the contents of the bundle. No wonder it stank! Inside was a half-hundredweight of fish and chicken heads along with their entrails! He informed me later that he had cadged them from a local fishmonger who had saved him several days' supply.

By this time the engine was lurching through the tunnel as though each gasp from its chimney-top would be its last. In the light from the firebox Dan resembled a priest of some weird black magic cult performing an evil ritual. When the gruesome contents of the bundle were exposed, he poured a gallon of thick, black cylinder oil over the lot, then re-tied the knot.

For a moment I thought Dan had gone completely mad. Grabbing hold of the soggy load, he wrestled it on to the blade of the shovel and heaved it with all his considerable strength at the firehole. It was too big to go through! It stuck in the hole sizzling and spluttering and emitting a disgusting odour! He became frantic and, with squelching blows, began belting it with the shovel until, just when I was contemplating leaping from the engine to escape the death-dealing fumes, it dropped through the firehole into the flames of the furnace.

Diving to the side of the cab in a desperate bid for air, I suddenly experienced one of those flashes of insight that sometimes come to man in a state of utter desperation. At last, I had solved the mystery of Dan's obnoxious bundle! Rolling back along the tunnel was a dense cloud of smoke laden with the stench of the burning entrails. When the bank engine entered that lot the only way to escape the putrid odour of the fumes would be to shove like mad! And how they shoved! Seconds later we lurched forward in an alarming burst of speed that sent me flying across the cab and, less than a minute later, we shot from the tunnel like a runaway train!

Regaining my composure after my unnerving experiences of the previous couple of hours with Dan, I breathed my fill of the fresh night air, then opened the firehole door so that the light from the fire afforded a better view of him. He was transformed. With tears streaming down his fat cheeks, he was perched on his stool like Humpty Dumpty, his feet dangling three inches from the footplate and his podgy hands clasping his enormous belly. He appeared to be struggling with himself, as though unable to release a tremendous accumulation of mirth that had built up inside him. Then, just when I was becoming fearful he might collapse in convulsions, he exploded into peels of Satanic laughter. Each time he got rid of a load, it seemed to build up again so that every twenty minutes throughout the rest of the trip he exploded time and time again.

My last view of Dan was when we left the shed after signing off duty just after dawn the next morning. Disdaining to walk with the unsociable creature, I followed ten yards behind. One moment he was waddling along straight as an arrow, the next he was falling about like a drunken man screaming and screeching with uncontrollable laughter as his mirth demanded release again. Who knows? Perhaps the Devil himself has a sense of humour.

8
Roly's Hard Ride

L ike the rock that sank a thousand ships, once seen, the face of
Black Jack Robinson was never to be forgotten. Indeed, his image
leaps into my mind like Satan on to a Victorian stage. With less than
five years to go to receiving his retirement clock, Black Jack had driven
his first locomotive before the turn of the century, and although I
wasn't around at the time, I'm absolutely certain the event provoked
not the slightest expression on his swarthy countenance.

That is what I remember most clearly about him – his face. Every
other feature of the man has faded with time, but that swarthy, morose
face projects through a myriad hazy memories like the summit of the
Eiger through layers of mist.

There wasn't a man at the Junction who could remember a single
occasion when his face had softened into a smile. This craggily
featured, uncommunicative engine driver appeared completely devoid
of emotion. So forbidding was his countenance that neither joy nor
sorrow, pleasure nor pain, found succour to linger there.

In the way of expression, the only extravagance Black Jack allowed
himself was the singing of any one of a dozen hymns – never the full
verse, just a few words snatched at random once or twice a day. Without
any apparent cause, he would burst into song without warning,
surprising whoever happened to be his fireman by the startling
abruptness of it. Sometimes commencing at the beginning of a verse,
sometimes in the middle, after a couple of lines he would stop abruptly
as he returned to his silent brooding. He was like a long inactive
volcano briefly erupting to remind those who lived on its slopes that it
was still a power to be reckoned with.

But then, appearances can be so deceptive. I mean, if Black Jack
Robinson was so completely insensitive to those around him, how did
he become embroiled in his endless feud with Roly Poly Farrel, a goods

guard at Darkcroft sidings? In view of the bitterness of the affair one can only conclude that once offended, Black Jack Robinson was the kind of man who never forgets. Certainly, if Roly Poly and he had been dogs, there would have been skin and hair flying every time they met. The terrible feud between the two railwaymen had gone on for so long that no one could recall how it had started, prophesying that the hatchet would be buried only when one or the other of them finally cocked his toes up.

The mystery surrounding the origin of the feud was the cause of much speculation and rumour. Could it have been a difference of religion, that dedication to peace and goodwill that so often leads to hatred – the ultimate paradox? Was it the welshing on an old loan, or perhaps a schoolboy enmity that defied adult wisdom? No one knew. The only certainty about the whole sorry relationship was that when Black Jack was at the controls at the front of a train and Roly occupied the van at the rear, anything could happen. When the two adversaries saw a chance of getting at each other it was exploited to the full with no holds barred.

The way the two men reacted when they passed each other said it all. With the short, fat Roly bristling like a dog defending a bone as Black Jack strode passed him as though he didn't exist, the atmosphere became charged with their mutual hatred.

Leaving a sidings at the start of a trip it always fell to the morose engine driver to make the first move. In those days most freight trains ran loose-coupled, which meant that from the moment the engine began to move forward it travelled about ten yards before the guard's van moved at all. With the evil intention of wrapping Roly round the hot stovepipe of his van as early as possible, Black Jack made certain that his locomotive traversed that ten yards in one great leap so that the brake van shot forward with the utmost violence.

Anticipating Black Jack's malicious intent, Roly would cling for dear life to anything to hand the moment he entered his van, then bide his time until the train was labouring up the first incline. Here, with the engine blasting on full regulator, he would screw on his handbrake to increase the train's load by the equivalent of another fifteen wagons.

On a descending gradient Roly would screw on his handbrake so hard that instead of the train coasting effortlessly down it, Black Jack would be compelled to open the regulator as though heading for Shap summit. On these occasions the brake van performed so much skidding that it arrived at its destination with square wheels.

Without expressing his elation in the slightest degree, a particularly crafty move Black Jack relished above all others was the one he executed when Roly was scheduled to be relieved en route. Slowing down the train to allow the relief guard to board the guards van, he would suddenly apply full steam so that poor Roly had to risk life and limb jumping to the ballast from the rapidly accelerating train.

But whatever evil prank Roly got up to to make Black Jack's life as miserable as possible during a journey, it always fell to his arch enemy to administer the coup de grâce. As their train entered the sidings of their destination, Black Jack would apply the brake with a single swipe of his hand so that the engine almost stood on its smokebox with the abruptness of it. Then, as each wagon collided with the one in front, he would sit quite still anticipating the violent thud as Roly's twenty-ton brake van rammed the already stationary wagons to butt the engine another five yards along the track. Fulfilled by the success of his evil stratagem and content in the belief that by this time Roly would be spreadeagled on the floor of his van after completing a somersault, Black Jack would give voice to a snatch of 'Oh What a Friend We Have in Jesus', put his feet up on the warming plate above the firehole and retreat into an impenetrable mood of black brooding.

Mercifully the two enemies didn't find themselves at the opposite ends of the same train often. To have allowed this fate would have been guilty of deliberately setting the scene for murder. In her infinite wisdom fate arranged their encounters just three or four times a year in the way of irresistible forays of capriciousness.

Had a score been kept of the tricks they played on each other during their time on the Iron Road, I am in no doubt that by the time they retired the score would have been about even, but this is not to say it was always tit-for-tat. On the day I worked as Black Jack's fireman on the Baintree to Darkcroft goods, the swarthy engine driver had things entirely his own way. That day above all others Mistress Fate smiled upon him as though he were her favourite son.

Why Roly failed to foresee the kind of trip he was in for when he boarded that ancient contraption of a guard's van we will never know, but then, as sometimes happens, the obvious sometimes remains hidden even to the sharpest scrutiny. A single word of protest on Roly's part and the van would have been changed at once for something more suitable for the journey. It was a relic of a van constructed long before the end of the last century. Only half the tare weight of the standard twenty-tonner, its four wheels were set on an extremely short wheelbase. It was of a type commonly known as a 'Boneshaker', which, because of their age, were usually restricted to short local journeys. The truth of the matter was that Roly was so deeply preoccupied with scheming ways of putting one over on his arch enemy, he realised his blunder only when we left Baintree at the start of the journey.

Recognising the malevolent possibilities in the ancient caboose the moment he set eyes on it, Black Jack made no such blunder. His excitement became apparent as we steamed alongside the already marshalled train to couple up to the other end when he suddenly burst into song! There was no mistaking the hymn – 'Onward Christian Soldiers' – sung with the fervour of a raving evangelist at the very gates of Hell!

Roly climbed into his van like a lamb to the slaughter. With the outlet signal already in the clear position, the moment he waved his green flag Black Jack snatched at the regulator like an executioner opening the trap door! Along the entire length of the train each wagon snatched with increasing force at the one behind in a manner that threatened every coupling, and, as though tied to an immensely powerful length of elastic at full tension, Roly's van shot forward like a greyhound from the traps. A flying start in the full sense of the term, we must have accelerated from nought to twenty miles per hour in five seconds flat! So violent was the start that Roly Poly Farrel embraced his red-hot stovepipe the moment he stepped inside!

Although it was nothing short of a miracle that every bone in Roly's body wasn't broken by the speed of our getaway from Baintree sidings, this was only the start of his ordeal. The rest of that trip of forty-five miles was destined to be an experience both he and I would remember to the end of our days. With the signals set clear for us as far as the eye could see, Black Jack exploited his unexpected opportunity to get one over on Roly to the full, and it wasn't until I finished my first stint with the shovel that I fully appreciated the kind of torture the unfortunate guard was being subjected to.

Looking back along the speeding freight train, I saw every one of the forty-three wagons running smoothly behind the engine, but the ancient contraption coupled to the last of them was jigging and prancing like a jester at court. Swivelling from side to side on its short wheelbase, it caused me to fear for its safety, and, as I imagined the wretched Roly being tossed about like a solitary pea in a drum, I began to doubt if he could still be conscious. Black Jack never looked back once. Completely absorbed in his determination to make the journey as hair-raising as lay within his power, he peered grimly through his eye-glass as though willing the signals to be set clear and gripping the regulator like a lethal weapon.

At Halford Junction, five miles into the journey, the Baintree goods was usually stopped to allow a passenger train to cross its path. Knowing that Roly would leap from his crazy van if we did so to pin down as many wagon brakes as the delay allowed, my fanatical driver began sounding the whistle like a maniac as we approached Halford signal box. Minutes ahead of schedule, we had ample time to clear the junction before the passenger train was due. Determined to maintain the train's momentum he continued whistling until, as he caught sight of the signal set clear for us, he lunged on the regulator and applied more steam.

Imagining the unfortunate guard bouncing off the four walls of his van with every jig and jolt, my anxiety increased with every mile, but I was nothing more than an observer, restrained from protesting to Black Jack by the certain knowledge that if he had been the guard and Roly the driver, the trip would have been exactly the same. With great difficulty I convinced myself my conscience was clear. After all, I was there to produce the steam to get the train to Darkcroft; if Black Jack chose to use it to break every bone in Roly's body, that was his business!

At Dutton we swung to the right on a severely canted stretch of line, enabling me to get a good view of the speeding wagons by looking back along the train as we took the curve. They were still running smoothly enough, but the archaic contraption of a guard's van was leaping and diving, twisting and jerking like a kite caught in a crosswind in its valiant protest at the indignity being imposed upon it in its dotage.

Black Jack tackled Plimpton bank with the regulator wide open, blasting up the one in fifty gradient like a thunderbolt. At the summit he hardly eased up. As we started to descend the other side, the guard's van momentarily disappeared from view and, fearful that it would fly off the end of the train as it mounted the crest, I looked back once more. When it finally appeared still attached to the train, my anxiety subsided and I resumed my work on the footplate. Mile after mile we continued to pound along the line with our nondescript freight train as though attempting to beat the world record for steam traction with the decrepit caboose in the rear performing its incredible dance.

With Entwistle Junction less than a mile ahead, my fears burgeoned once more. At Entwistle, threading their way through a forest of refineries and factories, so many lines converged that it was a work of art reading the signals. With Black Jack sounding the whistle like a maniac, we ploughed through numerous diamond crossings at breakneck speed. Convinced that the ancient guard's van stood no chance of selecting the correct line from the maze of tracks, I closed my eyes, opening them again only when the ragged chatter of the wheels changed to a smooth rhythm as we left the junction behind. To my intense relief, when I looked back along the train I saw the van still clinging to the last wagon like a tenacious terrier refusing to part with a bone.

Completing the journey in record time, we finally swung into the loop at Darkcroft sidings where, in his customary manner when Roly was the guard, Black Jack applied the brake with a mighty swipe of his hand. As the engine lurched to a standstill he closed the vacuum valve and an ominous silence descended, the only sound now being the metallic chatter of the buffers as the still moving wagons behind us ran into the stationary engine. A few seconds later we suddenly shot forward as the guard's van rammed the last wagon to butt the engine another yard along the loop and, for the first time since leaving Baintree, the entire train became still. With my nerves frayed by the experience and my heart beating loud enough to be heard all over the sidings, I stood breathing deeply as I tried to make sense of the diabolical feud between the swarthy gorilla on the other side of the footplate and the corpulent bulldog in the van on the end of the train.

The trip from Baintree to Darkcroft with Black Jack Robinson at the controls and Roly Poly Farrel in the guard's van was the most hair-raising I experienced throughout my time on the railway. Never before nor after the event did I encounter such blind hatred between two humans. And yet, despite the knowledge that there was nothing to choose between them, my concern at this moment was the welfare of the wretched Roly who, by this time, must have been reduced to a disjointed wreck.

In the welcome calmness that descended after our spectacular arrival, I leaned from the cab window to look anxiously back along the train for signs of Roly alighting from his van. As the minutes passed without any sign of him, my anxiety increased to the point at which I found myself wondering if he was alive at all!

Then, just as I was about to climb from the engine to go to his assistance, Roly's satchel hurtled to the ballast below and I experienced an immense feeling of relief. Clearly, if he could throw his satchel from the van he had to be conscious. As I continued to watch, like a man in a drunken stupor he himself appeared, gripping the handrails and lowering himself backwards with pain-racked movements down the steps of the ancient guard's van until he stood swaying uncertainly on terra firma. Slowly he turned about to face the wagons on the adjacent line and, holding out his arms, fell forward to support himself on the wagon facing him, with his head drooping between them as he struggled to find his bearings.

It was here that Black Jack crossed the cab to join me in observing the distressed guard in complete silence, and, as his miserable adversary pushed himself away from the wagon that supported him to retrieve his satchel, not a sign of emotion brushed his rock-like features. Fixing his gaze on the satchel as he swayed unsteadily on his feet, Roly lunged at it only to go staggering past it. Turning round as though in a trance, he lunged at it again, this time missing it by a mile to go sprawling full length on the ballast. After lying there a moment, he struggled to his feet and, eyeing the satchel all the time, made a feeble effort to brush himself down.

Suddenly, straightening himself up, he rushed at it once more and succeeded in getting a hold on the shoulder strap, which he threw over his head as he staggered about like an ungainly dancer. At last, finding some semblance of stability, he turned to face the engine and, for a few poignant moments, the two enemies glared at each other along the full length of the train. Neither made a sound. I found it impossible to fathom Black Jack's mood, but the defiance in Roly's very stance spoke volumes.

Without words, it shouted, 'Aye, all right, you've won that one, you bastard – but just you wait! The next time we meet I'll put one over on you as you won't forget in a hurry – you see if I don't!'

Continuing to stare at Black Jack in a final gesture of defiance a few moments longer, he spat on the ballast then staggered out of sight behind the wagons on the next road.

Without a word Black Jack returned to his own side of the cab where he sat on his stool and put his feet up on the warming plate, his face betraying not the faintest trace of emotion. There was no victory there, no hatred, not even a sign of gloating at having settled a score with his arch enemy. Still set in it's rock-like mould, his expression might have been chiselled in granite a thousand years before. Then, with an abruptness that startled me, he burst into song:

'The God of love my shepherd is,
His goodness faileth never.
I nothing lack if I am his…'

He stopped singing as abruptly as he had begun, then, as though infused by a warm, mysterious contentment, he gave a great sigh, settled himself more comfortably on his stool and seconds later he was dozing.

9
Timothy
Time-and-a-Bit

O n the face of things Timothy Mellor was the most dedicated engine driver on the old London Midland & Scottish Railway. He would go anywhere the lines led him for as long as they allowed him to remain at the controls. So reluctant was he to descend from the cab of his locomotive that had there been a bridge across the English Channel, I am convinced he would have expired from sheer exhaustion in some Chinese goods yard.

A non-smoker and a devout teetotaller, Timothy possessed not a single hobby or pastime to distract his thoughts from his job on the railway. His neighbours saw him as a tall, gaunt bachelor of sixty who was either going to work or returning home when everyone else in the street was going to bed. A quiet man who troubled no one, he resisted all attempts to engage him in conversation and rebuffed the womenfolk whenever they tried to gain access to his little terraced house on the pretext of doing a little tidying up.

Everyone in the street thought him crazy to put up with the long, erratic hours demanded by his job on the Iron Road. After all, being a bachelor, it wasn't as though he had a wife and family to maintain. Still, he was harmless enough and, if he didn't care, who were they to complain?

And yet, to those who knew him best of all, his workmates at Clanky Junction, Timothy Mellor was the most miserable grab-all ever to drive a locomotive.

It had to do with the way engine drivers got paid. Their working week was supposed to consist of six shifts of eight hours each, making forty-eight in all. But it wasn't as simple as this. When they worked after ten o'clock at night they received time-and-a-quarter; if they worked overtime after ten o'clock at night this was calculated at time-and-a-half. Further, when they worked on Sunday they received time-

and-three-quarters. So, depending on when they signed on and off duty, eight hours' work could earn ten hours' pay, twelve hours' pay or fourteen hours' pay.

It was this remarkable increase in the value of an hour's work that led to Timothy's strange behaviour. Early in his railway career he cultivated an insane urge to accumulate all the time-and-a-bit he could get his hands on. With the gold-lust of a forty-niner he would exchange a day trip for a night run at any time and agree to work a colleague's Sunday duty at the drop of a hat. The moment on a trip when his earnings changed from ordinary time to time-and-a-bit was as poignant as blast-off time on a rocket-site. Taking his watch from his pocket, he'd glance at it, then at his fireman, and, his voice trembling with excitement, announce, 'We're on time-an-a-bit now mate! It's time-an-a-bit from now on!'

The moment a new fireman climbed on board his engine, the money-grabbing engine driver gave him to understand at once just what he expected of him. I remember only too clearly how he tackled me.

'What d'yer come to work for, eh lad? Because you like it? 'Course you don't – you're like me, you come to work for money! That's all that matters in this life – money! Now, I'm gonna tell you this lad – you'll make more money wi' me than you made with all your other mates put together! What you've got to remember is this – after ten o'clock at night every shillin's one an' three. D'yer see? An if we can manage a bit of overtime after ten o'clock at night – every shillin's one an' six. Now, on Sundays it's better still – on Sundays every shillin's one an' nine!'

After rubbing his hands together, he continued, 'Aye, we could do wi' more Sundays in t'week – if we had more Sundays in t'week it 'ud be worth comin' to work for! Ordinary time's alright for livin' 'and to mouth – but if it's a little bit on one side you're after it's time-an-a-bit you want! D'yer see me meanin', lad?'

Going over to his own side of the cab, Timothy stuck his head over the side to see if the line was clear then addressed me again.

'Now, you do as I tell yer, lad, and by the time you an' me part company you'll have money in the bank.'

Before I could reply, he sounded the whistle, heaved on the regulator and we moved off the shed to commence the journey.

Within a few days of working with the old skinflint it became clear that my new driver was obsessed with the idea of making a fortune by the most painstaking method ever devised. His formula for getting rich was simply to create chaos along the lines, so that those in charge would be so pre-occupied with sorting it out that no one would notice his train steaming further and further into the distance away from the mundane world where a shilling was only a shilling to the golden land where it was worth one and threepence or one and sixpence. When he contemplated beyond this to the Sabbath when a shilling was worth one and ninepence, he entered a realm of sheer delirium.

I sampled Timothy's rare cunning on my very first trip with him. Earlier that night we had hauled an eastbound freight over the Pennines as far as Shipton, where, after being brought to a halt, we had exchanged footplates with a crew of a coal train bound for the West Coast. After ten weary hours on duty we were finally slowed by signals at Dickleton, a station about a mile from Clanky Junction, our home shed. Having in mind that our train had a further thirty miles or so to go to its destination, I became hopeful that a relief crew would be waiting on the station platform to take over. Sure enough, when I looked over the side of the engine I saw the shadowy outlines of a driver and fireman waiting in the darkness under the signal at the far end of the platform. The signal was set against us, and in my innocence I reached for my jacket.

In these circumstances it was customary for the driver to allow the relief crew to step on board when, after exchanging a few words with the men about to alight, the new driver would sound a couple of subdued pops on the whistle to inform the signalman that the relief had been executed and, with this, the signalman would lower the signal and allow the train to proceed. Completely unaware that to be relieved on a train with another thirty miles to go was anathema to my money-grabbing engine driver, I was astonished to hear him blow on the whistle the moment we entered the long platform!

Erroneously believing that the relief crew had taken over, the signalman lowered the signal in good faith, whereupon, obsessed by his blind desire to accumulate more time-an-a-bit, Timothy lunged on the regulator and, with the wagons almost leaping from the rails with the speed of our getaway, we left the mystified relief crew gesticulating on the platform! When we were switched to a loop three miles along the line to allow the relief to catch up with us, Timothy was completely undismayed, for, although he had been deprived of another thirty miles at the controls, he had wangled another hour of time-and-a-half for his secret hoard.

Timothy reduced time-cribbing to a fine art. Nothing that would allow him to glean an extra penny escaped his attention. He possessed the memory of one of those mortals who can reel off the winner of every horse-race since the inception of the sport, but instead of horses it was the passing time of every train that steamed along the lines.

The basic weakness of any railway system is that on normal double track there is no overtaking. At the height of the Steam Age, whenever a train got out of its 'path' through being delayed, there would be another on its tail in a matter of minutes. It was this weakness that Timothy exploited like a boxer plays on an open wound on his opponent's face.

Regardless of hold-ups at busy junctions and delays caused by breakdowns and fog, most engine drivers during the Steam Age made it a matter of pride to arrive at their destination on time. Timothy, however, was something of a mutant, a peculiar offshoot from the usual strain of engine driver. When he left a siding behind schedule he made no attempt whatsoever to make up for lost time. To him, every second's delay was money in the bank. He liked nothing more than being at the controls of a goods train clanking along at a snail's pace three miles from the nearest loop with an express passenger train on his tail blowing and snorting fit to burst its boiler and every signalman along the line tearing his hair out on the steps of his box urging him on with apoplectic gestures.

Where Timothy was concerned, when time-an-a-bit was in the offing, the nation's commerce could go to the Devil! Completely unperturbed, he'd stare back at the demented signalmen with a blank expression on his face, silently calculating how much he would be in pocket at the end of the trip.

Paradoxically, the only subject he discussed at any length was the question of the forty-hour week. The unions had been pressing for this for years. When I first heard him raise the matter I thought I was hearing things!

'Forty hours a week's enough for any man, lad! Man doesn't live by bread alone! He needs time for recreation – readin' an' enjoyin' the countryside! Oh aye, a fair day's pay fer a fair day's work, that's what I say. An extra day off, that's what we want!'

As he elaborated on his theory I began to think I had never heard such hypocrisy. The way he behaved didn't seem to square with his philosophy. If there was one thing he liked more than a fair day's pay for a fair day's work it was two days' pay for half a day's work. Then, right at the end of his puzzling discourse, I detected the twisted logic of what he was saying.

"Course, when we get a five-day week, they'll 'ave to pay them who work their rest day the same as we get on Sundays – time-an'-three-quarters! It'll be like 'avin' two Sundays in t'week then – every shillin' one an' nine!'

If it hadn't been for Timothy Time-an-a-Bit, the name of Thristleton might never have been inscribed in the annuls of railway legend. Before that Saturday when Timothy and I steamed to this remote village deep in the Pennines, few people had heard of the place. Even Timothy wasn't sure how to get there, but it wasn't the first time we had set out for a destination he wasn't exactly sure about. Indeed, whenever we found ourselves heading for a destination with which he was unfamiliar, he became quite excited in the hope that we would get lost finding the place!

Our instructions were to couple to a giant steam crane and a guard's van in the shed yard and proceed to Thristleton to assist in repairs to a railway bridge there. I knew at once that he had great expectations of the trip by the remark he made when I joined him on the engine.

'Have you brought plenty o' grub, lad? You're gonna need it on this trip.'

I found nothing alarming in his remark, for I had learned after only a week with him to bring an extra sandwich and another twist of tea and sugar just in case we found ourselves working overtime. When he continued, however, my consternation knew no bounds!

'Aye, it's gonna be time-an-three-quarters on this trip, son! It won't be long before every shillin's one an' nine!'

Even now, more than fifty years after the event, I can still recall my consternation at the implications of Timothy's amazing pronouncement. There was I, a light-footed scion of the local dance hall, a slayer with the girls, looking forward to my first Saturday night out for weeks – and there was Timothy informing me at seven o'clock on Saturday morning to expect having to work through into Sunday! After quickly calculating that there were still seventeen hours to the end of Saturday, a violent protest welled in my breast, but he choked back my words with an admonishment like that of a father chastising a wayward son.

'Oh, it's all right you, looking at me like that, lad – I'm tellin' yer! If you've any ideas about gettin' home tonight you'd better get rid of 'em!'

Before I could muster the words to reply we were moving off the shed towards the slip road where the steam crane and guard's van awaited us. I might have persisted in voicing my protest, but, the more I thought of the possibility of working into Sunday, the more diabolical it appeared.

Five hours later we came to rest at a signal miles from anywhere. The only other living creatures in sight were the sheep that grazed on the hills around us. When the signal dropped, we moved slowly forward to stop at a ramshackle signal box where a red flag hung from a window. Over the door in blistered, peeling paint was the name THRISTLETON. With a face as creased as the boards of his box, the signalman appeared at the window and opened it. He held a newspaper in his hand and, on his forehead, like a second pair of eyes, rested a battered pair of wire-rimmed spectacles. With the air of a man with all the time in the universe at his disposal, he shouted, 'Nay, tha's not clear o' t'points yet! Go 'ead a bit an' I'll turn thi into Yebers!'

Judging by the amount of rust on the rails ahead of us, the branch line where the signal box stood was hardly used and Yebers, as the signalman called it, was even more derelict. Indeed, both the branch line and Yebers evoked a strange feeling that the entire woebegone place had been abandoned by the railway company many years before. But then, someone must have been aware of its existence, or why would the engineers have been sent to repair the crumbling bridge?

Yebers was nothing more than a rusting, single-track spur of railway line hardly visible through a verdant overgrowth of grass and weeds. When we cleared the points the signalman waved us back and we began slowly to propel the guard's van and the steam crane along the ancient track towards a cluster of trees; after two hundred yards, the branch line and the signal box were no longer to be seen. It was for all the world as though we had been swallowed by the wild, rampant countryside in the middle of nowhere. I could hear a profusion of birds singing, and on each side of the rusting rails and between the half-sunken sleepers buttercups danced in the summer breeze before a swaying audience of bluebells higher up a slope. The place had a picnic atmosphere about it, and, as I breathed the sweet, scented air, I found myself becoming enchanted by the place.

Through the trees we came across a huge mound of rubble which, I learned later, was all that was left of Yeber's dyeworks, a Victorian factory that had gone out of business just after the First World War. Near the decaying bricks and stones a group of engineers stood waiting for us and, after a few more yards, they signalled us to stop and began to climb on to the steam crane like a gang of looters. As they got busy on the crumbling bridge that spanned the deserted lane below, Timothy and I started on our sandwiches. The time was twelve noon on Saturday.

'Now then, son, we've got plenty o' time. If you want to go fer a walk there's nowt stoppin' yer.'

Throwing his sandwich wrapping into the firebox, Timothy spoke for the first time since leaving the engine shed. His invitation seemed almost too good to be true. The hills surrounding us along with the deserted lane and the lush grass that stretched in all directions as far as the eye could see were just waiting to be explored. Eagerly abandoning the engine before he had time to change his mind, I slithered down the embankment to the deserted lane and set off with a swinging gait.

Thristleton was beginning to enchant me more and more. Out of sight of the engine and the engineers I found myself in a world that seemed to have been forgotten. I must have walked two miles without meeting a soul when, rounding a bend in the lane, I came across a cluster of cottages and the quaintest pub I had ever set eyes on. With the sun glaring from a cloudless sky I entered the coolness of the pub and, with strained manliness, asked for a pint of beer. The publican enquired whether I wanted mild or bitter. Not knowing the difference I plumped for bitter and placed a shilling on the bar. The effect of my first pint of beer was almost instant; after downing over half of it in one draught in a demonstration of my adulthood, my spirits began to sing.

The locals in the pub yarned and drank as though they lived by it, and I listened spellbound as they discussed a sheepdog trial. Later I became enthralled by a tale from a farm labourer who related how, after assisting in the building of a haystack to the boss's instructions, the whole thing had collapsed. Everyone laughed as he went on to tell how the farmer blamed everyone else for the calamity but himself and had gone off in a huff. When the farmer returned several hours later to behold a perfect stack, he criticised them for taking too long over the job and went off again with his tail between his legs.

The pleasant coolness of the pub's interior and the congeniality of the company made the minutes race like seconds and, before I realised how long I had been there, the landlord was shouting 'time'. Jumping to my feet I shot from the pub and ran all the way back to the engine half expecting a search party to meet me on the way; panting and spluttering, I climbed back on board to find Timothy calm as a vicar. He greeted me like a favourite uncle.

'Bin runnin', lad? What a' yer gerrin' all excited about? We've plenty o' time. Look, y'see that theer crag over there – near that clump o' trees? Go an' climb up that. I bet you can see for miles up there.'

I had noticed the crag Timothy indicated on my walk to the village. It was by far the highest point in the landscape. So, completely enraptured by the place, my earlier concern about losing my Saturday night out at the dance hall dispelled by the inebriation of my first pint of beer, I set off to climb it.

The view from the top of the crag was breathtaking. The rolling hills, the birds and the flash of sunlight on falling water were sights I would never forget and, after feasting my eyes in all directions, I finally lay in a trough of long grass and fell fast asleep.

Two hours later, at six o'clock exactly, I climbed back on board the engine.

'Back already, lad? Did you enjoy the view? Eh? Did you enjoy it?'

It was at this moment that I realised Timothy was up to something. I could sense it in every facet of his behaviour; the way he spoke, the way he looked at me and his obvious attempt to put me at ease. I answered him warily.

'Yes, it was grand, Tim, grand. Are we going now?'

'Aye, in a bit, lad, in a bit. We'll just 'ave another five minutes.'

It was at this point that the guard strolled up to the engine and, the moment he spoke, I knew for certain that there was a conspiracy.

'I've gorra nice brew on in the van, Tim. If you come an' join me when you're ready we'll 'ave a sup!'

After Timothy accepted the invitation, the guard returned to his van. With the engineers who met us on our arrival now gone, and with the peace and serenity of the English countryside all around us, the engine and the steam crane appeared like monstrous invaders. Aware that I was staring at him, Timothy indicated my stool.

'Sit down, lad! 'ave a smoke – a few more minutes won't harm anyone.'

Doing as he suggested, I sat on my stool facing him and lit a cigarette. Every second he appeared to become more agitated, glancing at his watch five times in the following five minutes. Then, at twenty minutes past six he released the brake, opened the regulator and we moved cautiously towards the signal behind the trees that would take us back on to the branch line. Several yards from the signal we stopped. He spoke to me again.

'Ah well, we'll give 'im a crow to tell 'im we're ready, eh lad?'

As he pulled on the whistle I noticed that his face bore a sly grin. When the signal remained against us he whistled again, but this time, when the sound of its last echo died in the Pennine hills, he turned to me with triumph in his eyes and said, 'He won't let us go, y'know lad – he won't let us go!'

Puzzled, I fired the obvious question.

'What do you mean, he won't let us go? He'll have to let us go shortly, won't he?'

As he made to reply, his face beamed radiantly.

'No, he won't let us go lad – he's gone home. That signal box shuts at six o'clock!'

Alarmed now, I crossed the cab and questioned him again.

'What time does he open again?'

Rubbing his hands together he announced what he had been scheming ever since we left the shed earlier that morning.

'He doesn't open again until eight o'clock tomorrow mornin'! Eh lad, we'll mek a bob or two on this trip. Oh aye, we will that!'

Noticing my jaw drop at the prospect of spending the rest of the night in the middle of nowhere, he continued.

'There's nowt to worry about, lad! I've brought enough grub for both of us. The guard's all for it. We can sleep in the guard's van – we've plenty o' tea an' sugar! We'll let the fire go out to save coal an' water and light it again first thing in the mornin'. Why, we'll make more brass

on this trip, lad, than we made all last week! Think o' the money, lad –
think o' the money!'

Allowing the fire to go out on a locomotive when on a trip was
tantamount to scuttling a ship. I protested.

'Let the fire go out? You'll get us both sacked! It's not a greenhouse
stove, y'know! How will we light it again?'

Looking at me as though I was still wet behind the ears, he replied,
'You worry too much, lad! When we set back through the trees to the
old dyeworks you'll find a pile o' timber higher than a house. I've not
been idle while you've bin away, y'know!'

Sure enough, when we reversed through the trees to the old bridge,
I beheld a stack of old timber big enough to satisfy Guy Fawkes himself.

And so it came about that Thristleton became fixed in my memory.
With eight hours at ordinary time, seven hours at time-and-a-quarter,
two hours at time-and-a-half and thirteen hours at time-and-three-
quarters, my following week's wages had to be stuffed into two tins
instead of the usual one.

Late that Saturday night, as I dozed fitfully on the hard floor of the
guard's van with my money-grabbing mate on the locker to my left and
the guard recumbent on the one on my right, Timothy Time-an-a-Bit
shook me awake. It was exactly midnight. As my eyes focused I saw him
peering at his watch in the weak moonlight penetrating the grimy
window of the van.

Becoming aware that I was paying attention, he declared, 'Are you
awake, lad? Eh? Are you awake? I just thought I'd let y'know – it's
Sunday now, lad – we're on time-an-three-quarters now! Can y'ear me?
I say we're on time-an-three-quarters now! Every shillin's one an' nine
from now on!'

With this he returned his watch to his pocket, eased himself back on
the locker and, supremely contented, went back to sleep.

I never discovered whether the signalman at Thristleton genuinely
forgot that he had put us down Yebers, or whether Timothy had squared
him with a few bob. Nor did I hear any more about the matter. But
then, the wiles and ways of Timothy Time-an-a-Bit were way beyond
my comprehension. Sad to say, when the old Devil died many years
later, they found two thousand pound notes stuffed in his mattress.
That was the mystery of it; after scheming and scraping for that little
bit extra for most of his lifetime, he went and left it all behind.

10
Same as Y'would Y'self

*L*ike all railways during the Steam Age, the London Midland & Scottish was governed by a system of laws that, for sheer drama, equalled anything enacted in the civil courts of the land. Unlike Civil Law, however, based as it is on precedent and the past rulings of judges, railway law was laid down in black and white, enshrined in a Rule Book containing more than two hundred rules and regulations covering the minutest details of railway practice.

Broadly speaking, the rules and regulations were formulated to protect the interests and property of the railway companies. It didn't seem to matter in the slightest that when they were applied to the letter the whole damn system ground to a standstill, an unfortunate feature resulting in the strange paradox that when the unions wanted to bring pressure to bear on the management, all they had to do was 'work to rule'.

An example of how things ought to have been done compared to how they were actually carried out was the way that goods trains were dealt with at exchange sidings. According to the procedure laid down in the Rule Book, when a train arrived on the loop at night, a signal would be lowered for the train to draw ahead until the guard's van cleared the points leading into the sidings. When clear of the points, the leading shunter would offer the driver a red light to stop the train, then, after shouting to the shunters stationed in the sidings to set the points for the appropriate road, he would display a green light to the driver, who would slowly reverse the train into the sidings until the buffers of the guard's van gently contacted those of the first vehicle in the road. Here, the brake of the van would be applied to secure it, then detached from the train. This done, the driver would be signalled to draw ahead clear of the points again, the shunter would shout for the points to be set for the appropriate road, and the driver would be signalled to reverse with a green light until the train again contacted the buffers of the first wagon in the road. Once again the brakes of the wagons would be pinned down, the shunt detached, and the driver signalled to draw ahead again for the next shunt. This slow, painstaking process would be repeated until all the wagons on the train had been shunted into the sidings and the engine finally dispatched to the shed.

What happened in reality, however, was quite different. When the train cleared the points leading into the sidings, the leading shunter would uncouple the guard's van, bawl to his minions stationed in the sidings to set the road, then signal the driver to 'hit 'em up' by swinging a white light frantically from side to side. At once, the driver would ram the wagons with full force to thump the uncoupled van into the sidings at breakneck speed, then, stopping abruptly, he would quickly reverse and draw ahead for the next shunt while the guard's van was careering into the sidings. Within minutes of the start of the operation, wagons would be hurtling into the sidings at split-second intervals being ridden by shunters lying across their brake-sticks rammed into the underframes of the wagons. Just before the wagons collided with those already in the roads, they would leap off their brake-sticks with the dexterity of circus performers a second before the deafening impact and run to meet the next shunt already careering into the sidings.

The practice was fraught with danger. A non-railwayman observing it at the time would have been impressed by the speed and alacrity of the shunters as they disposed of each train, seeing them as loyal, eager railway employees performing their duties with the utmost efficiency. But it was nothing of the kind; with no such signal as 'hit 'em up', the procedure was officially unauthorised, and yet at every freight sidings throughout the land it was adopted with impunity simply because it suited everyone. The railway company got its trains shunted in half the time, the Inspector and shunters returned quickly to resume their interminable game of crib, and the driver, fireman and guard got home to their beds sooner. Only when a derailment occurred or a wagon disintegrated with the excessive force of the shunt did the officials pounce to point out the illegality of the practice. The company couldn't lose – providing that nothing went wrong they turned a blind eye, but the moment a serious mishap occurred they appeared on the scene as though by magic to lay down the law like Moses from the mountain top!

The first intimation a driver received indicating that he was enmeshed in the company's disciplinary procedure was when he found an innocuous little note pinned to his timecard as he signed on or off duty. It would read something like:

DRIVER TOWNSEND: 385.
It is reported that on the 5th inst whilst working the 10.45 pm
Darkcroft-Elton goods, you collided with the buffers at Elton
wharf with undue force. Please explain.

Signed: W. C. Philpot
District Locomotive Superintendent

This was only the beginning of the process. In the event of the
Superintendent being unconvinced by the driver's explanation, he
would charge the culprit on what was called a 'Form 1'. This gave the
driver concerned the choice of pleading 'guilty as charged' and
accepting the punishment the Superintendent chose to inflict, such as
a reprimand or suspension from duty, or denying the charge and
appearing at an inquiry conducted by the Superintendent himself. For
the latter, the accused was allowed to be represented by a spokesman of
his choice.

If the accused was found guilty by the inquiry he would be informed
of his punishment on a 'Form 2', and, if he decided to appeal against it,
there would be a further inquiry at a higher level at which he would
again be allowed to be represented by a spokesman.

Carried to its final stage, the process could be both dramatic and
fascinating. With cases involving such light misdemeanours as late
running to serious derailments and collisions, all the fears, emotions
and humour of the human condition were displayed. Because of this, it
was slight wonder that the role of 'spokesman' assumed such
importance.

Over the years, Charlie Brown, or Brownie as he was called by the
men at the Junction, had established the reputation of being the finest
advocate the men had ever known. So great was the demand for his
services that he spent more time representing the men at inquiries than
at his real job of driving locomotives. Whether he passed a signal at
danger, over-ran the buffers or dropped his lead plugs through allowing
his boiler to run dry, a driver with Brownie as his spokesman would feel
confident of receiving the lightest punishment an inquiry could opt for.
It wasn't simply that the great man knew backwards every rule, clause
and amendment in the Rule Book, it also had to do with the way he
marshalled the facts of the case and timed his appealing gestures.

Brownie revelled in the role. Sometimes beautifully eloquent with
references to the Bible or one of our greater poets, sometimes blazing
at the injustice of the charge, and sometimes permitting a tear to seep
from his eye, the man was born to it. So powerful was the confidence
he exuded that after laying his troubles at the great man's feet, a driver
who had wrecked his train would walk away from him bearing a

glimmer of hope. It wasn't for nothing that the men said that he had missed his way. What Brownie achieved he did the hard way; with a more affluent start in life he would have gone far in the legal profession.

Wally Philpot, the District Locomotive Superintendent, was a pastmaster at making the men of Clanky Junction quake in their boots as he inflated the seriousness of their misdemeanours, but with Brownie as their spokesman, even he had to watch his Ps and Qs. Those who administer the law need to be more careful than most in observing them, and no one knew better than Brownie the immense satisfaction to be had in bringing to boot one of the bowler-hatted brigade.

If to Wally Philpot Brownie was a worthy adversary, to the men he represented he was almost infallible. No case was too trivial for his attention, and if he delighted in hearing the men say as he approached, 'Hey, here he is now. Go on, ask 'im – see what he says', he never showed it. Like a cricketer entering the pavilion to a standing ovation or a conductor responding to endless encores, Brownie bore his greatness with the modesty of the truly great.

But then, even the greatest cricketer has nightmares over the ill-timed stroke that had him caught for a duck before a great crowd at the Oval, and the most famous conductor sweats blood when recalling the night an over-enthusiastic French horn came in a second too soon, blasting out of existence the sweet trill of the flute in a rousing Rossini overture. With Brownie it was the night Bert Wheeler sidled up to him, asking if he could help him in connection with a little bit of trouble he had got into. Afterwards, whenever the great advocate recalled the event, his renowned confidence drained from his veins, leaving him momentarily unsure of himself.

Before that night Bert Wheeler and Brownie had never worked on the same footplate, but, despite this, when Bert sidled up to the great advocate as they waited for their train to be dealt with at Edenroyd sidings, saying, 'Eh, Brownie, I'm in a little bit of trouble like, er, d'yer think you could help me…', Brownie responded with the generosity for which he was famous:

'A bit o' trouble, you say, Bert? Well now, you know the old sayin', a trouble shared's a trouble halved! Go on, tell me all about it!'

If an angel of fate could have whispered into Brownie's ear at that moment, warning him of what he was inviting upon himself, how he would have stifled those words! Completely unknown to him, what he was about to endure would test to the limit not only his faith in humanity, but his tremendous faith in his own abilities.

Encouraged by Brownie's expansiveness, the troubled fireman sidled closer to the great advocate.

'Well, it was like this 'ere, Brownie – er, I broke loose in Boddington dip!'

Brownie smiled to himself. Wasn't it just typical? They were all the same – whenever they got into a little bit of trouble they got to worrying like pregnant spinsters!

'Boddington dip, you say? Then what the blazes are you worryin' about? Why, there's hardly a driver at the Junction who's not broken loose in Boddington dip some time or other! Why, some of the best lads at the place have come to grief there!'

What Brownie said was quite true. Boddington was no ordinary dip; it was more like two dips in one. Legend had it that it was the fault of a drunken ganger who, when laying the line before the turn of the century, after elevating the track out of the main dip, put an extra kink in it just for devilment. For those who knew it well it was a hazard, but for the unwary it was fatal. For Bert Wheeler there was an excuse; the night he broke loose happened to be the first time he had handled the controls in the capacity of a driver. Having passed his driver's examination only a month before, he had assumed the title of 'Spare driver'. This meant that he could be called upon from that day forward to occupy the driver's side of the cab whenever a regular driver failed to present himself for duty.

Already Brownie had assumed that what was being put to him was an open-and-shut case. Leaning back on his seat with his legs outstretched, his boots resting on the warming plate just above the firehole, he was quite relaxed.

'When did this 'ere happen, Bert?'

Bert sprang forward to reply.

'Last Thursday, Brownie, last Thursday night.'

Brownie became thoughtful, striving to recall the weather conditions prevailing on the night in question. After a few seconds he addressed his fireman again.

'Last Thursday night, y'say?'

'Aye, last Thursday night, Brownie.'

Suddenly Brownie straightened himself up.

'Hey, hey, there was a little fog hangin' about last Thursday, if I'm not mistaken! Not much to get excited about, but it's as well to bear it in mind.'

As Bert nodded eagerly, Brownie continued.

'Well, look here, Bert, tell me in your own words exactly what happened. There you were checkin' the train down the bank and at Boddington home signal you started to give her steam to tighten the couplin's – go on from there!'

Elated at Brownie's sympathetic response, Bert replied at once.

'That's right, I was checkin' the wagons down the bank, same as y'would Brownie, same as y'would y'self – an' at the home signal I opened her up to stretch the couplin's. Course it was the fog, y'see, Brownie – couldn't see we'd broken in two!'

Brownie stared at his fireman abruptly.

'Hey, hey, hold on a minute, Bert! The fog wasn't that bad! I said there was a touch of mist hangin' about, that's all! I mean, don't get carried away! In any case, a driver doesn't need eyes to tell him his train's broken in two – he feels it! God's truth, a blind man could tell!'

As though the case was cut and dried, he continued.

'Any road, stop worryin' about it. When you get the Form 1 chargin' yer, where it says do you want a spokesman, put "yes" an' underneath put my name. We'll have no trouble wi' this one. The blokes who laid the track at Boddington must have been drunk. They intended us to break loose there. It's the rummest bit o' track-layin' I've ever come across. In fact, Bert, when I look back on my railway career I've defended more blokes for breaking loose in Boddington dip than for any other crime in the book! Why they have two kinks in a railway line when one 'ud do I just don't know! I mean – a couple o' tons o' ballast – that's all it needs. I've told 'im, y'know! Oh aye, I've told Wally Philpot about it time an' time again! 'Course, all you get is that it 'ud cost too much!'

Brownie sighed.

'Anyway, Bert, stop worryin' as I say. Your first drivin' turn – a touch o' fog – I only wish every case was as straightforward! A simple reprimand, that's what it'll be – nothin' worse than a simple reprimand!'

As far as Brownie was concerned there was nothing more to be said. Filing away the relevant facts in his tidy mind he relaxed once more and turned his thoughts to the more important cases he had in hand. Bert, however, appeared troubled, as though he would have liked the conversation to have continued. For some reason, the miraculous calm that usually descended on those who unburdened themselves to the great advocate didn't materialise. Going back to his seat he crossed his legs, leaned on them with his elbows, and started biting his fingernails. Five minutes later, he got to his feet and crossed the cab to address Brownie again.

'Y'see, Brownie, if we hadn't been short o' water I wouldn't've passed that signal at danger!'

Brownie jerked, staring at his fireman as though trying to get him in focus.

'Signal? What flippin' signal?'

Hesitating, Bert said, 'Y'know, the one on the viaduct!'

With perplexity written large on his features, Brownie continued to stare at his fireman. Then, 'You mean after you coupled up to the rest of your train?'

'No, no, before!'

'Y'mean you didn't find out you'd broken in two until you got on the viaduct?'

Bert nodded. 'Aye.'

Brownie still didn't grasp the full meaning of his mate's new confession.

'But the viaduct's a mile past the dip! How do we get on the viaduct?'

Bert leapt to explain. 'It was the boiler, y'see, Brownie – there was no water showin' in the gauge glass and the tender was bone dry. All I could think of was gettin' to the water column – same as y'would Brownie, same as y'would y'self!'

Once again the great man's anxiety flared up and, with wild eyes, he questioned the miserable fireman once more to get the facts right.

'Now look, Bert, let's get things straight! After your train broke in two, you carried on another mile to Gleasby viaduct. Now, is that right, Bert?'

Bert nodded pensively.

'Now then, the signal at Gleasby was against you but you took it into your head to ignore the red light and pass it at danger. Now have I got it right, Bert?'

Bert nodded again, saying, 'Aye, that's right, Brownie, dead right. All I could think of was the boiler, y'see, same as y'would Brownie, same as y'would y'self!'

Brownie shook his head with incredulity.

'Well, that puts the top hat on it, that does! Why in Heaven's name didn't you tell me all this in the first place?'

Bert remained silent and, as Brownie pondered this new complication, he began to feel uneasy, faintly suspicious there might be more to his fireman's weary tale than met the eye.

During the brief silence that followed, Bert too became uneasy, afraid that the great man would refuse to act for him after all. So, to test the water, he plucked up courage to approach him again.

'What d'yer think, Brownie? D'yer think I've gorra chance? D'yer think you'll be able to do anythin' for me?'

Generous as always, but with a hint of impatience this time, Brownie replied, 'Oh aye, stop worryin', I tell yer! Just put my name on that there form like I tell yer and leave everythin' to me!'

Once again the hapless fireman was placated and returned to his seat while Brownie switched his thoughts with great difficulty to one of the more important cases he had in hand.

This seemed to be the end of the matter, and nothing further was said for a good ten minutes. Meantime, Brownie appeared to have regained his usual calmness as, leaning back on his stool, his thoughts probed the intricacies of the other case he was involved with. Suddenly his concentration was shattered when Bert piped up again.

'I mean, I wasn't long at the water column, Brownie, honest! I was going back for the rest of the train in no time at all!'

Alerted, the great advocate stared again at his fireman.

'You obtained a Wrong Line Order?'

Bert shook his head. 'I didn't think it mattered, Brownie.'

Brownie started.

'You didn't think it mattered? Y'mean you ran up the down line without permission?'

Bert nodded. 'Well, I wanted to get back to pick up the rest of the train as quick as I could! Same as y'would Brownie, same as y'would y'self!'

Brownie panicked.

'Well, I'll go to our house! I – I – I've never heard anything like it in all my life! An' I wish you wouldn't keep sayin' same as y'would y'self, cos I wouldn't have done any of the things you did that night! I mean, just fancy – runnin' up the down line without a Wrong Line Order! Why, I've never heard anythin' so diabolical in all my born days!'

Before he could digest the full significance of Bert's new confession, the tormented fireman revealed more.

'Aye, it was one thing after another, Brownie. In the heat of the moment I completely forgot them trap points. Same as y'would Brownie, same as y'would y'self.'

Suddenly remembering the trap points wickedly placed halfway up the incline that succeeded the dip, Brownie visibly sagged under a great wave of weakness. But that was what trap points were for – to derail a train running out of control in the wrong direction before it collided with one approaching.

For a moment it seemed as though Brownie had passed out completely. Still reclining on his seat with his feet resting on the warming plate above the firehole, his eyes were shut tight as though trying to blot out the terrible implications of his fireman's new revelation. Suddenly he opened his eyes and exploded. 'Little pigs an' flyin' fishes! You're tellin' me now you came off the rails!'

Hardly audibly, Bert replied, 'Aye.'

Brownie groaned. 'Oh, God almighty! Well, if I hadn't heard it with my own ears I wouldn't've believed it! Oh for God's sake!' He stared at his fireman in disbelief. 'D'yer know, Bert, you've done something to me tonight that no one has ever done before! You have! D'yer know what you've done, Bert? Eh? D'yer know what you've done? Well, I'll tell yer! You've plumbed the depths of incredulity, that's what you've done. For as long as I live nobody'll ever surprise me again!'

Bert said nothing as Brownie paused, searching for words with which to express his deep frustration.

'D'yer know, if you stood there and told me with your own lips that you finished up dropping your lead plugs – it'd leave me completely unmoved! It would, Bert! After what you've told me tonight – if you told me you dropped your flamin' plugs I wouldn't bat an eyelid! I mean it, Bert! I wouldn't turn a bloody hair!'

Sidling closer to his driver, Bert said, 'I'm really glad you said that, Brownie, cos I did.'

Jerking like Jimmy Cagney in one of his death throes, Brownie's boots slipped from the warming plate to thud loudly on the boards of the footplate, and he had to grab a steam valve to stop himself falling off his stool altogether. Startled by his driver's violent reaction, Bert scurried to his own side of the cab where, sitting on his stool, he crossed his legs, leaned on them with his elbows and started devouring his fingernails again. Suddenly Brownie screamed in torment.

'I want nothing to do with the case! D'yer hear me, Bert? I wouldn't touch it with a barge pole! An' I'll tell you summat else too, Bert – what you've told me tonight's destroyed my bloody faith in human nature! It has, Bert! Why, if a bloke violated as many civil laws as you've contravened company rules and regulations he'd get ten years behind bars! How did you pass your driver's exam when you go an' break almost every rule in the book the first time you take the controls? Oh no, I wouldn't touch it with a barge pole! I mean – I can't work miracles, Bert! Y'see that, don't yer? Oh no, I can't work miracles – I mean – I'm not Jesus Christ!'

Now the silence became heavy with the hopelessness of both men. With Bert gnawing his finger ends like a condemned man ten minutes before his execution and Brownie sitting upright on his stool twitching occasionally and moving his lips soundlessly, they appeared to have reached an impasse.

At last, after deep consideration and as though moved by the sight of his distraught fireman eating himself alive, the great advocate responded to his finer feelings.

'I mean, just think of the charges, Bert – breaking loose in Boddington dip; passing a signal at danger; runnin' up the down line without a Wrong Line Order; derailin' your train, and, to cap it all – droppin' your flamin' plugs! An' what have you got, eh Bert? Your first time at the controls an' a measly smudge o' fog that wouldn't upset a bloody homing pigeon! Y'see the position don't you, Bert? Eh? You see what I'm on about?'

In the absence of a reply from his despondent fireman, he became thoughtful again. Then, after another pause, he said, 'Y'know Bert, there's only one thing you can do – just one chance!' As though he hadn't heard a word Brownie said, Bert continued staring at the floor still devouring his finger ends.

'Aye, there's only one thing you can do – you'll have to plead domestic circumstances! In other words, you'll have to break their bloody hearts! And believe me lad, it'll have to be some story! Are you listenin' to me? Look at me when I'm talking to yer! I say it'll have to be some story. You'll have to tell 'em your missus ran off wi' the milkman leavin' yer wi' three kids to look after an' the authorities demandin' they be sent to an orphanage. Furthermore, she left you with higher purchase debts runnin' into hundreds o' pounds, the bailiffs on the doorstep, a house crawlin' wi' cockroaches an' the gas turned off! That's what you'll have to tell em – are y'listenin' to what I'm sayin'? I say that's what you'll have to tell em!'

As Brownie garnished this heart-rending plea he slowly began to live the scene. He began to imagine himself addressing Wally Philpot and the other officials on the inquiry board as clearly as if he were already there. Carried away by his reverie, he silently opened his case.

'Superintendent, Inspector, gentlemen (his protocol was always faultless). On behalf of Fireman Wheeler, I have to inform you that in investigating the circumstances of this unfortunate case, I came across such appalling circumstances in the domestic affairs of the accused that I hesitate to describe them to you in case you are sickened by them as much as I was! Such terrible circumstances it has never been my lot to behold in my entire life!'

It was certainly the most difficult case he had ever been asked to take, and yet, as he imagined himself addressing the grave officials, he actually saw them soften under the power of his eloquence.

'You know, Gentlemen, most of us have a cross to bear in this life, but after listening to what I have to tell you about the atrocious domestic circumstances of Fireman Wheeler, you will surely agree that no one has ever borne a heavier one than this unfortunate man!'

Here he saw himself fling out an arm in a great gesture of compassion. 'I ask you to think for a moment of those poor, destitute children!'

As Brownie continued to imagine himself pleading Bert's case he began to feel his confidence flooding back. Overcome by his own imaginary eloquence, real tears of compassion welled in his eyes.

'Surely, like me, you must find it impossible to imagine the turmoil that beset the innermost feelings of Fireman Wheeler as he left his miserable home to take the controls for the first time as a Spare driver – an occasion that should have been joyous with achievement, but which, because of his terrible domestic circumstances, was nothing but anguish. As men of the world – I ask you – how much torment can we expect a man to bear in this vale of tears?'

It was here that Brownie felt he had to take the case. Too much of a realist to believe he would get Bert off scot-free – the weary catalogue of his fireman's violations of the rules and regulations was far too serious for that – he felt confident that he would get him off with a token suspension. But, more than this, he was beginning to like the feel of the case. He saw great scope in it for his eloquence and gestures and, the more he thought of the possibilities it presented for him to exercise the skills for which he was both proud and famous, he was already relishing the prospect.

Bert thought that his mate had gone into a trance. Unaware of Brownie's dream he had begun to feel abandoned. With sickening clarity he had noticed how, when the great man offered his advice, he dropped the plural 'we' for the personal 'you', as though he had decided to wash his hands of the case altogether. With little hope and more than a little desperation, he decided to approach the great man once more.

Cautiously crossing the cab, he confronted him with trepidation.

'D'yer – d'yer think you'll be able to do anythin', Brownie? Will you take the case?'

For a moment Brownie stared at the downcast fireman as though he hadn't heard a word. Then, coming back to earth, he suddenly beamed a huge smile.

'What's that you said, Bert? Will I take the case? Of course I'll take the case – same as y'would Bert, same as y'would y'self lad!'

11
A Whistle on the Wind

*W*ally Philpot, the District Locomotive Superintendent, the Station Master of Westfield station and a Block Inspector, were assembled in secret conclave in Wally's office planning how to nab Billy Banks, the driver of the pickle train, for habitually sounding his whistle like a madman. This gross violation of the company's rules and regulations had come to Wally's notice from a report submitted almost six weeks earlier by the signalman of Westfield Quarry signal box. So damning were the words contained in the report that the three officials had concluded that the misdemeanour warranted not just a warning reprimand, but that the culprit should be caught in the act.

That the engine of the pickle train whistled at all at Westfield Quarry was most unusual, for there was hardly anything there to whistle for. The quarry after which the signal box was named had been closed for so long that the levers controlling the points and signal permitting entry to it were seized up through lack of use. The only time a driver had cause to whistle when approaching Westfield was when the main-line signal was set against him. In this event it would have been one long note; there was no need for a long and a short for 'left' or a long and two shorts for 'right', for there was no junction. Nor could it have been that the driver was whistling to warn the signalman that his train was running away out of control, for the line possessed not the merest pimple of a gradient.

The 'Tasty Pickle' factory adjoined the main line three miles before Westfield Quarry signal box on the down line. Every Saturday morning a train of empty vans was gently reversed down the line of the loading bay at the side of the factory. On contacting the buffers at the end of the line, the engine uncoupled, leaving the vans to be loaded with the following week's production. Six days later, on the Friday morning, duly sealed in airtight jars and immersed in spiced malt vinegar, the pickles left the factory on the pickle train to be distributed throughout the land.

That a trainload of such humble merchandise could trigger such a furore among railway officialdom is stark testimony to the truth of the old adage that the smallest pebble can cause an avalanche. Why the signalman's wrath hadn't been provoked long before he sent off his report is a matter for speculation, for the outrageous whistling had been going on for months. My own view is that the wind had a lot to do with it. On that November morning the wind was blowing in strong, prolonged gusts in exactly the same direction in which the train was travelling. This, along with the nature of the whistle itself – a prolonged wildly whooping whistle – made a confrontation between the signalman at Westfield and the driver of the pickle train inevitable.

Launched on a powerful gust of wind the moment it left the valve, that joyous, wildly whooping whistle rushed towards the signal box ahead of the train to fall upon the ears of the signalman with the impact of a gross obscenity.

Content in the knowledge that his down home and starting signals were set at clear for the pickle train, the signalman was making a pot of tea at the time. At that moment he was very much at peace with the world, singing 'Daisy, Daisy, Give Me Your Answer Do' at the top of his voice as he prepared his brew. When, with startling suddenness, that wildly whooping engine whistle smote his ear-drums, he was transformed into a raging maniac!

Dropping the aluminium teapot into the sink with a loud clatter, he rushed to the window, slid it open and glared up the line at the approaching pickle train as it rounded the curve at Westfield station. Resolving at once to get to the bottom of the matter, he leapt to his levers, threw his starting signal back to danger and immediately hung a red flag from the window.

Even before Billy Banks, the cause of all the commotion, noticed the signal reverse against him, it went without saying that he would meet the situation with supreme calmness. This had to do with what can only be described as 'Occupational Genetics'. Billy Banks, you see, was a 'Wessy' man, and the main characteristic of this breed of engine driver was a complete disregard of formality.

When the old London & North Western, Midland and Lancashire & Yorkshire railways merged to form the London Midland & Scottish, the senior firemen found that they could transfer to any part of the system to gain promotion to driver. To Clanky Junction, the largest locomotive shed on the entire system, they came in droves. A driver whose career began on the old Midland Railway, with its tradition of

spit and polish, was referred to as 'One of our people'. A Lancashire &
Yorkshire driver was known simply as a 'Lanky man'.

A driver who originated on the London & North Western, however,
differed from the others in almost every respect. For one thing the old
LNWR applied no restriction as to the height of its recruits, for which
reason a remarkably large number of 'Wessy' men were on the short
side. Furthermore, they seemed to have very little regard for rules, rank
or regalia! Whether he was at the controls of a decrepit shunting engine
or the 'Royal Scot', a 'Wessy' driver would probably be a short man
wearing a muffler, cloth cap and clogs. It was generally believed that
most of them sold the uniform issued to them each year the moment
they got through the shed gates.

Such was the appearance of Billy Banks as he braked the pickle train
to a standstill under the window of the signal box displaying the red
flag. I know, for I was his fireman on that occasion. Although the
signalman was poised to say something at once, it was Billy who got in
first.

'Are you in a changeable frame o' mind this mornin' or summat? First
the signal's for us, then it's agin us! What d'yer think we are – a bloody
dodgem car or what?'

Taking advantage of the pause at the end of Billy's question, the
signalman commenced his somewhat frustrated attack.

'What's all the commotion about?'

Innocently, Billy asked, 'Commotion? What commotion?'

Red in the face, the signalman continued. 'All that flamin' cock-o-
doodle- doin' coming through the station! What kind o' whistle d'yer
call that? God's truth – I wouldn't be surprised if you've caused half a
dozen premature births in the town with all that racket! What's it all
about, for God's sake?'

Billy replied, 'Ah, well, I thought I saw summat on t'line y'see.'

The outraged signalman stared with incredulity. 'You saw summat on
t'line? What d'yer mean, you saw summat on t'line?'

Unabashed, Billy explained: 'Well, between you 'n' me it looked like
a goat.'

Here Billy's cloth-capped head swivelled round on his muffler to face
me. 'Do you reckon it was a goat, mate?'

Eager to give Billy all my support, I said, 'Could've been a goat Bill,
but to be quite honest I thought it was a donkey.'

Billy looked hopefully at the signalman. 'There, you see, whatever it
was it had four legs an' a tail!'

Suspecting that he was having his leg pulled, the signalman exerted
his full authority.

'Oh aye, well you listen to me, driver – goat, donkey or flamin' giraffe

– you just watch it, that's all! If I hear that flamin' cock-a-doodle-doin' again I'll have you on the carpet good an' proper!'

Of course, it was against the grain of any 'Wessy' man to show meekness in the face of authority. With rich sarcasm, Billy replied, 'Come on, man, let's be on our way – you'll have these pickles gerrin jealous o' that face o' yours if we stay here much longer!'

With a final glare and a belligerent thrust of his jaw, the signalman withdrew the red flag, slammed shut the window and pulled the lever to operate the signal and, with a defiant if subdued 'crow' on the whistle, Billy opened the regulator and the pickle train blasted from the signal box to resume its journey.

Apart from Billy himself, only I knew of his secret joy. He had discovered it almost six months before when, quite by chance, his gaze fell upon the bedroom window of a modest red-bricked house situated on a level lower than the railway line as we approached Westfield station. There, at the back of the bedroom, he caught sight of a hand waving feebly. So desperate was the gesture that he waved back, but before he could get a better view of the bedridden occupant we were out of sight rounding the curve. The discovery played on Billy's mind and, six weeks later, when we again found ourselves on the pickle train, he stared harder to get a better view of the occupant. Once again he saw the hand waving feebly, but this time he could see behind the hand the ailing face of a bedridden woman straining her head off the pillow to catch sight of him.

A host of questions began to crowd Billy's mind. Who was she? How long had she been bedridden? What was the nature of her illness? What was her name? It never occurred to him that she might have waved to every train that passed. For the little 'Wessy' driver she waved only to him and, when he began to speculate on how long she had been trying to make contact with him he was tortured by feelings of guilt.

From that day forth, as though to make up for lost time, he started sounding the whistle to announce our approach whenever we found ourselves on the pickle train. At first it was just one long note, but, as time went by, he got carried away by his enthusiasm and began adding more and more variations as we steamed passed. After four trips it sounded more like a joyous solo part in a concerto for engine whistle!

The unknown woman lying in that modest little house came to mean so much to Billy that he began to call her his 'Sweetheart', and, before reaching for the whistle on our approach, he would shout across the footplate to me.

'Hey, come on, lad – come an' wave to me sweetheart – you're gonna miss her!'

Then, leaving the house behind as the last note of the whistle died on the air, he'd turn to face me with a broad, proud smile on his face.

The signalman's threat to have Billy on the carpet for his wild whistling did nothing to deter the little driver when it came his turn to work the pickle train again six weeks later. That day, having learned from further enquiries that Billy was at the controls, the signalman's ears were trained on Westfield station curve like the reflectors of a radio telescope. This time, with the wind at right angles to the direction of the train, the sound came to his ears muffled, but he heard it all right – he was ready for it. The defiant attitude of the driver when he had stopped us six weeks earlier, along with his remark relating his face to the pickles, had rankled him. Now he had a personal score to settle and he was reaching for pen and paper before the last note died on the wind.

'Whistling like a madman' and 'Shattering the peace and quietness of the town' were some of the words he put down, and when the Block Inspector and the Station Master discussed the matter, they decided to consult the Locomotive Superintendent himself.

It took Wally Philpot no time at all to trace the name of the culprit. Following up the dates provided by the signalman he delved into the rosters and came up with Billy's name within minutes. He had it in front of him when the Inspector and the Station Master kept their appointment and, in less than fifteen minutes, their plan for nabbing him in the act was cut and dried.

With the conspiracy well and truly laid, a dismal, rain-swept day saw two officials lurking on the down platform of Westfield station, and, as the time for the pickle train to pass drew near, garbed in sombre railway raincoats and bowler hats, they crouched behind the gent's lavatory like two ghouls in a graveyard. They were oblivious of the driving rain and biting wind, for, to such as these, a mission to expose a gross violation of the rules and regulations was nothing less than a sacred duty. Little did they know that their cause was lost even before they took up their vigil.

The day the signalman stopped the pickle train at Westfield quarry Billy Banks had been a very disappointed man. That day, when he peered into the bedroom of his ailing 'Sweetheart', the room had been empty. He had seen the bed clearly enough, but there was no head straining from the pillow, no hand feebly waving. Six weeks later, when the signalman heard the wild whistling that provoked him into reaching at once for pen and paper, he failed to detect the note of despair as the whistle trailed into silence, for this was the day that Billy's worst fears were realised. Not only had there been no sign of his 'Sweetheart', there were no curtains at the window, no bed, no anything. The house was empty.

On the day that the grim-faced pair crouched cocksure of a catch behind the wall of the gent's lavatory on Westfield station platform, Billy Banks had neither heart nor cause to sound the whistle. To the chagrin of the two conspirators the pickle train steamed through the station without so much as a wisp of steam at her whistle valve. Unaware of Billy's sadness and thoroughly dejected at the failure of their mission, the two officials slunk away to scheme fresh plans for catching miscreants who violated the rules and regulations.

The next time we worked the pickle train the little house by the side of the line had changed completely. We noticed that the unkempt garden had been tidied, and a child, only a few weeks old, reposed in a brand new perambulator outside the back door. New curtains hung at the windows and the woodwork had been given a fresh coat of paint. As Billy observed the changes he said, thoughtfully, 'Oh aye, she's passed on, y'know, mate – me sweetheart – I say she's passed on. There's nothin' so sure.'

Afterwards, as though privately mourning, he remained completely silent to the end of the trip.

Scientists tell us that sound waves radiate in all directions from their source, diminishing in force the further they travel until, finally, when the energy of the waves is exhausted, the air becomes still and the sound is lost forever. And yet, although it happened more than fifty years ago and both Billy Banks and his 'Sweetheart' are long dead, I hear that wildly whooping whistle of joy spiralling through the morning air frequently in my inner conscience and, whenever I hear it, I always wonder to which of them it meant the most.

12
A Wagon Bottom
for Christmas

A hundred years ago one could travel by rail from Manchester to Liverpool in forty minutes. Even more remarkable, one could travel by the same means from Manchester to London in three hours fifteen minutes. And yet, despite little or no improvement in these times to the very end of the Steam Age, aspiring brains were constantly at work striving to improve efficiency. Year after year the locomotives became more powerful, the signalling systems more complicated and the rules and regulations more and more difficult to apply. While some of the ideas blazed but briefly across the firmament, others were applied with tremendous enthusiasm in the vain hope that because of them the Steam Age might last forever.

And yet, no matter how they stood up in theory, every idea emanating from the 'Brains' department possessed a fatal flaw: no matter how grand or trivial in concept, almost all of them failed to take into account the wicked little factor mysteriously referred to as the 'human element'.

Take, for example, the genius who peddled the idea that when coal is reduced to the size of one's fist it burns at its most efficient. After countless trials he was proved to be absolutely right and won the support of the most eminent coalologists of the time. But, you know, he never convinced Henry Peacock.

Henry was a fireman on the old London Midland & Scottish Railway who simply abhorred large cobs and possessed an equally strong aversion to using the coal-pick. With Henry, if a cob rolled down the tender on to the shovelling plate that would just pass through the circumference of the firehole, it had to go in as it was. Confronted by a cob as big as himself, he'd glare at it with manic hatred, declaring, 'Bastard cobs!' Whereupon, panting and sweating with exertion, he would wrestle with it to the side of the engine and, in a great explosion of effort, hurl it over the side of the speeding train to the ballast. The moment it landed it would bowl and bounce along until it finally shattered into a thousand fragments as it slammed against the wall of a platelayer's hut or some other obstruction, and, as it disintegrated, Henry's face would assume the expression of a man who had just disposed of an inconvenient corpse.

The arrival of the mechanical coaling plant on the technological scene imbued the bowler-hatted officials with an irrepressible fever of excitement. This was the quantum leap that they had been waiting for – the most important development since the innovation of the signal box. Measured by the two criteria of technological advance – the amount of time saved or labour displaced – the idea promised savings in manpower of such proportions that its conception was considered to be close to immaculate.

Prior to the installation of these marvellous constructions, the locomotives were coaled by the brute force of coaling gangs shovelling the coal from wagons on an elevated ramp directly into the tenders. As one engine left the queue replenished, another would join the queue to await its turn.

With everyone in management believing that the new innovation was flawless, the construction of the new coaling plants proceeded with haste, slowly coming to dominate the skyline at every engine shed throughout the land. The one they erected at Clanky Junction was enormous. Appearing like a gigantic tombstone on stilts, it towered above everything for miles around. At the pull of a switch a twenty-ton wagon of coal was hoisted to the top where it turned completely over to empty its load into a cavernous hopper with a noise like thunder. It could devour ten such wagons without getting the least congested. Straddling two lines at the inlet to the shed, it could coal four locomotives simultaneously in a quarter of the time it had taken the old coaling gang to coal one.

No wonder the bowler-hatted battalions were keen to see it operating. There were four men to a shift coaling the locomotives by the old method; twelve men employed throughout the twenty-four hours. Now, at a stroke, their labour was obsolete.

Fortunately for the men of the redundant coaling gangs, the new contraption appeared on the scene when the railways were booming. Instead of being dismissed from the Junction, they were dispersed throughout the shed on simple labouring jobs. Nevertheless their earnings were reduced to less than half their previous wages, for when coaling the engines by the old method they had been paid by the ton; by buckling down to it they more than doubled their wages. Now, as they swept the shed roads, laboured in the sand-dryer or assisted the fitters, they cursed the inventor of the new coaling plant with Luddite bitterness.

Alas, within a few days of its grand debut, the bowler-hatted brigade learned to their chagrin that, like everything else designed by man, the wondrous new plant had its faults. The first to reveal itself was that for every ton of coal it fed into the tender of a locomotive, a hundredweight spilled over the side to the ground below. Had it been left to its own devices it would have buried itself in coal within a week.

Greatly concerned, the officials made frantic efforts to solve the problem, but, although they made slight improvements, it soon became apparent that a man would be required to clear the spillage from the base of the hopper. Even before the fault revealed itself, it was understood that a man would have to be employed to send the wagons up and down the towering construction; if now they had to employ another to clear the spillage, the optimistic claim that the new contraption was a major labour-saver would be somewhat tarnished. And so, with characteristic guile, they decided to combine both operations and offer the job to a volunteer from the deposed coaling gang.

When, after considering what was involved in the job on offer, the members of the coaling gang saw only a back-breaking future with a mere pittance at the end of the week, they turned it down flat. Finally, by offering a penny an hour above the rate of a labourer, they enticed little Johnny Sparrow to take it on.

Whether or not Johnny Sparrow knew or was capable of knowing what he was letting himself in for is difficult to judge. Most of the men in the coaling gang said he was 'thick', while the more generous amongst them expressed the less vindictive opinion that he was a little on the simple side. Suffice to say that Johnny Sparrow not only accepted the job, but he stuck at it for the rest of his working life. It turned out to be the most arduous job I ever saw a man perform. Sending the wagons to the top of the hopper was as simple as pulling a switch, but clearing the spillage was cruel, back-breaking work.

By the time he went home at the end of the day, the ground at the base of the hopper was bare as a freshly cleared table, but when he returned the next morning there were tons to shift. After years on the job his back became permanently bent, and whenever he came into view as he weaved his way between the queuing locomotives, he would be covered in coal dust from the steel-capped toes of his boots to the top of his bald head.

Small in stature, no taller than five feet, Johnny Sparrow's body was like a highly tempered spring that seemed to re-wind itself whenever he paused in his arduous labour. He was entirely sinew and muscle without an ounce of fat anywhere on his frame. Deprived of anything resembling an education as a child, he was barely literate; no matter how long one engaged him in conversation, his only response was to repeat over and over again the phrase, 'Aye, that's right – that's right.'

And yet, despite the general opinion of the coaling gang that he was 'thick', Johnny organised his new job in a manner that denied this. Knowing from long experience that using a size twelve shovel on uneven ground was asking for trouble, he scoured every nook and cranny of the vast engine shed and pestered the foreman fitter until he acquired enough steel plate to cover every inch of the area on which the spillage landed. Under the dropped door of the wagon into which he shovelled the stuff he managed to have placed a huge square of quarter-inch steel plate of which he was especially proud.

Shovelling the spillage into a gigantic steel wheelbarrow, he would trundle it to the wagon and tip the contents on to the steel plate. He would do this five times. Then, pausing to ease his back, he would shovel the huge mound higher than his head into the wagon, then set off for another relay.

When, at the end of each weary day, the wagon was full, he'd release the brakes and lever it with a heavy pinch-bar along the line until it came to rest on the section that acted as the lift to take the wagons to the top of the hopper. Then, pinning down the brakes again, he would enter his little cabin and pull the switch to send the wagon to the top of the huge construction to disgorge its load into the gigantic maw. When the wagon returned to the ground empty, he would lever it back to the buffers, drop the door and proceed to fill it again.

What with this, clearing up the ashes and smokebox spar left by the disposal men as they cleaned the fires of the incoming locomotives, and sending the wagons of new coal to the top of the hopper, Johnny's labours never ceased from the beginning of the day to the end. The new coaling plant, albeit a technological miracle, was a hard master.

With the problem of the spillage solved, the new contraption slowly lost its aura of wonder to become just another commonplace feature of the engine shed, and, as the excitement subsided, Johnny was left alone to perform his back-breaking labour in peace.

For six months the new mechanical marvel functioned without a hitch, and, with Johnny slaving away hardly noticed, both he and the new coaling plant became taken for granted. Then, to the consternation of those who believed in its infallibility, it suddenly convulsed to a halt without warning. The shed foreman on duty at the time was old Redneck, a man noted for his highly volatile temper. When he heard of the catastrophe, he took off his bowler hat and threw it to the floor of his office in a wild display of frustration.

It was Johnny himself who discovered the cause of the problem; when he pulled the switch to lower an empty wagon from the top of the hopper it arrived on the ground without a bottom in it. Puzzled by his discovery, it took him a little time to realise its full significance, but, within five minutes of his informing the first official he caught sight of, he was surrounded by a gaggle of the bowler-hatted brigade in a high state of excitement.

'D'you mean to say the wagon bottom's in the hopper?'

Johnny nodded. 'Aye, that's right, that's right.'

The officials looked aghast. Another piped up.

'Are you sure it didn't go up like that?'

Johnny nodded again. 'Aye, that's right, that's right.'

Understandably, the officials were rather confused as to the hopper attendant's explanation, and another of their number stepped forward to break the deadlock in communications.

'Now look here, Sparrow, tell us in your own words – did the wagon have coal in it when you sent it to the top of the hopper?'

Johnny explained again exactly in his own words: 'Aye, that's right, that's right.'

Completely flummoxed, the bowler-hatted officials stared at the coal-black hopper attendant at a loss to know how to proceed.

It took three days to extract the wagon bottom from the innards of the coal hopper, during which time the bowler-hatted brigade vied with each other in suggesting solutions to the problem. Meanwhile the engines needed coaling. Immediately the hopper ground to a standstill a queue of locomotives began to form at the inlet, threatening to block the main line, and with the signalman on the telephone every five minutes urging old Redneck to do something about it, the shed foreman with the volatile temper was becoming more agitated by the minute.

Instructing his office lad to summon every member of the redundant coaling team to his office, he impatiently awaited their appearance, then, addressing them gravely, he informed them that they would have to resume coaling the engines by shovel for as long as the emergency lasted. With a queue of thirty locomotives already lined up at the old coaling ramp, his desperation was so great that without protest he agreed to their insistence on tonnage money, and, jubilant with great expectations, the coalers rushed from his office to collect their shovels. As far as they were concerned, the wagon bottom could remain lodged in the bowels of the hopper for ever.

That Johnny Sparrow never revealed exactly how the wagon bottom had hurtled down with the coal wasn't entirely due to his stunted vocabulary. He had something to hide. After several weeks on the job he had made a remarkable discovery. One day, after sending a loaded wagon to the top, he found that when he reversed the switch to bring it down it responded instantly. Moreover, he found that when he pulled and pushed the switch in rapid succession he could make a twenty-ton wagon of coal perform a dance more than a hundred feet in the air. This remarkable discovery filled him with a sense of wonder at the power he commanded and, like a child when it first discovers that by pulling a cat's tail he can make it screech, he found the sensation pleasing.

Johnny paid dearly for his innocent peccadillo, the effect of the breakdown on him contrasting sharply with that on the coaling gang. The latter, making the most of the lucrative opportunity afforded them by the hopper's severe bout of constipation, more than doubled their wages. Johnny's fate was more cruel. Called upon to assist the fitters in the difficult task of clearing the blockage, he had to climb to the very top of the huge construction and descend into its cavernous maw where, for three days, at the bidding of his more highly skilled masters, he pulled and prised the entangled timbers in an atmosphere where every movement agitated layers of choking coal dust. At the end of the ordeal he was glad to get back to the back-breaking task of clearing the spillage.

With the obstruction finally extracted, the newfangled coaling plant was declared fit to resume its wondrous function and, under the anxious gaze of the inevitable gaggle of bowler-hatted officials, the first wagons were sent to the top. When everything went smoothly, the officials departed with renewed confidence and the men of the redundant coaling gang were once again dispersed throughout the shed on their less lucrative jobs of sweeping up and fetching and carrying of various sorts. Soon the disruptive event slipped into history and little Johnny Sparrow was abandoned once again to bend and shovel and trundle his gigantic wheelbarrow through the back-breaking days.

And yet, despite the restored smooth functioning of the coaling plant, things were not quite as they were before. In the minds of the redundant coaling gang something rankled. With the fruits of their bonanza well and truly spent, a certain consideration began to creep into their conversation, especially in the tackhouse at scoff-time. It was shortly after their unexpected windfall that Alf first gave voice to it.

'Suppose, just suppose, mind you, he could do it whenever he wanted?'

Alf's remark was so pregnant with subtle meanings that it caused a long silence to descend upon his mates as they proceeded to probe it to the bone. At last, slowly shaking his head, Tommy gave his verdict.

'No Alf, it was just a one-off – a loose bottom, that's all it was – a chance in a million.'

Alf was unconvinced: 'Aye, p'r'aps you're right, Tommy, but all I'm sayin' is just suppose you're wrong. I mean, if he could do it whenever he wanted – we'd be quids in. That's all I'm sayin', Tommy. Don't yer see?'

Here Andy subscribed his twopennyworth: 'Aye, an' suppose he can do it whenever he likes, who's to say he would? Y'know what he's like, Alf, he doesn't understand a blind thing you say to 'im! He's as thick as a coal engine's boiler! If he found 'is shovel full o' gold dust he'd throw it in the bloody wagon! That's why they put 'im on the job – only a bloke who's twopence in the shillin' 'ud do it for the money he gets!'

Despite the lack of enthusiasm on the part of his mates, Alf persisted: 'I know, Andy, I know, lad, but just suppose. That's all I'm sayin' – I'm not puttin' it any higher than that – but just suppose he could do it whenever he had a mind to – don't y'see?'

The seed of hope that Alf sowed in the minds of his cronies germinated like a dandelion in a fallow field and, not long afterwards, Johnny Sparrow found himself becoming very popular. Like all the men at the Junction, he signed on and off duty at the north end of the shed, and it was here that one morning he was most surprised to find himself being greeted like a celebrity.

'How's it going, Johnny lad? Are you all right? Have you lost any more wagon bottoms lately?'

'Hiya, Johnny! Is that coaling plant behavin' itself? You're doin' a grand job lookin' after a machine like that! They're not payin' you half enough, Johnny!'

Johnny Sparrow didn't know what to make of it all. Few of the men ever spoke to him, most of them believing that he was a simpleton, the rest refraining from engaging him in conversation to avoid embarrassment. Now everything appeared to have changed. From a shunned recluse he had become a man of significance almost overnight.

As the weeks went by, the demoted coaling gang's campaign to soften him up increased in intensity until, one evening, after he had trudged through the shed the quarter of a mile to the north end to sign off, he found himself surrounded by four burly coalers who proceeded to slap him on the back like a long-lost friend. Before he realised what was happening, he was hustled into the empty tackhouse where, with one on guard at the door, the other three pressured him for a good twenty minutes.

Apart from the coalers and Johnny himself, no one knows what happened that evening in the tackhouse. What is perfectly clear in hindsight, however, is that the coalers extracted from Johnny the knowledge that he could inflict a chronic bout of constipation on the newfangled coaling plant whenever he chose to. What is even more important, he must have offered his full co-operation.

Two weeks before Christmas, just in time to fatten the festive wage-packets of the coaling gang, the magnificent contraption of a coaling hopper juddered to a halt once more with a wagon bottom buried deep in its vitals. When the news of the calamity broke, Johnny was surrounded by a group of officials to be assailed by accusations. Old Redneck had a near fit, and within fifteen minutes Wally Philpot summoned all his official underlings to his office. Meanwhile, as the panic increased, the redundant coaling gang hovered in the background becoming more and more intoxicated with visions of opulence.

Once again, as the old coaling ramp echoed with the boisterous banter and grunts of the coalers as they doubled their wages, little Johnny Sparrow found himself crawling about the cavernous maw of the hopper, lacerating his hands and knees on the sharp edges of the coal and breathing in clouds of coal dust as he performed all the heavy work to extract the stubborn obstruction he himself had lodged there.

As he struggled with a huge balk of timber in the grimy bowels of the hopper, a bowler-hatted figure appeared, silhouetted against a small patch of bright blue sky in the opening high above him. The official shouted down to him, his voice echoing in the vast chamber of the hopper.

'Come on, Johnny, put your back into it! It's costing the company thousands of pounds paying them money-grabbing coalers while this thing's out of order! They're making a fortune. You know they're on tonnage, don't yer?'

These were the words that inflamed Johnny's suspicions. This it was that made him realise that he had been made a fool of, and the revelation expanded his vocabulary as he vented his feelings whenever he had time to dwell on the matter: 'The bastards! The crafty bastards!'

As with the previous calamity, time healed everything after a few weeks, everything but a gnawing suspicion deep in Johnny's subconscious. He had thoroughly enjoyed his brief popularity. Suddenly finding himself one of the lads after years of being shunned had given him a feeling of self-esteem that he had never known previously, but, when all the back-slapping and jocular greetings ceased immediately after the event, he found himself abandoned once more.

In time, Johnny's smouldering grudge against the coalers faded as he resumed his back-breaking tasks of clearing the spillage and satisfying the gargantuan appetite of the hopper. Had his loneliness been accompanied by idleness his smouldering grudge might have turned to hatred, but shovelling fifteen tons of coal higher than one's head every day in all weathers gives little opportunity for a grudge to fester, and before the week was out he resumed his painstaking labour as though nothing had happened.

Inexorably, Christmas came round again and, whatever others chose to forget, the deposed coaling gang clung to the memory of their fat wage-packets of the previous year with the tenacity of a miser anticipating a visit to his secret hoard. Three weeks before the holiday Johnny suddenly found himself once again subjected to ribald greetings and vigorous back-slapping, but this time his dormant grudge against the coalers leapt to the surface of his mind like a rekindled flame. Oh no, they wouldn't succeed in making a fool of him this time! Oh no, not again! Whenever he saw them approaching, Johnny set himself to walk straight through them.

'Hiya, Johnny lad! It's nearly time y'know, Johnny! Don't forget the old wagon bottom, eh, Johnny?'

Despite the back-slapping, he continued to walk straight through them without faltering in his stride, saying only, 'Aye, that's right, that's right.'

Without let-up they harassed him for days until, getting no sign of co-operation from the wary hopper attendant, they assembled at a quiet, out of the way corner on one of the shed roads and argued amongst themselves.

'It's gonna be too late! If it doesn't 'appen tomorrer it'll be too late for the Christmas wages! What're we gonna do?'

This was the pessimistic Tommy. Seeing the need for a little inspiration, Alf stepped into the breach.

'Now look here, lads, there's only one thing we can do. We'll have to go an' see 'im – p'r'aps offer 'im summat.'

Andy interjected at once. 'Offer 'im summat? Wadyer mean, offer 'im summat?'

Alf expanded: 'Make it worth his while, that's what I mean! Don't forget, he got nowt last time! We'll just 'ave to cast a sprat to catch the mackerel!'

For a moment they stared at him blankly. Then, as each of their faces broke into a sly grin, unanimity was finally achieved.

On the morning of the very last day that the event would benefit the Christmas wages, Johnny found himself surrounded by the members of the deposed coaling gang as he shovelled a fresh mound of spillage into the wagon. Stepping forward from the ring in a suppressed state of anxiety, Alf addressed the coal-grimed Johnny.

'Now look 'ere, Johnny lad – what about this wagon bottom? I mean, what've we done to yer? If it doesn't 'appen today it's gonna be too late. Y'see that, don't yer, Johnny?'

Ignoring him completely, Johnny continued shovelling.

'I mean, it's only once a year when all's said an' done! Can't y'see y'way clear to fixin' it, Johnny? Just for Christmas like?'

Still ignoring him, Johnny continued his shovelling of the spillage into the wagon. Alf persisted in his plea.

'Is it the money, Johnny? Eh? Is it the money that's stoppin' yer? Come on, Johnny, out with it!'

The rhythm of the little man's shovel never faltered as he got down to the last of the mound of coal, and it was here that Alf delivered what he considered to be the coup de grâce.

'I mean, if it's the money that's stoppin' yer, we'll give yer a quid, Johnny!'

To his astonishment Johnny showed not the slightest interest in his proposition. Instead, throwing his shovel into the wheelbarrow, he grasped the handles and trundled it to the base of the coaling plant. His apparent disinterest in Alf's offer was deceptive, for secretly his thoughts were racing. A quid indeed! Did they think he was a complete idiot?

Out of the corner of his eye he observed the redundant coalers following behind him. As he lowered the wheelbarrow they stopped several feet away. Taking hold of his shovel, he was just about to start reloading the barrow when Alf resumed his appeal. This time there was the pleading note of a mendicant in his voice.

'Come on, Johnny, tell us what's stoppin' yer! I tell yer – if it's the money – we'll give you a quid!' Then, as Johnny continued to ignore him, he added, 'A quid apiece, Johnny – a quid apiece lad!'

Now they were talking! A quid apiece! There were twelve men in the old coaling gang, four on each shift. Twelve quid! Deep in the recesses of Johnny's uncomplicated mind a tiny worm of avarice began to wriggle to the surface, its progress clearly showing in his demeanour as he stopped shovelling and turned to face the coalers.

Anxious to get back to the north end of the shed where their duties lay, Alf brought the bargaining to a close.

'Right then, Johnny? We can take it you'll be seein' to things then – just for Christmas like?'

For the first time that morning, Johnny spoke. 'Aye, that's right, that's right.'

With this, the jubilant coalers scuttled back to the north end of the shed to await the event.

Two hours later the wagon that Johnny sent to the top of the hopper performed a spectacular tango a hundred and fifty feet in the air. After tipping its load it took two steps backwards, two steps forwards, three steps backwards and three steps forwards. Then, with the lunge of a Latin American professional, a huge leap backwards and a huge leap forwards! It wasn't just the wagon bottom that hurtled down into the coal that Christmas, breaking away from its four anchor points on the lift section of the line – the whole damn wagon went in! Anticipating the event at the north end of the shed, the men of the coaling gang already had their shovels in their hands when old Redneck came screaming through the shed to instruct them.

For the new coaling plant to convulse to a halt one Christmas would no doubt have been accepted as an unfortunate accident. To occur twice in succession was not simply an unlikely coincidence, it was an insult to the intelligence of Wally Philpot, the District Locomotive Superintendent, When, immediately after the debacle, little Johnny Sparrow was escorted through the shed yard to appear on the mat, he was confronted on his appearance by a raging Wally with old Redneck and three more bowler-hatted officials standing gravely in the background. Wally attacked at once.

'Tell me, Sparrow – tell me why it only happens at Christmas? We never have trouble any other time of the year! Tell me why?'

As the Superintendent impaled the quaking Johnny on his stare, the little hopper attendant became completely bereft of speech.

'I'm waiting, Sparrow! Don't just stand there, man – tell me – go on – tell me why it only happens at Christmas! It's true, isn't it?'

Johnny gulped quite audibly under the onslaught: 'Aye, that's right.'

Wally flew at him. 'I'll say it's right – and you know more about it than you're prepared to admit, Sparrow!'

At a safe distance outside, Alf, delegated by the rest of the coaling gang, leaned nonchalantly with his back to the wall of Wally's office at the side of the frosted window listening to every word of Johnny's interrogation through an open fanlight. Unseen by him, Wally raised himself from his armchair, stood to his full height and, thrusting his face to within inches of that of the miserable Johnny, almost screamed at him, 'It's got to stop, Sparrow! D'yer hear me? It's got to stop! By hell, it's got to stop! You know what it is, don't you, Sparrow? I say, you know what it is? It's downright sabotage – that's what it is, Sparrow! Downright bloody sabotage!'

Without taking his eyes off the miserable culprit in front of him, he paused for several seconds, then, maintaining his withering stare, slowly lowered himself back into his armchair to retreat into a brief spell of deep thought. Then, arriving at a decision, he glared at Johnny afresh.

'Now I'll tell you what I'm going to do, Sparrow! I'm going to forget all about it. I'm going to forget it ever happened. During your long service with the company you've kept a clean sheet up to now and, when you leave this office, so it will remain.'

On the face of it this appeared an extremely magnanimous gesture on the part of the Superintendent, but it was nothing of the kind. The crafty old devil knew only too well he would have to engage two men to perform the work of clearing the spillage and replenishing the hopper with coal if he sacked Johnny Sparrow. Nevertheless, completely unaware of Wally's ulterior motive, the guilt-ridden Johnny felt an immense wave of relief as he heard the decision. For a moment his spirits soared, only to plummet again when the enraged Superintendent leaned towards him again in a most threatening manner.

'But I'll tell you this, Sparrow. If it happens again – just once more, mind you – as sure as my name's Wallace Cecil Philpot, I'll have your bloody guts for garters!'

Here, pointing to the door of his office with all the veins on his head and neck bulging with temper, he screamed, 'Get out!'

Of course the Superintendent was absolutely right – it was nothing less than downright sabotage. But sometimes in this funny old world it appears that right and wrong depend on which end of the stick one has hold of. As Alf remarked when he reported back to his mates in the tackhouse, 'He raised the roof! He did! He raved like a bloody lunatic! There was no need to carry on like that! I mean, what the bloody hell's Christmas without a bob or two?'

13
Dirty Work at Diddler's Ferry

*S*o erratic and unpredictable were the hours worked by the men who manned the locomotives during the Steam Age that their lives became permanently disorientated. With the rest of the family enjoying meat, mash and peas on their return from work in the evening, an engine driver joining them straight from his bed would expect egg and bacon. Likewise, returning home at four o'clock in the morning he would look forward to finding a full dinner between two plates ready to pop in the oven. After eating this in the silence of the dawn, he would settle back in his armchair just like a man who had returned from work in the evening and browse through the newspaper. Then, after a ruminative pipe of tobacco or a cigarette, he would wind up his watch after noting the time, then make his way upstairs to bed silently hoping that his sleep wouldn't be disturbed by the whistling postman, the bottle-rattling milkman or the exuberant cries of children dawdling to school.

From a twelve-hour day at the beginning of the Steam Age, it became an eight-hour day towards the end. But this was only a formality – cold print on an agreement contracted between the companies and the unions. When a driver and his fireman signed on for a trip, their day's work ended only when they arrived back at the engine shed or at some distant barracks. Somewhere in the musty archives will be recorded the longest spell at the controls endured by some engine driver long dead, but even I know of one driver and his stoker who remained on the footplate for thirty-six hours. Fourteen and fifteen hours were common even when the first diesel made its appearance.

Many a restless neighbour parted the curtains of his bedroom at the first light of dawn to see the engine driver who lived nearby taking his dog for a walk. But then the man at the window and the man in the street belonged to different worlds – one governed by the rotation of the earth on its axis, the other by the wheels of a railway that required the men to drive them throughout the day and night in all seasons.

In the line of promotion, the Spare Link was the first group that a driver and fireman entered on being appointed to their grade. These were the men who worked the extra trains that coped with a flood of exports to the docks, an exodus to the seaside due to an exceptionally hot summer, or substituted for absent crews during a 'flu epidemic. At Clanky Junction the Spare Link consisted of eight crews listed to sign on duty at three-hourly intervals twice round the clock. When word came that a special train was required to run, or if another crew missed their rostered train, a knocker-up would be dispatched at once to rouse from their beds the first available crew in the Spare Link, leaving the next pair on the roster to be called when the demand arose.

The only thing the men of the Spare Link knew for certain was that after they signed off a trip they couldn't be called for another until they had rested for ten hours (later twelve). Never knowing where they would find themselves one day to the next, and called upon to handle every type of locomotive on the system, it was a hard school in which their physical endurance and their railway skills were tested to the limit. In such circumstances, where the end of the week was no more significant than the beginning, where the hours of darkness were no more inhibiting than the hours of daylight, and where time became an endless vista of disjointed sleep and long hours of work, a carefree Sunday with its attendant lie-in became as enticing in its rarity as a cool pool in an arid desert.

It was this uncertainty that lay behind Harry Kemp's anxiety. One of the drivers in the Spare Link, Harry had good cause to worry, for Saturday the fifteenth of July was destined to be one of the most important days in his life. He had never felt more confident. Ever since Jacob Purdy, a driver he had fired for years before, had got him interested in poultry, he had kept and bred old English game birds, or bantams as they are commonly known. By following the shows, reading everything he could find on the subject and experimenting as eagerly as Mendel himself in the science of cross-breeding, he had become devoted to the proud little birds. Not that he was prejudiced; he would discuss pigeons, canaries and budgerigars with anyone who fancied them, but, for Harry, the old English game bird was the aristocrat of the feathered world, and he would sacrifice almost anything to ensure that those he kept enjoyed the best of everything.

To say that he was devoted to the birds would be succumbing to sentimentality, for in truth he was ruthless in culling those that failed to meet his high standards. The slightest sign of weakness or poor colouring and they had to go. Mind you, those that met the grade lived in the lap of luxury – nothing but the best corn and a damp-free cote for those that took his fancy. Furthermore, the merest sign of a parasite and he would sacrifice his precious sleep to dust them with delousing powder.

Now, at long last, he was convinced that he had achieved what he had set out to accomplish so many years before. He had bred a champion. Every available moment he stood watching that proud little black-red cock as though he had fashioned it with his own hands. Its perfection was startling. Seeing it strutting round the pen with its head aloof and a myriad colours reflecting from the brilliant sheen of its feathers filled him with immense pride.

Usually practical and single-minded with his brood, with this one he became rather sentimental. He had never given a name to one of his birds during the ten years he had kept them, but one day, as he stood watching them strutting round the pen in a blaze of sunlight, a remarkable thing happened. Quite suddenly the black-red cockerel changed into the shape of Wally Philpot, the District Locomotive Superintendent, strutting among the engines on the shed roads on one of his surprise inspections. It was truly amazing. One minute he saw the black-red cockerel, the next, Wally Philpot, head aloof and hands behind his back as he cast sly glances in every direction so that all might tremble. The mirage lasted for no more than a second, but it was enough for Harry. Believing it to be an omen, he called the bird 'Wally' from that day forth.

Unable to fault it in mien, form or colouring, Harry entered 'Wally' in the local show to be held in the Mechanics Institute on Saturday 15 July and, as the day approached, his excitement began to get the better of him. By nature a man who took things as they came, be it long hours of overtime, lodging away from home or an engine with hardly a breath of steam in her, he now started fretting lest something turned up to prevent his attendance at the show. Above every other consideration, on Saturday 15 July he just had to finish early.

His first disappointment was when he calculated that on Monday of that week his name would be the last on the roster. This meant that he would be called from home to sign on duty between nine o'clock and midnight on the first day of the fatal week. He knew only too well what this portended. To start the week on the latest of lates and ensure that he was at home in time to present 'Wally' at the show at ten o'clock on Saturday morning wasn't going to be easy to achieve. And yet, if the perfect specimen of a gamecock he had bred after years of patient matings was going to grace the showbench with his presence, by hook or by crook he had to do it.

Harry's plan was to apply all his craft and cunning to avoid all overtime by pestering every signalman for a clear road so that he could be called for duty progressively earlier each day. It was a daunting task, but by concentrating on the problem with the utmost diligence, he succeeded in being called for duty at ten o'clock on the Friday night before the big day. Even if he didn't arrive home until eight o'clock the following morning, after a wash and a quick snack he'd have 'Wally' in his basket ready for showing at ten. His prospects appeared so promising that he began to feel intoxicated.

At half past three on the morning of the great day, the hopes of Harry Kemp had never been more buoyant, but ten minutes later, when his train was switched to the loop at Diddler's Ferry to allow a fitted freight to pass, they plummeted dismally.

Worse was yet to come. As he brought his lumbering coal train to a stand at the end of the loop to await a path he saw something that made his heart sink. There, waiting in the sidings three roads away, was the fish ready to leave with Roger Wylie at the controls. To be home by nine o'clock Harry would have to leave Diddler's Ferry at four at the latest. If he could manage this he would be at Darkcroft, his destination, in four hours, but, with the fish competing for a path, his chances were not promising. The situation was one he hadn't bargained for. Roger Wylie, alias Roger the Dodger, was renowned for manipulating his finishing times. With a wife who happened to be a cousin of old Redneck, the shed foreman, he enjoyed an advantage few could equal. Furthermore, Roger the Dodger's desire to finish early was just as fierce as Harry's, the only difference being that while Harry's was a desire of a lifetime, the Dodger's was a weekly passion.

At about the time Harry Kemp became enchanted by the charms of old English game birds, Roger the Dodger became envious of the adulation showered on those who entertained the Saturday night gatherings at the shed social club. Deciding one Saturday night to unleash his own talents on the audience, he strode to the microphone during the first break in the proceedings and, without so much as an 'Excuse me' or 'I beg your pardon', launched into a rendering of 'O Solo Mio'. Had his performance possessed the slightest merit the audience would have applauded generously. As it was, with a voice that knew neither pitch nor tone and trembled sickeningly whenever he tried to hold a note, the rendering was abysmal. The howls of derision that greeted it were intended to drive him from the stage for good, but, handicapped by a skin thicker than that of a rhinoceros, the Dodger took it to mean that they adored him!

So powerful was the Dodger's conceit that when he overheard a driver refer to him as the working man's Caruso he took it as a complement. There was no restraining the man. Shortly after his agonising debut he had cards printed bearing the words:

Mr Roger Wylie. Tenor.
Weddings and parties catered for.
Modest fee.

Whenever he was on nights, his sole aim was to get home as early as possible every Saturday morning when, after a recuperative sleep of six or seven hours, he would tog himself up in dress suit and dicky bow ready to inflict his lethal talent once more.

It was a cruel stroke of misfortune that the two trains, one driven by Harry, the other by the Dodger, should cross paths at Diddler's Ferry. With the impeccable black-red gamecock looming large in his thoughts, Harry was close to desperation.

'Would you believe it!'

Fully aware of his driver's desire to finish early, his fireman crossed the cab.

'What did yer say, Harry?'

Pointing despondently towards the sidings, Harry replied, 'The Dodger – he's beaten us to it. He's there, see, already to go wi' the fish.'

Sure enough, as the fireman looked towards the fish train engine he saw the figure of the Dodger silhouetted in the firelight of the cab. His sympathy went out to his driver at once, for he knew only too well that on a Saturday morning at the height of summer, a lowly coal train stood little chance of preference on the main line.

If at that moment Harry Kemp had suddenly acquired the power to disintegrate the fish train and the Dodger with it in a puff of smoke, he would have exercised it without hesitation. Instead, he stood deep in thought on the footplate of his locomotive racking his brains for a solution to the problem that threatened his greatest ambition.

With his thoughts sparking in wild tangents, he continued to stare into the sidings until, quite suddenly, something aroused his interest. In the soft pool of light cast by the high lamp situated where the roads fanned out into the sidings, he saw the leading shunter emerge from the cabin and approach the Dodger's engine. After a few seconds the Dodger and his fireman descended to the ballast and joined him. Then, after a few words with each other, the three of them walked the short distance to the shunter's cabin and disappeared inside. Long experience told Harry that the Dodger and his mate had been invited to join a card school, and it was at that moment that he conceived a diabolical plan to save the day. He addressed his fireman excitedly.

'Hey, Tommy, we can still do it! Look, there's no one on his engine! Him an' his mate have gone in the cabin for a game o' crib! I'm sure of it! Go an' have a look what they're doin' – have a sly look through the window!'

As loyal to his driver as most of his kind, Tommy descended to the ballast and approached the shunter's cabin stealthily. A few seconds later he returned with his findings.

'You're right Harry – they've just started a game o' crib – the guard an' all!'

Harry's excitement increased.

'Lovely – we've gorrim, Tommy. Now look, he's got about twenty vans on his train – we're gonna pin down all his brakes. Are you with me?'

Startled by the audacity of the plan but knowing how desperate his driver was to launch 'Wally' on the golden road to feathered fame, he felt honour-bound to co-operate.

'Of course I'm with yer!'

Grabbing the brake-stick, he declared, 'Come on – what're we waitin' for?'

Leap-frogging past each other, they proceeded along the fish train in the darkness pinning down every brake. Reaching the vacant guard's van and perspiring freely, Harry noticed that the buffers of the van rested right up against the buffers of the first wagon of an almost full road of freight. On impulse, and unable to resist the temptation glaring him in the face, he ducked under the buffers and coupled the fish train to what must have amounted to a further seven hundred tons of freight. As the two conspirators got back to their engine, Harry addressed his fireman again.

'Right, Tommy, you get back on the engine while I go an' 'ave a quiet word with the signalman.'

Harry entered the signal box breezily.

'Good mornin' signalman! What are our chances then?'

Pulling feverishly on his levers, the signalman replied, 'Are you the fish?'

'No, Darkcroft coal.'

The signalman looked astonished. 'The coal? Oh, you've no chance, driver! Why, the fish 'as been waitin' fer a road for half an hour! I've the milk, the mail an' a couple o' banana trains afore he goes – an' he'll have to go, I can tell yer! Y'know what it's like this time o' year – there'll be a couple o' specials on his tail in next to no time!'

Strangely, this was exactly what Harry hoped to hear. He had gone to the signal box to sow a seed of doubt and, if the signalman's manner was anything to go by, it would fall on fertile soil. He released the seed.

'Ah, but will he, signalman? Will he?'

This time the signalman looked puzzled.

'Will he? Will he what?'

With the seed of doubt sown, Harry proceeded to nourish it.

'Will he go? Y'know whose drivin' the fish tonight, don't yer? It's the

Dodger – Roger the Dodger – a man wi' more money in the bank than Rockefeller – an' all from time-cribbing! He's known for it from Land's End to John o' Groats!'

Despite the momentary expression of doubt that brushed the signalman's face, he resisted the bait.

'Oh, he'll have to gerra move on, driver!'

Throwing back his levers as the milk train thundered past the box, he shouted above the noise, 'Oh aye, he'll have to go all right when I give him the signal. He will that! He'll have to go like a bat out of hell!'

Then, as the clamour of the milk train died in the distance and his telegraph jangled to warn him of the approach of the mail, he continued, 'Any road, driver, what's all the hurry? You're well afore time! Darkcroft coal isn't due to leave for another hour at least! An' anyway, y'know as well as I do it's fish afore coal every time! I mean, lerrus be fair driver – lerrus be fair!'

Here, with nothing else for it, Harry told the signalman all about 'Wally' and his imminent debut on the showbench.

When, during Harry's revelations regarding 'Wally', the signalman revealed that he too was a poultryman, the desperate driver was imbued by a fresh surge of optimism and returned to his warning about Roger the Dodger.

'I hope you don't misunderstand me, signalman. If I thought the fish would get a move on I wouldn't be standin' here botherin' yer. It's just that I know 'im of old. You mark my words, it'll take 'im ten minutes to get out of the sidings and another ten to pass your starting signal! Now, if you could see your way to giving me a chance to go first, why, I'd be through your section faster 'n a greyhound wi' a red-hot poker an inch from it's arse!'

Pulling the signals for the approaching mail train, the signalman repeated the inviolable laws of railway preference, but this time his litany lacked the conviction he had shown previously.

'Aye, I see what y'mean, driver, but as I keep tellin' yer, he is the fish when all's said an' done – an' fish comes afore coal every time. Y'see that, don't yer? I mean, lerrus be fair.'

As the roar of the mail train assaulted the signal box then died in the distance, he threw back his levers and approached Harry as though he had come to a decision.

'All right driver, I'll tell yer what I'll do – I mean, he is the fish when all's said an' done – but any road, what I'll do is this – I'll give 'im his chance when the last banana's gone through an' if he's not makin' an effort to get away I'll have 'im stopped and give you a chance.'

The signalman looked at Harry questioningly. 'Now then, how's that suit yer? I can't be fairer than that, now can I?'

Harry was more than satisfied. The very thought of the Dodger getting away sharpish with all the brakes on his train pinned down and coupled to another seven hundred tons of freight into the bargain made him want to split his sides laughing, but, restraining the impulse, he thanked the signalman.

'That's very good of you, signalman. That's all I want. Thank you very much.'

With this, followed by a signalman very pleased with his compromise, he opened the door of the signal box to leave. As they stood at the top of the steps the engine driver was assailed by another impulse to burst out laughing, but, pulling himself together, he gripped the handrails and, watched by his benefactor, descended the steps with dignity.

As the last of the banana trains roared past the sidings Harry and his fireman heard the outlet signal clatter to the lower quadrant and, almost at once, the door of the shunter's cabin flew open to disgorge the Dodger and his mate along with the guard. Seconds later the dawn sky was rent by a shower of sparks shooting from the chimney of the Dodger's engine as it strained in vain to move the enormous load it was coupled to. With more sparks streaming from the madly slipping wheels, the working man's Caruso tried again and again to get his train moving, but it was all in vain.

With the seed of doubt Harry had sown now in full flower, the signalman telephoned the Inspector at once.

'Stop the fish! Let's be 'avin' the coal! No, no, no, stop the fish, I tell yer – let's be 'avin' the coal! I don't care what you say – he's not stoppin' my bloody railway – let's be 'avin' the coal!'

The Inspector reached the outlet signal just as the Dodger and his fireman were making to descend to the ballast to investigate the remarkable resistance preventing their train from leaving the sidings. Displaying a red light from his handlamp, he shouted for them to remain where they were, then, offering a green light to the coal train, he shouted, 'Right Darkcroft! Let's be 'avin' yer!'

Although slightly reassured by the knowledge that no one had seen him immobilising the fish train, Harry Kemp knew beyond doubt that suspicion would fall on him if the matter came to the attention of higher powers, but nothing would have restrained him that morning. Regardless of any consequences, he was prepared to make any sacrifice, no matter how painful, to ensure that his proud little black-red bantam cock received his due on the showbench. Crowing triumphantly on the whistle, he blasted from Diddler's Ferry loop as though assisted by a bank engine, not forgetting to shout his thanks to the signalman above the deafening clamour from the chimney-top as he shot past the signal box.

14
The Bold Drum Major

During the nine months that Bill Dickenson had been Ernie Brewer's fireman, he had never seen his driver so agitated. It had been going on for more than a fortnight. Whenever their train came to rest in a sidings or was stopped at a signal, he had taken to crossing the footplate to his side of the cab to deliver such terrible outbursts of pent-up anger that he was becoming anxious for his driver's state of mind.

Before the formation of the Clanky Junction brass band, Bill had always found his mate a genial, good-natured soul interested only in his home and his job on the railway. Now, almost overnight, he had become transformed into a man full of cares and tribulations capable of wild gestures and alarming tirades that ceased only when their train got moving again. Bill knew that it was going to happen any minute now as their train clattered to a halt in Dickleton loop. Sure enough, the moment Ernie applied the brake and closed the valve, he was standing in front of him, his face tortured by some terrible torment.

'It's right, y'know, Bill! You ask anyone who knows anythin' about brass bands – they'll tell yer! Without question the drum major's the leader of the band – never mind the big drummer! I mean, you've only got to think about it – how does he know when to strike up? Tell me that, Bill! If the big drummer's the leader of the band, why have a drum major at all? I mean, it's plain common sense, Bill! Without the man wi' the mace there'd be bloody chaos! 'Course, what can you expect? He's as thick as wheel sprag! He belts the flamin' drum like a man wi' a grudge! He wouldn't last five minutes in a military band, y'know, Bill! I'm tellin' yer, not five bloody minutes! Bang – bang – bang – why, every bloody bang's the same! You know what he's short of, don't you, Bill? Eh? I say, you know what he's short of? Finesse, that's what he's short of! He's got about as much finesse as a shoveller on a shit cart!'

In a manner expressing all his disgust, the distraught engine driver returned to his own side of the cab to stare fiercely across the sidings. Then, after an uncomfortable silence lasting several minutes, he returned to confront his fireman again and launched into another tirade.

'Y'know what he says, Bill? Eh? Y'know what the idiot says? He says the drum major's there just to guide the band round the streets! Now then, what d'yer think o' that, eh, Bill? It just shows what he knows, doesn't it? 'Course, he's had no experience, Bill! He never played a drum in his life till Harry Smith died!'

Pausing once more, Ernie took a step closer to his fireman and, looking at him most confidentially, said, 'Course, you know what it is, Bill, don't yer? Eh? I say, you know what it is? It's gone to his head, Bill, that's what it's done! It's gone to his flamin' head!'

Really you could put down the trouble between Ernie Brewer and the big drummer to teething problems. After all, the Clanky Junction brass band had been in existence only six months. Looking back on its formation, it was touch and go whether it would succeed at all. The staggering cost of new instruments and uniforms almost doomed the idea to failure right from the start. It was only when someone suggested that they should buy the paraphernalia of a local band that had packed up through lack of support that things got under way.

There was never the slightest doubt as to the choice of drum major; in his army days Ernie Brewer had borne the mace for his regimental band. He had never lost his military bearing, and from the day that the committee invited him to join, he had applied himself in true military fashion. Finding the second-hand mace they gave him too heavy and lacking that delicate balance that enabled a drum major worth his salt to handle it as though it was part of him, he spent hours whittling it down. On his return home from a late trip in the early hours of the morning he practised marching up and down his back garden even while his neighbours were still in their beds. He finally got his mace so finely balanced that he could throw it in the air and catch it again as though it was tied to his hand by an invisible length of elastic.

The great day, when the band would perform in public for the first time, was to be the first Saturday in June. This was the day the Clanky Junction social club held its annual gala. This event had been held on the football ground for more than twenty years, but this time, in addition to the athletes and dancing troupes, the proceedings would commence with their very own band marching three times round the ground.

After the march-past the band would form up in front of the stand where the entire committee and no less a personage than Wallace Cecil Philpot, the District Locomotive Superintendent himself, would be looking on. It was going to be a day to remember, and if Ernie Brewer was an example of the rest of the band, their debut was going to be the highlight of the occasion.

Like Ernie Brewer, Harry Smith, the big drummer, had been invited to join the band at the very beginning. For as long as anyone could remember Harry had played with the local Salvation Army band. They reckoned that he could play almost any instrument there was, but he chose to play the big drum with the Clanky Junction band simply to give someone younger the chance to learn the rudiments of music. Every practice night Harry would be present instructing and encouraging the younger players in the pursuit that had given him so much pleasure throughout his life.

The two men showed respect for each other right from the start. Furthermore, Harry recognised Ernie as the leader of the band without question. He said as much as they broke rank after their first practice march.

'Well, Ernie, though I say it meself, you're a pleasure to march behind.'

That's what Harry had said, and Ernie's reply revealed beyond a shadow of doubt that the respect was mutual.

'It's very good of you to say so, Harry, but, y'know, when I'm out in front wi' me mace I'm not exactly dreamin' meself. I'll tell you summat Harry – you've got music in your hands, lad, music in your hands.'

Yes, Ernie Brewer and Harry Smith were men who could work together. One could see this only too clearly in the way they shared the burden of the big drum as they left the football field after a practice march.

And then, quite suddenly and with only three weeks to go to the big day, Harry Smith collapsed and died. Many of the bandsmen wanted to cancel their gala appearance altogether in simple respect to their departed colleague, but Ernie Brewer argued strongly against this. Had not Harry Smith's heart and soul been dedicated to perfecting the band's performance for the gala? Wouldn't he have wanted more than anything in the world for the band to make a glorious debut? And anyway, what more fitting tribute could the band pay to his memory than to form up for a minute's silence in front of the Clanky Junction fraternity? And so, persuaded by Ernie's obvious sincerity, the band committee decided to seek the services of another big drummer and go ahead with their plans as arranged.

The untimely demise of Harry Smith gave Charlie Buckle the opportunity he had been waiting for ever since the formation of the band. It wasn't that he possessed any experience on the instrument, or any musical talent whatsoever, it was just that he fancied himself stationed right in the centre of the band with the big drum on his chest.

Charlie Buckle, you see, was a short man, and, like many short men, he possessed a strong desire to impose his presence on the world. He bowled the band committee clean over with his enthusiasm when they asked him to demonstrate his ability with the drum sticks, but then this was only to be expected. What better way exists for a short feller to command the world's attention than by bashing away at a big drum? Before he delivered half a dozen swipes at the drum as he paraded across the committee room floor the members had their fingers in their ears, their pleas for him to stop being completely ignored until they finally got him to cease with a little muscular persuasion.

In fairness to the committee, it has to be understood that they acted under duress. Not only was Charlie Buckle the only candidate for the vacancy, but there was only a fortnight to go to the big event. The minutes of the meeting speak for themselves:

APPOINTMENT OF NEW BIG DRUMMER

In view of the short time available before the annual gala, it was decided to appoint Charles Buckle to the position. It was unanimously agreed that whilst more skill could be desired, enthusiasm was there in abundance. The position will be reviewed after the gala.

It was here that Ernie Brewer's terrible torment commenced. The very first day that Charlie Buckle accompanied the band on a practice march, the indomitable drummer exposed his true nature for all to behold. As the others in the band straggled from the dressing room towards the football field, he was already out there bashing away at his drum like a man possessed. Ernie had to leg it like a four-minute-miler to get in front with his mace as the rest of the bandsmen, hampered by their instruments, jostled and tripped in ragged pursuit. By the time that they achieved some kind of formation, Charlie was halfway round the pitch belting the drum like a man drumming up a crowd for a circus performance.

That evening the practice was a disaster. The bandsmen were so out of breath that the notes that came from their instruments emerged as painful howls – as though the tubes were tied in knots. The only bandsman to derive any satisfaction from the event was Charlie Buckle himself. He alone excelled as, completely insensitive to the chaos he created in his wake, his devastating drum-beats reverberated over the town like death-dealing thunder claps.

The following day, as his train came to rest in Wentworth sidings, Ernie crossed the footplate once again to unburden himself to his patient fireman.

'He's thick, Bill! He is! He's thick! I wouldn't mind if you could tell him anythin', but it's like talkin' to a stone! D'yer know, Bill, with a drum on his chest an' a couple o' sticks in his hands he'd walk through a brick wall without knowin' it! You can't just throw a big drum on your chest and start playin' it, Bill! There's more to a big drum than meets the eye! You'd think he was bloody Napoleon Bonaparte the way he goes on, Bill! He'll burst it, y'know! He will! You mark my words – he'll burst that bloody drum as sure as God made little apples!'

With a despairing shake of his head Ernie returned to his own side of the cab to brood further on the cause of his torment, and, as Bill leaned forward, his ears straining to make sense of his distraught mate's incoherent mutterings, the tortured driver turned to face him again.

'D'yer know, Bill, if Harry Smith could see the way he's performin' he'd turn in his grave! He would, Bill! If he could just see the pompous little swine bashin' away at that drum he'd turn in his grave!'

As Ernie Brewer's desperation deepened he began to look haggard. Knowing less about brass bands than a midwife knows about navvying, Bill Dickenson felt quite helpless. Before the formation of the band Ernie Brewer had been one of the most amicable drivers he had worked with, a pleasure to share the footplate with. Now he was becoming concerned about him, but, apart from shaking his head in disbelief as his driver bared his agony, there wasn't much he could do.

When the band dispersed after its last practice before the big day, Ernie Brewer was a bag of nerves. The lads in the band had tried every stratagem they could think of to curb the devastating enthusiasm of the indomitable Charlie Buckle. They had hidden his drum, telling him where to find it only when they were formed up ready to move off; they had remonstrated with him on the finer points of bandsmanship; they had even stationed Alf Wignal behind him with his trombone with strict instructions to poke him in the back of the neck with his slide whenever he threatened to run amok. But it was all to no avail. As the big day drew ever nearer the conviction began to grow among the bandsmen that when they paraded in public for the first time, something catastrophic was going to occur. Indeed, when Ernie read his horoscope in a newspaper he casually picked up in the tackhouse before leaving the shed one day, this conviction intensified. It read: 'Something will occur at the end of the week that you have been expecting for some time.'

When he came to don his second-hand uniform on the morning of the gala, Ernie's nerves almost broke completely. The man who had worn it previously must have been shaped like an Egyptian water jar! His wife, Beryl, had altered it once, but he had been so pre-occupied with the antics of Charlie Buckle that he had neglected to try it on.

Now, as he observed himself in the mirror, his face clouded with disappointment. Apart from being an inch short in the sleeves and a little loose at the waist, the tunic wasn't so bad, but the trousers – oh, the trousers!

Irritably, he shouted upstairs to his wife. 'Beryl!'

Alarmed at the urgency in his voice, she rushed downstairs.

'Ernie! Whatever's the matter?'

Her husband's raw nerves sounded in his voice.

'What's the matter? Look!'

Holding up the back of the tunic, he whined, 'I can't go like this! Look at the pants! They'll think I've got duck's disease!'

Beryl had to work fast; the band mustered at two o'clock and with Ernie planning to catch the one o'clock bus a few yards along the street, there was no time to practice her amateur tailoring skills. But she would have to do something. She couldn't have her husband's trousers falling to his ankles on his first parade, especially since she intended to follow him later to witness the occasion.

After Ernie took off his trousers to hand them to her, he sat in an armchair in his underpants getting increasingly anxious as Beryl set to work on them. Folding the material into a crude tuck, she quickly ran it through her sewing machine, fervently hoping that his tunic would conceal her handiwork, then, going into the kitchen, she took out her ironing board and pressed the repair with the hot iron. Satisfied that she had done her best in the time available, she returned to the living room and handed them back to husband who, to her relief, climbed into them without examining the repair. Dressing himself hurriedly, he fastened his snow-white gauntlets under his left epaulette, adjusted his cap, grabbed his mace and, with a light kiss to his wife's cheek, left to catch the bus.

Outside the house a queue had formed at the bus stop. The sound of the door opening caused the people to turn their heads, and the moment Ernie met their gaze he turned quickly and darted back into the house.

'It's no good, Beryl, I can't go like this, everybody's staring at me!'

Worried by the way her husband's nerves had been showing signs of wear in recent weeks, Beryl coaxed him.

'Get off with your bother! They're just admiring your smart uniform, that's all! If you don't go soon you'll miss the bus. You'll have me late, too, love, and I'm looking forward so much to watching your first parade.'

After holding a mirror behind him as he stood on a chair in front of a wall mirror, she calmed his nerves and, finally placated, he left just in time to catch the bus.

Ernie's ill-fitting trousers marked only the beginning of his day of torment. As he stepped smartly on to the platform of the bus his mace somehow became entangled in the handrail, and, under the maddening gaze of the other passengers, he struggled desperately to free it. Succeeding at last, he leaned it against the side of the bus under the stairs and sat on the side seat opposite to allow him to keep an eye on it. It was at this moment, as he stared unwaveringly ahead to deflect the embarrassing glances of his fellow passengers, that the image of Charlie Buckle's face stole into his mind, and he scowled involuntarily as a murderous desire to strangle the man threatened to overwhelm him.

At the football ground, packed with the off-duty men of Clanky Junction along with their wives and families in their best summer clothes, the stand was a sea of colour. Leaning like a square of toy soldiers about to totter, the low, white-washed fence surrounding the pitch gleamed white in the welcome sunshine. With the sun beaming on them, the heads of hundreds of children bobbed about restlessly as they waited impatiently for the gala to begin, and, lying about on the meagre patches of grass, the ripe-limbed girls of the dancing troupes awaited their moment of glory.

The traditional red-nosed drunkard staggered past with his lamp post over his shoulder followed by a ripple of laughter from the crowd. The ground smelled of ice-cream and toffee, of shoe polish and scent, and, close to the dressing room where a temporary bar had been erected, engine drivers and their firemen congregated in their best suits engulfed by an odour of wholesome beer that wafted over the assembled people on the gentle summer airs.

A cheer swelled from the crowd when, exactly on time, the bandsmen emerged from the dressing room, formed in a tight circle round the diminutive figure of the big drummer. As a temporary precaution the drum sticks had been entrusted to another bandsman who carried them thrust down his tunic with instructions to hand them over to Charlie Buckle only after the minute's silence. After paying their last respects to the memory of Harry Smith, Ernie Brewer would execute a smart right turn, raise his mace and, after a couple of beats on the big drum, the band would step out to the tune of 'Old Comrades' on their first circuit of the field.

Alas, their plan came to nought. The moment he was handed the drum sticks at the end of the minute's silence, the indomitable Charlie Buckle smote the drum two mighty swipes before Ernie got his mace balanced and was off, weaving his way through the ranks of the startled bandsmen as though they didn't exist!

With the bandsmen leaping about like cats on a spiked roof as they struggled to get into formation, Charlie forged blindly ahead with a terribly determined look on his face. Bang! Bang! Bang! As each explosive wave of devastating sound bounced off the wall of the football ground it collided with another wave less than a yard behind it. Every other noise, the sound of the instruments, the cheers of the crowd, was blasted into oblivion by the rhythmic explosions from Charlie's drum. As far as the big drummer was concerned, this was going to be his day and nothing anyone might do was going to deprive him of it!

Twice round the pitch they straggled confused and bewildered, wincing with pain at every blow Charlie struck and resolving more and more firmly with each ragged step that the moment the gala was over they'd get rid of him for good!

Then, as they straggled past the stand for the third time, a miracle happened. Unable to withstand the incessant battering being inflicted upon it by the wildly flailing arms of the incorrigible Charlie Buckle, the big drum burst and, like a flash of sunlight on a grey day, the melodious sounds of the instruments flooded over the crowd for the first time. As the trombonist jumped into the breach to supply the beat, the bandsmen instantly assumed a new bearing. It was as though the band had been playing for a week into a giant tube and someone had just pulled the cork to allow 'Colonel Bogey' to come into his own. Realising what had happened, the bandsmen stepped out with renewed faith and, as years fell off Ernie Brewer's shoulders, his mace took on the swing of a guardsman's.

In front of the stand where the committee and the Superintendent stood watching, Ernie threw the mace high in the air and, to the cheers of the crowd, caught it smartly and stepped out like a grenadier. Spurred on by the cheers, he threw it again and again, finally sending it as high as the stand. Catching it without the slightest falter in the swing of his arms or the measure of his step, he swelled his chest to fill even the oversized tunic he was wearing, and, his confidence restored, his pride knew no bounds.

As Ernie Brewer remarked to his fireman as they walked together for a pint afterwards, 'It's been a great day, hasn't it, Bill? Eh? Don't y'think it's been a great day? I'll tell you summat else, too, Bill, I'll bet old Harry Smith smiled in his grave.'

There was something quite strange about the behaviour of Charlie Buckle that day. When his drum burst he didn't turn a hair. With arms flailing he continued belting away at the ruined instrument as though nothing had happened. Some said he did this to save face with the crowd, but Ernie wouldn't have it. He reckoned that it was simply that he was too stupid to tell the difference.

15
The Downfall of
Sammy the Magpie

*T*he crowd of passengers awaiting the arrival of the nine forty pm boat train on number twelve platform of Central station was larger than usual. It was always the same as Christmas approached; after working in England for most of the year, hundreds of Irish migrants returned home for a welcome reunion with their families. The crowd was thickest on the most illuminated part of the platform, in the middle, where the refreshment room was situated, branching outwards in both directions like the wings of a giant bird.

As though deterred by the shadows that fell upon the end of the platform where the guard's van would come to rest, the crowd stopped short, leaving a small area of platform to a solitary traveller who paced up and down with his head bowed in deep concentration.

Making his turn at the door of the porter's room, the restless traveller strode past a huge mound of parcels waiting to be loaded in the guard's van of the expected train and continued to the very end of the platform. There, after peering into the darkness as though listening for the sound of the approaching train, he turned about and retraced his steps. It was after he had done this several times, just as he peered into the night at the end of the platform, that a very remarkable thing happened. Behind his back a large cardboard carton leapt forward from the mound of parcels!

Although the lone traveller was forced to change his line of direction to avoid stumbling over the carton on his way back to the porter's room, this remarkable event went completely unnoticed by him. Stranger still, just before he made his turn at the porter's room, the carton reared up as though to leap forward again, but, lowering itself to the platform as though possessing a mind of its own, it decided to lie doggo. Biding its time until the traveller paced to the end of the platform to peer into the night again, it suddenly leapt forward once more. When the traveller retraced his steps this time, he had no need to make a detour round the carton, for there was a path a yard wide between it and the mound of parcels. Yet he still appeared not to have noticed anything unusual.

Then, just before he made his turn once more as he reached the porter's room, the carton reared up and leapt clean over the edge of the platform to the line below. After landing on the ballast, it reared up again, mounted the first line it came to, slid along the sleeper and cleared the second line. Its timing was perfect; no sooner had it cleared the second line than, with a deafening roar, the nine forty boat train plunged into the station.

There was nothing supernatural about the behaviour of that cardboard carton when it abandoned the mound of parcels; it happened to be attached to a small grappling hook tied to a length of stout cord. On the other end of the cord, ensconced on a little shunting engine standing in the shadows of the station on an adjacent line, was Sammy the Magpie. It was simply that this was one of the more refined methods he adopted to expropriate some desirable piece of merchandise he had a mind to possess.

Hauling the carton on board his engine, Sammy the Magpie ripped it open and surveyed the contents with a well-practised eye. Plucked, cleaned and ready for the oven, the carton contained three succulent geese. There was hardly anything to choose between them. With his expert eye he selected one that appeared to be slightly plumper than the others, wrapped it in several sheets of newspaper and tied it with a piece of string he had ready for the purpose.

Making a loop in the string, he took off his jacket and hung the goose around his neck. Then putting on his jacket again he fastened it over the goose and caressed the resultant bulge. Adjusting its position until he was satisfied that he could carry it home without suspicion, he unslung it from his neck and placed it in his food locker for the time when his relief would climb on board.

When this was done he offered his fireman a choice of the remaining birds. Declining the offer with a disdainful shake of his head, his fireman turned his back on him. Completely undismayed, Sammy gathered up the loose packing that had fallen to the footplate, stuffed it back into the carton containing the rejected geese and slung the lot into the firebox to destroy the incriminating evidence.

In those days the delightful smells of Christmas, the scent of the mistletoe and holly that lay in heaps on the platforms and the aromatic smoke that drifted from the cigars that forested in the mouths of the passengers as the festive day approached, pervaded even a railway station. The night Sammy the Magpie slung the unwanted geese into the firebox of his engine, the quality of Central station's atmosphere was enriched alarmingly. The aroma of overdone roast goose billowing from the chimney of his engine penetrated every nook and cranny of the lofty building where it lingered for days afterwards.

Throughout his career at Clanky Junction, Sammy the Magpie was an embarrassment to every fireman who worked with him. Whenever he climbed from the cab of his engine on one of his exploratory strolls, one never knew what he would return with. On different occasions he had been known to climb back on board with a brand-new bicycle, a roll of carpet and a complete set of encyclopaedias. One fireman told of his alarm when he observed him surveying with covetous eyes a cattle wagon loaded with beef on the hoof! Fortunately the task of concealing such a prize defied even Sammy's corrupted ingenuity and, when he turned away from the cattle truck defeated, his fireman sighed with relief.

Everything about Sammy the Magpie's appearance was baggy; he was a large man by any standard, but with overalls and jacket three sizes too large, he gave the impression that when he was made the gentle hand of nature had faltered in her design. His jacket alone would have sheltered a Boy Scout troop. At a distance he appeared like a giant figure in wax melting at the edges.

A casual observer might have attributed his appearance to sheer bad taste, but on looking closer he would have noticed that every pocket in his attire had been clumsily enlarged. By the simple knack of putting two and two together, those who worked with him soon realised that every aspect of Sammy's appearance was cunningly designed to facilitate his light-fingered pastime.

That no one informed on him was almost entirely due to the fact that he was such a marvellous driver to get on with. On the longest trips he took a stint on the shovel, and with his tea and cigarettes he was generous to a fault. Of course one never knew for certain if the tea and cigarettes really belonged to him, but at least the spirit was there. Because of his amiable disposition there was a kind of esprit de corps, which, although permitting you to turn your back on him as he sorted his ill-gotten gains and deny him any assistance whatsoever, nevertheless prevented you from ever spilling the beans.

If, in purloining the carton of geese, Sammy demonstrated his refined cunning, his tactics when travelling in the spare parcel van on the six fifteen to Bealham revealed a cunning bordering on genius. We travelled as passengers on the six fifteen to Bealham every six weeks to relieve a goods train there. From Central station the line climbed steadily for twenty-five miles to Dalton tunnel. Immediately on entering the tunnel the line plunged steeply, losing in the remaining ten miles to Bealham much of the height it had gained.

Getting to work the moment the passenger train left Central station, Sammy rummaged through the parcels, weighing up the information on the labels and feeling the contents of the parcels with the expertise of a customs official. Finally selecting one that took his fancy, he carried it to the window to stand with it between his feet. Then, when the train reached the summit of the gradient and entered the tunnel, he waited until it was well inside, opened the window and flung the parcel from the van so that it cleared the adjoining line.

Half an hour after alighting from the passenger train at Bealham, we were labouring back along the same railway the way we had come on the footplate of a heavily loaded goods train. The ten miles to Dalton tunnel demanded every ounce of steam a fireman could raise, and by the time the small circle of daylight came in sight at the end of the tunnel, the engine was blasting at long intervals at the chimney-top as it strained to reach the summit.

With the train moving at a snail's pace, Sammy descended the steps of the engine and, waiting until he saw the parcel in the light from the tunnel mouth, jumped to the ballast. Hurrying forward, he took hold of the parcel and re-boarded the engine. Now it was just a question of trying the contents for size under his bell-tent of a jacket, destroying the wrapping in the flames of the firebox, and another piece of merchandise vanished without trace.

Of course they nabbed him. I suppose it was inevitable really. After all, to steal once or twice on impulse might lead to nothing more than a guilty conscience, but to adopt the vile practice as a way of life was laughing in the face of probability. When they finally apprehended him it was something of an anti-climax. Everyone thought that when his time came he would go out in a blaze of glory – say, enticing a bull elephant from a circus train at the dead of night, or stuffing his voluminous pockets with gold bars secreted from a bullion train. But it was nothing like that at all. On the day he was caught red-handed it was as though all his craft and cunning had deserted him.

The scene of his downfall was Mouldham fish dock. The moment he spied the giant codfish lying on a hand-truck next to a pile of fishboxes, he became so excited that I thought he was starting a fit. He couldn't wait to get at it! Before I finished screwing on the handbrake he jumped from the engine to go striding towards it like a man under hypnosis. This wasn't like him at all! Previously all his escapades had been cleverly planned and efficiently executed, but now he was behaving like a clumsy apprentice!

Fearlessly gripping the huge codfish by the gills with one hand, he began feverishly to undo the button at the waist of his overalls with the other. Lifting the fish as high as he could he almost ruptured himself attempting to slide it down his overall leg. He failed miserably. Standing on tiptoe and stretching as high as he could, he tried again. This time he succeeded in inserting the tail of the fish in the opening and began jumping up and down like an ungainly ballet dancer until its head was lower than his collar. Satisfied that the fish was safely lodged down the leg of his overalls, he buttoned his jacket and retreated from the scene like a lumbago-ridden Long John Silver.

The hand that nabbed him shot from behind a stack of fishboxes when he was no more than a few paces from the engine, and when the bowler hat appeared behind the arm, it was only too clear that the game was up.

It goes without saying that they fired him. Oh yes, an engine driver could derail his train, smash through a set of buffers or even be an hour late with the Royal Train without getting fired, but pinch a codfish, or even an orange for that matter, and he had to go.

When they raided Sammy's modest terraced house in Paradise Street it took a huge pantechnicon to retrieve the loot. What a revelation this proved to be! From a parcel of funeral shrouds to a case of whisky, almost every item of merchandise ever transported by rail was represented there. And yet, like the genial character he was, Sammy the Magpie gave the warders at the clink no trouble at all. A model prisoner, he was out in no time and found a job driving a pot-bellied saddle tank at the local gasworks where, contentedly, he worked until his retirement many years later.

Like all sensational happenings, the exposure and final incarceration of Sammy the Magpie lost all its interest value after a few months, and I, along with everyone else at the Junction, forgot about him.

And then, one night several months later, the jet on my gas stove suddenly extinguished itself with a loud plop as I was boiling an egg on returning home in the early hours of the morning. I had to strike many matches before I ignited it again, and as one after another I discarded the spent matches, at the height of my frustration the image of Sammy the Magpie zoomed into my thoughts as large as life and, quite involuntarily, I found myself exclaiming, 'Oh no! He's not up to his tricks again, surely!'

In a lightning fantasy I saw it all! I saw him drilling through the plates of the gasometer with a Trapp & Prickit do-it-yourself drill in one hand and a can of water in the other to dowse the sparks! I saw him capture the gas in a balloon by holding it to the hole and tying its neck to retain it. After hammering home a pointed peg to stop the leak, he held up the balloon and performed a little dance of triumph. A fantasy triggered by frustration? Maybe, but I'll tell you this – if a method of pilfering gas from a gasometer had been possible, Sammy the Magpie would have been the first to crack it!

16
The Agony in a Quarter of Boiled Ham

*W*henever the thoughts of those who manned the locomotives during the Steam Age drift into a mood of nostalgia, the sights and sounds of the railway surface in their minds like rocks in an ebb tide on a misty shore. Once again they feel the vibrations of pounding pistons through the footplate as the engine blasts up a stiff gradient, and even on the sunniest of days they see nothing but black night as they peer anxiously for the signals through a flowing mane of smoke.

Sometimes the scene is of silent snow-clad hills with a lonely train snaking its way to some distant city. They see the countryside radiant in its summer dress and children waving; and then the rain that strives with wind-driven fury to resist the inexorable progress of the speeding train. There are lights too: red, green and yellow, reflected from wet rails an hour before dawn, and the swaying tail-lamp of a freight train suddenly swallowed by the black mouth of a tunnel.

Such images and any one of a thousand more steal into my mind at times, and yet, no matter how varied the kaleidoscope of memory arranges the pattern, there is always one that materialises time and time again. Beyond the maze of tracks of the shed roads, the water columns and more than a hundred locomotives in various stages of preparedness, beyond the wagons and the mountains of coal the shed devoured daily, I see the sombre outlines of the company barracks standing like prison blocks in all their gaunt, Victorian grimness.

These stark monuments to the meanness of the old railway companies were where the engine crews from distant cities lodged between trips. Like an old skinflint atoning for his meanness, the Steam Age did yield one or two more pleasant hostels towards the end of its time, but for almost a hundred years it afforded little more than the comfort of the workhouse for its weary engine crews.

Rising three or four storeys, each one traced by a line of tiny

windows, these forbidding buildings were invariably situated within the
walls of the shed perimeter. The only explanation for this strange fact
is that the fathers of the Iron Road believed that it would have been
fatal to subject the tired bodies of the occupants to a period of
restfulness after being so severely jarred and jolted by the bucking and
lurching of their locomotives on their outward journey. Perhaps they
believed that the tranquillity of a peaceful slumber might have
rendered them completely unfit for the return journey. And so, to avoid
such a calamity, they saw to it that the barracks shook and trembled
throughout their slumber, be it day or night, with the vibrations of an
endless procession of locomotives, whistling shrilly and blowing off
steam less than twenty yards from the dormitory windows.

To complete the therapy, just in case they managed to overcome the
vibrations and clamour of the shed yard to sink into slumber, any
possibility of a pleasant dream was denied them by the periodic thunder
of the coaling plant that continued to disgorge the coal into the tenders
of the locomotives throughout the twenty-four hours.

In the austere, institutional tradition of the age, the company
barracks catered for nothing more than the basic human needs of
eating, sleeping and cleanliness. Most of the ground floor was taken up
by the dining room, in which plain, scrubbed tables and un-upholstered
dining chairs stood in stark lines against the bottle-green and cream of
the unplastered walls. The frugality of the place was further enhanced
by the complete absence of floor coverings, exposing the drab
earthenware tiles to the lacerating boots and clogs of the endless
procession of engine crews who made the best of its meagre comfort.

Adjoining the dining room was the kitchen, which housed several
enormous gas stoves overhung by a collection of frying pans of such
enormous dimensions that they could only have been cast and
launched at John Brown's shipyard. Next to the kitchen was the sluice
where, on opposite walls, a line of huge wash-basins confronted an
equally stark line of urinals and several lavatory cubicles.

The upper storeys housed the sleeping quarters, rows of tiny cubicles
partitioned by wooden screens. Each of these contained a single bed
with a straw mattress covered by regulation sheets and blankets of the
coarsest weave, each of which was adorned by the company crest.
Beneath each bed, in respectful seclusion, lurked a regulation jerry-pot
of uniform design with delicate hair cracks in the glaze, bearing clear
testimony to many years of careful conservation on the part of a long
succession of janitors and their wives whose duty it was to manage the
hostels.

To conclude that these depressing surroundings in any way subdued
the spirits of the men who lodged there between trips would be to

ignore entirely the wonderful resilience of the men who manned the locomotives during the Steam Age. An example of this has to do with the enormous fireplace that took up most of the wall at the end of the dining room. Had this been replenished from the meagre allowance of coal allocated to the barracks by the railway company, it wouldn't have warmed a fly in a matchbox, but out in the shed yard less than twenty-five paces from the front door was enough coal to fuel the Atlantic fleet on a round-the-world cruise.

I never experienced a solitary occasion when the fireplace of any barracks I entered wasn't crammed with as many cobs as it would hold throughout the day and night. Entering such warmth after labouring through fog, rain or snow for hours on end was enough to revive the most wretched spirit. This, along with oceans of hot water and the prospect of a tasty fry-up, was sheer ecstasy to an engine driver and his fireman after a trip through a foul night, especially when it was rounded off later in sharing tales of the Iron Road with men from all corners of the land.

Occupied by enginemen from many parts of the land and echoing with their contrasting accents, the atmosphere of the barracks became transformed. So erratic were the rosters they worked that after two of them had struck up a friendship born of a common interest then left to go their own ways, it could be months before they renewed their acquaintance. When this occurred it was a joyous occasion celebrated by a cosy yarn before the great fireplace. To record the stories that were related about the railways and the serious discussions that ensued on every subject under the sun would be an impossible task. Needless to say, the characters who commanded the stage there were legion. The one I recall most vividly is Benjamin Judd.

The feature that distinguished Benjamin from the others drivers at the Junction was his glib tongue. Suggest that you were considering purchasing a new suit and he would offer his services at once. Hint that you had recently purchased a new lawnmower and he would explain how much you were out of pocket through not consulting him first. Ben was a mobile bazaar. In matters relating to supplying the material needs of mankind he set himself up as an expert, claiming that he could supply anything anyone needed at a cheaper price and better quality than anyone else.

In whatever town he found himself he spent every available minute of his off-duty hours mooching round the shops and market feeling the quality and comparing the prices of the goods displayed. The market that flourished only a cock-stride from the Junction knew him well. Indeed, old Nat Cohen who ran a stall there for most of his life greeted Ben like a brother whenever he saw him approaching.

What more could Nat wish for? For a small discount Ben introduced his merchandise to a large part of the British Isles. A hearth rug for one of his contacts, a shirt for another and a velour trilby for someone else – one couldn't ask him for the wrong item. With contacts in every craft and trade, Benjamin Judd made quite a bit on the side during his life on the Iron Road.

Unfortunately Ben wasn't really fully equipped for the role of merchant, for although he possessed the main prerequisite, a glib tongue, in other vital departments he was sadly lacking. His great failing was that he recorded neither the orders he received nor the money he pocketed. Relying on his somewhat hazy memory, a pound he took from a driver expecting a new shirt he would use on the spur of the moment to purchase something else that took his fancy. To complicate matters further, when the rosters changed he never knew when he would meet those for whom he had outstanding orders. Periodically his business affairs got into such a hopeless state that he invented a ruse he called upon from time to time to placate infuriated customers, who, having paid a deposit, had been waiting months to receive the goods. For a small consideration he persuaded a clerk in the office to type a small notice in the 'Stop Press' column of a daily newspaper. It read:

CITY WAREHOUSE DESTROYED IN FIERCE BLAZE
DAMAGE ESTIMATED AT THOUSANDS OF POUNDS

Greased and grubby with years of wear, it was this cutting he produced from his pocket whenever an exasperated customer threatened him with retribution as he pleaded for more time. When you add all this to the ever-present hazards inherent in a job on the Iron Road, working on the same footplate as Driver Benjamin Judd could be quite hair-raising at times.

Had it not been for the Second World War and the advent of rationing, Ben's lucrative sideline might have sunk without trace under the sheer weight of the threatened recriminations of his erstwhile customers throughout the land. Indeed, had one or two of his more offended clients got hold of him, his very survival would have been in doubt.

It was during the war that Ben's business prospects took a turn for the better. As epidemics with undertakers and bankruptcies with bailiffs, so it was with Ben. Every catastrophe has a beneficiary somewhere. The promise of half a dozen eggs or a pound of sugar blinded even the most doubtful to the uncertainty of delivery. Towards the end of the war and immediately afterwards, when rationing was biting deepest, a square meal was something one experienced once a week. It was then that scrag-end and cheese became luxuries. Even corned beef assumed the allure of a delicacy. Through all this Ben was living on the fat of the land. Furthermore, he boasted about it!

'You can't beat a bit o' red salmon!' he'd shout, flourishing the tin as everyone else in the company picked at their meagre fare.

It was only too obvious that he was courting disaster, but sadly his tongue had a mind of its own that led him into alarming situations from which he had great difficulty in extricating himself.

Entering Gainford barracks at two o'clock that morning we found everything cosy as always. The self-satisfied look on Ben's face I attributed to the money he had taken from the shed foreman in exchange for the parcel he had handed him when we signed off duty. As we breezed into the dining room the scene that confronted us was typical of the place. Relaxing in the waves of heat emanating from the enormous fireplace, a cluster of engine drivers, bib-braced and union-shirted, yarned about their experiences. At a far table, watched by several onlookers, a tense game of crib was in progress, and here and there individual drivers rested, quietly browsing through their newspapers.

Going over to one of the tables we opened our lodging baskets and reserved a chair apiece by placing our food parcels on the table in front of them. Ben chose one with its back to the wall and I settled for the one facing him. Next to Ben's parcel rested three more unattended.

Having gone through the ritual of reserving our places, we placed our togs and baskets in a locker then proceeded to the sluice for a wash. A little Wigan driver in the last stages of drying his ears acknowledged us with a barely perceptible nod, while a burly Carlisle driver, stripped to the waist and wallowing in a huge wash-basin brimful of hot water, bellowed, 'Had a good trip?' As Benjamin answered in good measure, I turned on the taps and prepared to wash.

At this point the little Wiganer left the sluice and entered the dining room to commence his meal and, with Ben prattling on about the trip and the burly Carlisle driver replying through a nest of bubbles, their conversation appeared to be blossoming. After a quick wash I wiped myself dry and, leaving Ben and the Carlisle driver to a conversation that was becoming more involved by the minute, I re-entered the dining room. Taking a mug from a cupboard I made my tea and, sitting at the table, started on my cheese sandwiches.

It was then that my gaze settled on the little Wigan driver two places to the right of the chair Ben had reserved. He was a strange character we had met before on our last trip to Gainford, when, as was his custom, Ben had bombarded him with a barrage of probing questions designed to ensnare him into his circle of clients. On that occasion all Ben's efforts had been wasted, for the Wiganer was a man of few words – the kind of man one would have to know a long time before qualifying for his confidence. As I looked at him he seemed hypnotised by a point on the wall behind me and, staring straight at it, he gulped his food as though anxious to have done with it.

After about ten minutes, with the sound of the Carlisle driver still blowing and snorting in the sluice, Ben appeared. Going to the cupboard he took a mug and, after brewing his tea, joined me at the table. As he sat down facing me, the little Wiganer suddenly gathered the newspaper wrapping into his hands and, screwing it up, left the table and threw it on the fire. Then, without a glance at anyone, he left for the dormitories.

As Ben sat down he started to rub his hands together in an exaggerated display of anticipation. I knew only too well what to expect next, for I had shared the same footplate with him for almost a year. Unwrapping his food parcel with flamboyant movements of his hands until the contents were exposed, he leaned back on his chair and exclaimed, 'Ah well – I know what I've got for scoff tonight!'

Pausing, he glanced round the room expectantly. Getting no response he clapped his hands together in what could have been another gesture of anticipation, but which I knew to be a further attempt to summon attention. Then, raising his voice higher, he repeated, 'Oh aye, I know what I'm 'avin' for scoff all right!'

This time his announcement had its intended effect. Startled by the unusual hullabaloo at the table, the firemen in the card school and the drivers round the fireplace all looked up, while those hidden behind newspapers lowered them simultaneously to stare questioningly over the top of them. Sensing like a veteran actor that he now had everyone's attention, Ben proceeded to enlighten them.

'Aye, a nice bit o' boiled ham on best butter, that's what I've got for scoff!'

Spurning both modesty and diplomacy, Ben's tongue now took over completely.

'If I've said it once I've said it a thousand times – there's nowt like a bit o' boiled ham on best butter! I wouldn't give you tuppence a ton for corned beef! Oh no, not tuppence a ton! If you've got a bit o' boiled ham on best butter you're a lucky man!'

Winking at the others at the card table, a fireman retorted, 'The wife friendly wi' the grocer when you're away on a double trip?'

Ben ignored the bait. 'I'm tellin' yer, there's nothin' like it! I'm right partial to it – I have it, oh, three or four times a week – don't I, mate?'

He looked at me, but, having heard it all before, I just nodded. Then, under the envious eyes of his audience, he opened his first sandwich and held it out so all could see the delicate pink slices of ham. Slapping the sandwich together again he took his first bite and, chewing with exaggerated pleasure, finally swallowed. Holding back his head in ecstasy he said, 'Eh, I tell yer, that was bloody lovely that was – absolutely bloody lovely!'

Clearly sickened by Ben's boastful behaviour, the assembled enginemen slowly resumed their previous interests and, with the card game restarted, the drivers round the fire scraping their chairs closer together and the news-browsers raising their newspapers back to eye level, the atmosphere resumed its cosy ambience, leaving Ben eating in silence.

From the sluice came the sound of the burly Carlisle driver singing at the top of his voice. The words of the song lacked definition, the vowels exaggerated and the consonants non-existent, and although he couldn't be seen, it was quite evident that he had removed his false teeth and was subjecting them to a severe scrubbing.

At last, when Ben was down to his last sandwich, the Carlisle driver appeared in the doorway of the dining room beaming like the sun in June. Making for the hob where his mug was warming, he proceeded to mash his tea and, carrying it to the table, he squeezed between the wall and Ben's chair to sit beside him. Suddenly, his hand still on the back of his chair as he was about to pull it out, he froze. Alerted by his hesitation, Ben looked up at him over his shoulder. Shooting out an arm and pointing to Ben's last morsel of food, the Carlisle driver shouted, 'Hey! You've swopped my flamin' sandwiches for yours!'

Swallowing abruptly, Ben looked momentarily dazed. Then, finding his voice, he exclaimed, 'What's that you say?'

In a most belligerent tone his accuser replied, 'Them's mine! You've scoffed my bloody butties!'

Ben shook his head in disbelief. 'I've what? I've scoffed your butties? Why, I've never heard anythin' so ridiculous in all my life! I've just been tellin' the lads here – I 'ave boiled ham three an' four times a week! I'm partial to it!'

Here Ben turned to me. 'Tell him, mate – don't I have boiled ham reg'lar?'

Weary of Ben's boastfulness, I nodded in grudging loyalty, but it left the Carlisle driver completely unimpressed.

'I'm tellin yer, you've swopped your parcel for mine – look!'

Taking hold of the food parcel in front of his chair, he held it under Ben's nose.

'See! The *Daily Dispatch*! I don't get the bloody *Dispatch* – I get the *News Chronicle* like what's in front of you! Anyway, my wife told me what she was puttin' up for me before I left home! Boiled 'am, she said!'

For several moments the two men glared at each other in silence, the Carlisle man having the advantage of looking down on Ben. It was the latter who broke the silence.

'Now look here, mate, whether you get the *News Chronicle* or the *Exchange an' Mart* has nothing whatever to do with it – if what you say's true, you've nothin' to worry about. If I've swopped your parcel for mine, inside mine there (he pointed to the Carlisle man's parcel) you'll find a nice bit o' boiled 'am on best butter! Now go on, open it!'

With everyone's attention focused on the two men arguing at the table, the burly Carlisle man began unwrapping the food parcel with Ben urging him on.

'Go on, open it! If what you say's true, boiled 'am on best butter – that's what you'll find in there!'

Exposing the contents, the Carlisle driver took out the top sandwich, turned back the uppermost slice of bread and immediately shoved it under Ben's nose. The filling was jam – bread and jam! Staring at it in disbelief, Ben started to whine.

'I don't believe it! It's a trick! A bloody trick! I've never brought bread an' jam to work in me life!'

As the Carlisle driver drew closer to him in a menacing manner, Ben raised an arm to restrain him.

'Now there's no need to get shirty! Just tell me when you're here again an' I'll fetch you 'alf a pound o' boiled 'am – won't I, mate?'

There was more than a hint of desperation in Ben's voice as he appealed to me, but before I could respond with my customary nod, the Carlisle driver threw the jam sandwich on the table. Then, grabbing Ben by the bib of his overalls, he yanked him to his feet and, thrusting his face within inches of Ben's, growled, 'A'right, mate, I'll say no more about it now, but I'll be here again the day after tomorrer – an' I'll be waitin' for yer!'

It was then, as I watched the Carlisle driver release his hold on Ben's overalls, that a strange thing occurred. Quite suddenly the image of the little Wiganer flashed into my thoughts again, and instantly I knew that Ben was as innocent as a new-born lamb! Although it didn't seem important at the time, my recollection of him gathering up his food wrapping suddenly took on more significance. I had noticed the heading of the newspaper – it was the *News Chronicle*! This, along with his furtive manner and the haste with which he devoured the sandwiches and left for his bed, convinced me beyond all doubt that he was the cause of Ben's tribulation.

Ben was quite right – I had never seen him once bringing jam sandwiches for his scoff, nor would I have expected him to! A man who could procure tins of red salmon, half pounds of boiled ham and legs of pork to sell to his favoured clients wasn't going to starve himself on jam sandwiches! My immediate impulse was to brand the crafty little Wiganer as the culprit, but something stopped me. My time with Benjamin had been a wearisome experience. What with his glib tongue, his boastfulness and his endless broken promises, I was beginning to suspect that his reputation was tarnishing my own. And so, to my eternal shame, I left him squirming under the menacing glare of the burly Carlisle driver and nonchalantly resumed the consumption of my cheese sandwiches.

17
The Birdwatcher

*I*n any large assembly of men it is almost certain that the vast majority will belong to that unspectacular mass of conscientious citizens, generally pleasant and hard working, into which most of us blend only too gladly. The man who arrives determined to impress the gathering with the joke of the year soon finds others eager to beat it with one even more hilarious, and he who stands at the bar drinking directly from the bottle like an Australian from the outback soon finds anyone can do it if they try. To be human is to behave humanly and, in this, we are all very much of a sameness.

In the case of Percy Sidebottom, however, uniqueness was realised. It wasn't merely that he was a Peeping Tom, but that he was the most dedicated Peeping Tom the world has ever known – a man who will be remembered until the last man to work at Clanky Junction during the Steam Age passes the final signal along the loop of Eternity.

No doubt there will be those who will consider this a rash claim to make in view of the reputation of that classic practitioner of the art who lived in Coventry, but believe me, Percy Sidebottom had that gentleman licked to a frazzle.

The amazing thing about the man was that he made no secret of his weakness, or pleasure, depending on how you look at it. There wasn't a single man at the Junction who didn't know of his exploits. Everyone knew of the two gigantic pockets concealed in the lining of his jacket in which he carried a complete set of implements for making his spyholes. Among these was a bradawl, a miniature drill and a carefully designed lever for prising away the panels in train compartments. In addition to these he possessed a slim torchlight and, for his fieldwork, a small but powerful pair of binoculars.

Percy's appearance gave no clue whatever to his unusual pursuit. In his Sunday best he would pass for a vicar in mufti any day of the week, and in the presence of the ladies he was a model of charm and consideration. If he saw a woman struggling to lower a pram down a kerb he would leap to her assistance like Sir Walter Raleigh himself. Mind you, if you continued to observe him you would see him administer a tentative pat on her backside as she turned to thank him, but then who would suggest that this was a sign of depravity?

Yes, in the way of gentlemanly manners, Percy excelled. On a crowded bus he would be the first to his feet to offer his seat to a standing woman and, if one happened to be ten yards behind him heading for the same door, he would rushed forward to hold it open like a butler to allow her to precede him. Furthermore, whenever he walked along the main shopping street during his off-duty hours, he would raise his hat to anyone in a skirt.

On the rare occasions when he found himself with a work-free Sunday, he would accompany his wife and daughter to church to join in the singing of hymns from Ancient & Modern as devoutly as anyone present. He was certainly a competent engine driver; there were dozens of firemen at the Junction who would testify to this. And yet the merest glimpse of an exposed feminine thigh or cleavage would provoke him into taking the craziest risks to life and limb to get a better view of it. He would notice a bathroom light come on half a mile away, and the sight of a courting couple getting to grips in the compartment of a train would send him scuttling into the shadows of the station to observe their antics until the train left the station.

His workmates at the Junction speculated endlessly on the mystery of how Percy Sidebottom became afflicted by his strange obsession. Some of them concluded that his wife was probably the kind of woman who withheld the normal activities a man expects from his marriage, while others suggested that it might have been due to his having hated his mother as a child. When one opined that it was probably due to his being dominated by his wife, some of the others concurred, saying that she did happen to be on the big side and no doubt took a bit of handling. One old driver, noted for his penetrating insight into human behaviour, reckoned that it was almost certainly the result of being deprived of mother's milk when an infant. Whatever the true explanation of Percy's compelling affliction, whenever the men at the Junction related the details of his latest exploit, it always concluded by an explosion of belly laughs.

It was only to be expected that Percy's irresistible compulsion to be a spectator at those moments of human behaviour normally pursued in private would lead to trouble at some time or other, but the fact that he was never apprehended is not only remarkable but clear testimony to his wiliness. One of his escapades, however, came very close to exposing his pastime to the world at large.

When he noticed the light come on in the bathroom of the 'Weavers Arms', it was close to midnight. In his eagerness to investigate, however, he made the fatal mistake of overlooking how brilliant the moon was shining. It was this that almost led to his downfall.

He was driving the engine on the coal yard shunt at the time. The moment he saw the light come on he asked his fireman to take the controls on the pretext of his having to answer an urgent call of nature. In the sense that it was the call of a nature peculiar to Percy, this was quite true, but the lad who happened to be his fireman was too young a fledgling to be familiar with the strange ways of his driver.

Jumping eagerly from the little saddle tank engine, he hastened along the sleepers in the darkness in the direction of the 'Weavers', where the track ran over a viaduct level with the upper storey of the pub. For the sake of privacy a previous landlord had fitted frosted glass to the lower pane of the bathroom window, but, being a man of normal perceptions, he had given no consideration whatsoever to the vantage point afforded by the tall signal situated directly behind the pub.

Percy knew the signal only too well, for he had climbed it many times, the landlady of the 'Weavers Arms' being one of his favourite subjects. His turn to work the coal yard shunt came round every eight weeks, and by the kind of observation that comes naturally to a man of Percy's disposition, he had discovered that she took a bath every Monday and Thursday.

The landlady of the 'Weavers' was no Venus. How could she be at fifty-eight years of age? As with all of us at this stage of life, time had taken its toll. But then Percy wasn't a man seeking a vision of beauty – he was simply a burglar who stole other people's privacy.

He had been at the top of the signal post long enough to witness the landlady step warily into the steaming bath when the landlord took it into his head to check the bolt on the door of his back yard. He saw Percy almost at once, a crouching black figure perched at the top of the signal post like a monkey up a stick, clearly silhouetted against a brilliant moon.

Before Percy became aware he had been discovered, the landlord, accompanied by two favoured after-time drinkers, had scrambled up the railway embankment to the tracks and surrounded the signal post at the foot of the ladder. Severely impaired by having imbibed more than was good for them, however, the approach of the pub posse was noisily chaotic. Cursing loudly, their first attack ended with them falling in a heap at the foot of the signal ladder as they fought each other for the glory of being the first to ascend.

Fully roused from his nocturnal vigil by this time, Percy decided to descend the ladder in a mock counter-offensive, and when the landlord finally disentangled himself from the others and began to climb the ladder, Percy shook it violently. Undeterred, the landlord continued his advance up the signal, whereupon Percy, descending lower to meet him, stamped on his fingers with his boots; howling with pain, the landlord slid back to the ballast on top of his two colleagues. After another attempt that produced the same result, the three men decided to bide their time at the foot of the signal post, cocksure of a catch. After all, how else could their quarry escape?

By this time lights were appearing in the bedrooms of the houses adjacent to the pub as the occupants sought to investigate the cause of the commotion. The beleaguered Percy became anxious. Why didn't the signal drop to the clear position? It was time! He started to pray silently, for despite his wickedness Percy was a religious man.

Loaded with fine coal destined for Bevington Power Station forty miles away, a heavily laden coal train was scheduled to leave Torkington sidings just round the curve. Being in his element, Percy knew this. If the signalman brought the train to a standstill at the signal he knew his chance of escaping would be extremely thin. However, his prayer was answered. With a loud clatter the signal dropped to the lower quadrant and his hopes revived. When, a minute later, the lumbering coal train rounded the curve, the desperate Peeping Tom descended the ladder to within ten feet of the ballast, causing the inebriated posse to believe that he had decided to give himself up.

But no such thought prevailed in Percy's mind. As the heavily laden coal train rumbled past the signal he leapt from the signal post to sink knee-deep in the fine coal and, with the train accelerating on its way to Bevington, the disappointed members of the posse could only shake their fists with rage as Percy made his getaway.

Percy's highest hopes were realised when, a quarter of a mile further up the line, the coal train was slowed almost to a standstill by signals as it approached East Junction. Clambering from the wagon to hang on the side, he awaited his chance and dropped to the ballast. Half an hour later, covered in coal dust, his feet raw where they had been chafed by the brittle grains of coal that had trickled through the openings in his boots, he climbed back on board the little saddle tank, strangely elated that another of his peculiar escapades had, despite all obstacles, been highly successful.

Of course, it had to come my turn to make his acquaintance; as a young spare fireman, one worked with them all in time. This misfortune occurred during an exceptionally bitter winter when the signal posts were hairy with hoar frost and the breath came from one's nostrils like steam. So many trains had been cancelled because of frozen points and solidified signal pulleys that the Yorkshire pitheads were clogged by mountains of coal. At the first sign of a thaw, Percy and I were instructed to travel as passengers on a train to Broyston, board an engine there and lug a coal train back to Dankworth sidings.

The train that Percy and I boarded at Central station was almost empty. After a few words of idle conversation I lost all interest in him. Even our short acquaintance was enough to indicate that we had very little in common. At that stage of my experience at the Junction I only half believed the stories I heard about him, attributing the more bizarre aspects of his notoriety to the wild imaginings of the story-tellers.

The train was of the old-fashioned type with separate compartments throughout, and Percy appeared particularly finicky about selecting the one we should occupy. Conducting me along the whole length of the train and a good part of the way back before selecting a compartment, it never occurred to me that he was reconnoitring the train with a view to selecting a subject for his diabolical pastime. Finally, entering the one he indicated, I settled on the seat facing the engine while he occupied the seat facing me.

With the compartment to ourselves, I snuggled down in my overcoat, pulled out a current issue of a motor cycling magazine and turned to an article on a new two-stroke that had come on the market equipped with a new carburettor and, although I was vaguely aware of Percy's presence, I became so engrossed in the article that he might not have been there at all.

As the train sped through the frozen night-time landscape, I considered gear ratios, piston bores and miles per gallon, then, closing my eyes, began to calculate the amount of overtime and Sunday work I would need to earn enough money to exchange my own rusty contraption of a motorbike for the sleek model illustrated in the magazine. It was a long, discouraging calculation that gave no cause for optimism, and soon, seduced by the rhythmic swaying of the train and the heat from the steampipes under the seats, I fell asleep.

Suddenly something roused me to wakefulness and, looking round the compartment, I was startled to see the studded soles of Percy's boots framed in the open window! Believing that by some strange circumstance he had fallen through the window of the speeding train, I darted from my seat to commence pulling on his legs with all my strength, but it slowly dawned on me that he was resisting all my efforts to save him! Every six inches I gained on each heave was immediately reduced to three by his counter-heave! Convinced now that he was bent on suicide, I commenced pulling with superhuman strength until, slowly, he began to inch his way back through the window.

The moment he got back inside he turned on me blazing with resentment and, with tortured comprehension, I listened wide-eyed with incredulity as he addressed me.

'What bloody game's on? What d'yer think you're playin' at? Don't y'know there's a couple next door, or what?'

Momentarily I was lost for words. As far as the female half of humanity was concerned, a pretty face or a pair of shapely, nylon-clad legs attracted me no less than any other young man, but to hang outside an express train to observe a courting couple at play in the next compartment was more than my imagination could cope with. As I called him every kind of pervert, he simply shrugged his shoulders and grinned. Then, with a final shrug, as though he was afraid of missing something, he wriggled back through the window of the speeding train to resume his spying.

Although the hours of darkness afforded a greater degree of concealment, it wasn't only at night that he needed to satisfy his perverted curiosity. Daylight too presented opportunities. For most of their length the myriad tracks of those days traversed the countryside where courting couples wandered. The flash of a colourful skirt against the green of a meadow as a lover and his lass strolled blissfully through the grass would have him reaching immediately for his binoculars. On a moving train he would peer through the lenses until the train rounded a curve; in sidings he would lie full-length on top of the cab even as the engine shunted up and down with his fireman at the controls.

When he damaged his spine falling thirty feet over a parapet endeavouring to improve his viewing position, everyone at the Junction thought his antics were doomed. The event provoked very little sympathy among his workmates, most of them declaring that it was only what he deserved, while others laughed their sides sore at the news. Sad to relate, his strange affliction was too deeply ingrained to be deflected by a disjointed spine. Despite being permanently braced in a steel-ribbed corset and confined to shunting duties in the surrounding sidings for the remainder of his time on the railway, he resumed his pathological mania the moment he returned to work.

Years later, retired and living alone, he took in a newly married couple as lodgers. It was Percy himself who, on a visit to see his old mates at the Junction, revealed how he had climbed into the loft to bore a small spyhole in the ceiling of his lodgers' bedroom directly overlooking their bed. Knowing nothing of this, the new wife praised Percy to her neighbours, telling them how often he washed her soiled dishes and did her shopping.

Right to the end of his life he persisted in raising his hat to anyone in a skirt and assisting young mothers to lower their prams down kerbs. He continued to attend church every Sunday to sing lustily from Ancient & Modern and, when he finally died, the women in the street watched his coffin leave the house through a mist of tears, saying what a perfect gentleman he had been.

18
The Ghost of
Grummit Tunnel

*S*o many years have gone by since the Ghost of Grummit Tunnel played his tantalising tricks on those who entered his domain under the Pennines that one would have to search long and hard to find anyone alive who remembers his pranks. Not that one can blame the ghost for its diminished notoriety for, after all, when humans abandon its haunt, what can a ghost do to ensure its immortality?

The railway line linking Bleakmoor on one side of the Pennines and Whitburn on the other was one of the first to be declared redundant towards the end of the Steam Age. Nowadays the tunnel is nothing more than a useless hole in a desolate hillside, and if the ghost still haunts its dank interior, only the bats will know.

Being of a practical turn of mind, the majority of the men at Clanky Junction didn't really believe a ghost-haunted Grummit. To most of them it was nothing more than a convenient fiction to which they could attribute the uncanny incidents that occurred with unusual frequency in the dark, dripping interior of the mile-long tunnel. It was also a useful scapegoat used by the craftier drivers to torment gullible young firemen on their first trips on the main line. Even so, a small but significant minority refrained from ridiculing the ghost just to be on the safe side. After all, not too far from the engine shed there were at least two spiritualist establishments known to be attended by a substantial number of men from the Junction with a strong desire to make contact with life beyond the grave, not to mention those of a timid disposition who, while disclaiming belief in the superstition that misfortune descends on those who walk under a ladder, never did so on the grounds that it was better to be safe than sorry.

When young fireman Tommy Gray found the cork of his tea bottle missing along with half his tea, he couldn't believe his eyes! Although he searched high and low for the cork as the train emerged from the tunnel on the Yorkshire side of the Pennines, it wasn't to be found anywhere! Furthermore, there was neither sign nor scent of the missing tea, and even after only a year at the Junction he knew very well that when tea spills on to a hot steel plate it produces a distinct aroma. When he observed his driver's bottle standing brimful next to his with its cork intact on the warming plate just above the firehole, he became suspicious. The more he thought of it he found it increasingly difficult to dispel the image of his mate snaking out an arm in the darkness of the tunnel's interior, swigging half his tea and disposing of the cork over the side of the engine! To believe this was the last thing he wanted, but, looking at the matter quite impartially, there seemed to be no other explanation. So he decided to tackle his mate about it.

When he crossed the footplate to confront him, his driver had his head through the cab window as he eased open the regulator to tackle the approaching gradient. With temerity, Tommy gave a gentle tug on his driver's sleeve.

'Hey, Bert, did you swipe my tea back in the tunnel?'

Feeling the tug on his sleeve Bert turned to face the young fireman. 'What's that y'say, Tommy?'

Pointing to the half-empty tea-bottle on the warming plate, Tommy repeated, 'Me tea – look – it's 'alf empty an' no cork in the bottle. Did y'ave a swig o' mine by mistake in the tunnel?'

The driver's face bore an expression of such unblemished innocence that the young fireman suddenly felt guilty in accusing him. 'I mean, I can't find the cork an' there's no sign of the spilt tea!'

Eyeing the half-empty bottle, the driver shook his head in a magnificent display of incredulity.

'Well, would you believe it? Y'say you can't find the cork?'

With equal incredulity Tommy replied, 'No. I've looked everywhere – there's no sign of it! What's more, there's no sign of the spilt tea neither!'

As the train began to punch its way up the gradient, the two men stared at each other, the driver as innocent as a choirboy and the young fireman showing the first signs of suspicion. Tommy probed further.

'I mean, if the cork had blown under pressure the tea would've spurted all over the place, wouldn't it? I mean, when tea spills on a hot plate you can smell it, can't yer?'

In a most reassuring manner his driver replied, 'Of course you can, lad, of course you can!' Then, his expression changing to one of deep concern, he continued, 'But I hope you don't think I've had it, Tommy! I hope you don't think that!'

Leaving the young fireman unsure of himself, Bert stuck his head through the cab window to observe the signals while Tommy got down to a fresh burst of shovelling, still troubled by thoughts of his missing tea. Completing his stint with the shovel, the young fireman decided to approach his driver again, and, going over to him, he tugged on his sleeve once more. Satisfied that the signals were coming up green all the way, the driver withdrew his head and turned to face his worried fireman.

'Well, what d'yer think happened to me tea then, Bert?'

Looking him straight in the eyes, Bert replied, 'Well, there's only one thing for it, isn't there, lad? I haven't had it – you say you haven't had it – that leaves only one explanation, doesn't it?'

Tommy looked at him enquiringly. 'What d'yer mean, Bert? What explanation?'

Disdainfully, Bert replied, 'The ghost, lad – the ghost! It must have been the ghost that nicked your tea!'

After remaining deadly serious for a moment, Tommy suddenly shook with laughter. Recovering himself, he bellowed, 'The ghost! What flippin' ghost? What a'yer talkin' about, Bert? You an' your ghost! It was you that nicked it, wasn't it? Eh? It was you that snaked your hand out in the tunnel and pinched me tea and threw the cork over the side! You an' your ghost! You're 'avin' me on, aren't yer?'

Bert's previous disdain changed to innocence again. 'Now, what would I want wi' your tea, eh, lad? Haven't I gorra bottle o' me own? Me? Pinch your tea? Why, I'd never do such a thing!'

Darting to the window to glance at the signals again, he quickly returned and, very seriously, said, 'I'll tell you summat else, Tommy lad! When you've been through that tunnel as often as I have you'll show a little more respect for the ghost. You mark my words!'

Anxious not to press his accusation to the point of threatening his good working relationship with his driver, the young fireman decided to let the matter drop and concentrated on maintaining a good head of steam throughout the rest of the journey. As for the ghost, its reputation suffered no harm, for although the young fireman refused to be overawed when the driver related the incident to his cronies, it would help to keep the legend alive.

When the six thirty freight from Dankworth became mysteriously uncoupled while running through the tunnel, however, the ghost demonstrated its malevolence in no uncertain manner. Like every mile of track from John's End to the Land of Groats, the section through Grummit Tunnel demanded a distinctive technique. On sighting the starting signal at Grummit West, the driver would shut off steam to allow the wagons to close up behind until the entire train was coasting through the tunnel with slack couplings. The moment he saw the light at the end of the tunnel at Grummit East, he would carefully apply steam again to stretch the couplings before opening up fully to climb a mile-long gradient. Then, after mounting the summit of the incline, he would allow the wagons to close up ready for another descent. By this method the train would continue running as smoothly as a drop of water running down a waxed board.

The driver of the Dankworth freight had done it a thousand times before. Passing the starter at Grummit West, he closed the regulator and entered the tunnel at the speed he always did and coasted through as sweetly as always. And yet, as he ran out of the tunnel to take the gradient, he got the shock of his life! Instead of the forty wagons with which he had entered the tunnel, he emerged with only six!

When a loose-coupled freight train of those days broke in two because the driver had handled the controls clumsily, there was a sickening jolt that sent the men on the footplate reeling. On this occasion the driver, the fireman and the guard swore that they had felt absolutely nothing. Furthermore, when the shackle and the drawbar hook were examined, they were found to be as good as new. And yet, despite the driver's solemn assurance that he had in no way snatched at the regulator and the guard's equally solemn assurance that he had never laid a hand on the brake in his van, both men were reprimanded by the investigating enquiry that followed. For many of the men at the Junction, however, the verdict was most unjust. As far as they were concerned, the break-loose had occurred simply because the ghost had been in one of its more malevolent moods on the day that the train passed through the tunnel.

Over the years the credence given to the existence of the ghost rose and fell according to its moods; soaring when some inexplicable incident occurred in the tunnel, then diminishing again when it chose to lie doggo. But when George Henry Bennett claimed that he had actually seen the ghost with his own eyes, many of the sceptics began to waver.

'Like Dracula,' he said it was, 'wi' a gapin' cavern of a mouth and great big holes where it's eyes should've been!'

After his experience George Henry wasn't half the man he had been previously. Known as a self-confident character, he became morose as he silently brooded on the matter. When another driver approached him in the tackhouse suggesting that the oppressive darkness of the tunnel had triggered an hallucination, George Henry lost his temper.

'I saw it, I tell yer! I bloody well saw it!'

That I was the only one at the Junction to learn the truth about George Henry's encounter with the Ghost of Grummit Tunnel came about because I was the last fireman to work with Jimmy the Scouse before he retired from the railway for good. As we commenced our scoff at two o'clock in the morning on an ancient Aspinall loco in Dankworth sidings, Jimmy drifted into one of those reminiscing moods that come to a man at the end of his working life, and, after holding my eager attention with tales of times before I was born, he suddenly fell silent.

As I continued to look at him, anticipating more, I formed the impression that he was silently debating with himself whether or not to reveal a long-kept secret. Then, just as I was about to say something to revive his interest, he cleared his throat and looked at me in what I can only describe as a confidential manner. Suddenly, he said, 'I'm going to tell you summat now, son, that I've never told a soul before.'

He said this as though he was anxious to unburden himself – to straighten things out, so to speak, before he left the railway for good. And so, with no one still living to be embarrassed by its telling, the story of how George Henry Bennett came face to face with the Ghost of Grummit Tunnel can now be told.

Before he became George Henry's regular fireman, the life of Jimmy the Scouse had been full to overflowing. The fact that he had entered railway service at a time when promotion was stagnant, with no prospect of being promoted to driver until he had served another twenty years on the shovel, dismayed him not the slightest. This small, wiry, slightly bow-legged man threw himself with great enthusiasm into every activity that Clanky Junction had to offer. He was elected to every committee at the shed; the horticultural society, the social club, the Mutual Improvement Society and the football team all valued his opinion with the highest regard and, whenever one observed him talking to a group of his colleagues, his words came eagerly, like a disciple of the good life stirring the horde from its lethargy.

Jimmy's domestic life was equally successful. His wife Florence doted on him. When someone called at his house to seek his advice when he happened to be at work, she would say, 'Leave it with me, love, I'll tell him. My Jimmy'll see to it, don't you worry.'

And see to it he would, not as a favour, but as a duty. It was Florence who revealed that when Jimmy couldn't get to sleep on returning home from a trip through the night, he would go downstairs, proceed to dismantle the gas stove, clean every part of it, then return to bed to sleep as soundly as a warrior after a battle. That was Jimmy the Scouse – a doer, a man who took life by the scruff of the neck to shake every ounce out of it.

It was this eagerness to get to grips with life that rendered Jimmy completely oblivious to his own appearance. Bequeathed by nature with a scalp that was utterly barren, he boasted not the tiniest tuft of fuzz. And yet, bald as a shelled egg, he didn't seem to mind in the slightest. He judged himself as he judged others – not by how he appeared, but by what he did, and, exhilarating in everything life had to offer, the paucity by which nature endowed his appearance seemed to concern him not one little bit.

George Henry Bennett, although the same age as Jimmy the Scouse, started work at the Junction a month before the latter to catch a great wave of promotion that saw him qualify as a driver seven years ahead of Jimmy. In pay and status this gave George Henry an advantage over his workmate never to be adjusted. But this wasn't the only advantage George Henry enjoyed, for nature too had favoured him. While Jimmy the Scouse blasted along the Iron Road with his cap concealing a head glistening with nakedness, the noble head of George Henry Bennett was crowned by a verdant mass of tight, auburn curls.

From his earliest years George Henry Bennett had wallowed in the admiration of all the females of the species with whom he came into contact, and suffered the envy of the males. When his mother had pushed him proudly along the streets in his pram, she was stopped by her women neighbours at every opportunity so that they could admire him closer. A truly favoured boy, as a youth he was demurely eyed by the girls, each one hoping that she would be the one to fondle his curls to the end of her days, while the boys in the school yard vented their envy in outbursts of spiteful tortures both verbal and physical. Eventually the highly sought honour of marrying George Henry fell to Hilda, to whom, by the time Jimmy became his fireman, he had been married for thirty years. At first Hilda had revelled in the envious glances of her rivals, but as time went by she discovered that even perfection has its drawbacks.

This grossly unfair bounty bestowed on George Henry Bennett quite randomly by nature had a devastating effect on his behaviour. Countless times a day, wherever he happened to be, he would stand with legs apart, slowly take off his cap to allow the world to see, toss back his head, then slowly run his fingers through his tight clusters of verdant curls. He had performed this remarkable display so often throughout his life that it had become a conditional reflex triggered the moment he saw someone glancing in his direction. It was the same when he arrived home after every trip on the Iron Road. The moment he stepped over the threshold, he would pause to attract Hilda's attention, go through the ritual with strained casualness, then stride to the kitchen with manly gait, believing that his wife was watching him with unbounded admiration. What George Henry didn't know, however, was that for many years Hilda had taken to grimacing behind his back on these occasions, fervently praying for a cluster of grey hairs or a bald patch to invade his curls to puncture his terrible conceit.

It was only to be expected that when George Henry Bennett and

Jimmy the Scouse came to share the same footplate as regular mates, their relationship would be fraught with the strife that afflicts the haves and have nots the world over. Until their first trip together George Henry had seen Jimmy's bald pate only at a distance. When he saw it at close quarters he was appalled! And yet, to his chagrin, despite flaunting his own verdant growth to Jimmy's gaze a hundred times during their first weeks together, instead of being impressed his bald-headed fireman showed not the slightest interest.

As a matter of fact, unknown to George Henry, Jimmy the Scouse, after noticing the frequency with which his driver fingered his hair, had come to the conclusion that he suffered from a persistent form of dermatitis of the scalp. Not that he would ever have mentioned it, for Jimmy was the kind of man who minded his own business. On the other hand, George Henry was completely non-plussed, unable to understand how a man as bald as Jimmy could face the world without feeling a powerful sense of deprivation.

One day, about a month after they came together, Jimmy took off his cap to wipe the perspiration from his head after a long stint with the shovel. As his glistening bald pate revealed itself to George Henry's gaze in all its stark nakedness, the startled driver stared hard at it in disbelief. He just had to say something.

'D'yer do nothin' for it, Jimmy?'

With a vacant expression on his face, Jimmy replied, 'What was that?'

George Henry repeated his question. 'I say, d'yer do nothin' for it?'

That Jimmy hadn't an inkling of what George Henry was talking about showed clearly on his face.

'Do nothin' for it? What d'yer mean, do nothin' for it? Do nothin' for what, for Christ's sake?'

George Henry elaborated.

'Your baldness – doesn't it bother you?'

For the first time since they came together as mates on the same footplate, Jimmy displayed his hackles.

'Does it bother you or summat? Eh? Does it bother you? Are yer tellin' me I've got to keep me cap on so's not to upset yer?'

The belligerence in Jimmy's manner prompted his driver to adopt what he considered to be a more conciliatory tone.

'Hey, now then, Jimmy, I didn't mean it like that. I was just wonderin', that's all. I mean, how does the missus take it? They can be funny about such things at times.'

Jimmy flew at him. 'Oh, they can, can they? Well you listen to me, Goldilocks – if yer don't mind yer own business I'll flatten them bloody nancy curls o' yours wi' the shovel!'

The ferocity of Jimmy's response reduced George Henry to silence, and for the rest of the trip they observed an uneasy truce, casting sly glances when each thought the other wasn't looking.

The strained relationship between the two men smouldered at this level for several days as they maintained an uneasy silence wherever they steamed along the lines. On the occasions when they had to have mutual co-operation, they resorted to abrupt sign language.

The angry words of Jimmy the Scouse and the increased frequency of George Henry's bouts of preening as his fireman kept his cap firmly on his head were only the outward signs of the rift in their relationship. Upon Jimmy's psyche, however, his driver's taunts had an unseen effect. When he got home after each trip he found himself staring at his reflection in the mirror, feeling like the natives of New Guinea must have felt when the missionaries taught them that nakedness was sinful.

When George Henry brought Jimmy a potion of honey and ginger to rub into his scalp as a peace offering, the outraged fireman grabbed hold of it and flung it in the firebox in a frenzy.

'That's what I think of your bloody concoction! Who d'yer think y'are? Now I'm tellin' yer for the last time – any more of it an' I'll throw you in the bloody firebox after it!'

Pausing in his outburst to stare at the driver, he continued, 'I'm warnin' yer – mind yer own business or I'll really lose me temper!'

Impervious to Jimmy's torment, George Henry administered the final insult as the two men sat apart in the porter's room of a remote station in the Pennines waiting with several other engine crews to relieve a westbound freight train. The time being just before dawn, the conversation was desultory, punctuated by an occasional snore from those who had succumbed to the heat from the enormous firegrate. Quite suddenly, one of the other drivers complimented George Henry on his fine head of hair after observing him run his fingers through it. When the driver made his comment George Henry had already replaced his cap, but sensing more mileage for his ego, he quickly raised it again with a flourish, saying, 'Not bad fer a man of fifty-five is it?'

After extracting every ounce of flattery from his admirer, he replaced his cap again and, nudging Jimmy, he said, 'Show 'em yours, Jimmy!'

Squirming under the curiosity-enlivened gazes of all the others at the table as they swivelled their heads to stare at him, Jimmy got up from the table and stalked from the porter's room, consumed by a vile temper.

Eager for revenge to assuage the deep hurt inflicted on him by the conceited taunts of his driver, it didn't take Jimmy long to work out a plan of action. Shortly after they were brought together as regular mates he had observed a weakness in his driver; a fine head of hair he might have, but he was as nervous as a kitten at the controls. With his hand hovering constantly over the brake, at forty miles an hour he thought he was breaking the sound barrier. It was this nervousness that Jimmy resolved to exploit.

The day they worked the Bickerton goods through Grummit Tunnel, Jimmy the Scouse arrived at the engine bearing a parcel containing an old mop-head to which he had attached a loop of elastic and one of those black masks children wear when playing bandits. Making sure he boarded the engine long before George Henry, he stowed the parcel in his locker and bided his time.

Getting to work on his plan the moment the train entered the tunnel, he opened the firehole door an inch to allow a thin curtain of dazzling light to partition the cab; this made the two men almost invisible to each other. Furthermore, the illumination had the effect of reflecting George Henry's face in his eyeglass, whereupon, suddenly finding himself staring at his own visage as in a mirror, he took off his cap at once and, holding his head first one way then the other, started to admire his hair like a prima donna.

With his driver completely absorbed in self-admiration, Jimmy the Scouse acted quickly. Quietly opening his locker, he took out the parcel and swung himself round the cab of the engine until he stood on the framing. Taking off his cap, he stuffed it down his overalls and, taking the mop-head, placed it on his head with the elastic under his chin, Then, putting on the black mask, he made his way along the framing of the swaying locomotive and, rounding the smokebox, proceeded along the framing on the other side towards the cab. He could see George Henry quite clearly now through the eyeglass, but, his view obliterated by the glare from the firebox, the driver was completely unaware of his approach.

Halfway to the cab, Jimmy took out his false teeth and stuffed them safely in his pocket. Now he was ready to give George Henry the fright of his life. As he made to cover the remaining distance to the cab, he was amazed to see his driver still preening himself, patting his curls like a ballerina about to take the stage and cocking his head to one side to view the effect.

The discovery that George Henry practised his aggravating conceit even in the seclusion of a tunnel fired Jimmy with greater determination. Hooking his left arm under the handrail along the boiler casing, he inserted two fingers in each side of his toothless mouth and pulled his cheeks apart in a ghastly contortion. More a ghoul than a ghost, he thrust his head forward, grimacing evilly at his driver, but although his horribly distorted face was hardly a foot from the eyeglass, George Henry made no response.

Discarding all caution, Jimmy thrust his head further forward and, pulling his cheeks even wider with his fingers, squashed his nose against the eyeglass. Suddenly, with eyes staring wildly and his mouth opening and closing like that of a dying fish, the terrified driver began to quaking on his stool as he beheld the ghastliest vision he had ever set eyes on!

Retreating quickly, Jimmy threw the mop-head and mask into the tunnel, reinserted his false teeth and scrambled back round the boiler of the swaying engine to the cab. The whole operation had taken only a few minutes, but the effect on George Henry was devastating. When the train emerged from the tunnel Jimmy saw that his driver's face was as white as a shroud.

Of a nervous disposition by nature, George Henry never recovered from the shock inflicted by the ghastly image that briefly stared at him through his eyeglass. A month after the event he applied to be brought off main-line duties on the grounds of nervous debility. With a doctor's note to support his request, he was appointed to the job of permanent shedman on nights, responsible for moving unmanned engines along the pits to allow more to be stabled behind them, and relocating those failed by the fitters. In addition to this he would perform the odd shunt as the situation demanded. Apart from the permanent night work, it was a cushy job that allowed him to mope in the tackhouse as he awaited further instructions from the foreman, where, night after night, he sat staring into the flames of the fire in isolation as the steam-raisers, bar-lads and the men who knocked up the drivers played crib behind him.

From time to time the tackhouse door would open to reveal a driver who had brought a young fireman to show him the living proof of the existence of the ghost and, as George Henry sat silently observing the flames, his hair now grey and a faraway look in his eyes, the driver would whisper, 'That's 'im I was tellin' you about – he saw it with his own eyes.'

But George Henry, unaware of their presence, would continue to stare into the flames.

19
The Cruel Hand
of Fate

*B*efore that fateful foggy night he was just plain Eddie Price, middling twenties and a fireman on the old London Midland & Scottish Railway. With nothing about his appearance to distinguish him markedly from the others at the shed, he was just a typical man of the shovel waiting to step on to that golden rung on the ladder of promotion that would take him across the footplate to the other side of the cab to take the controls as a regular driver.

On the night that Eddie earned his nickname a glutinous fog enveloped the entire North of England, shrouding the landscape so long that some of the fogmen whose duty it was to place detonators on the line had abandoned their posts wearily, leaving the trains to grope their way through the earthbound cloud as best they could.

Of all the capricious moods of the British weather, it was the clammy, sulphur-laden fogs that engine drivers feared the most. Through flood, snowdrift and hail they would pound with stoic determination, displaying all the age-old aggression of man against the elements. In fog, however, the fear of the unseen strained their senses to the point of rawness. In such conditions every engine driver experienced some time in his life the spine-chilling feeling that he had lost his bearings and passed a signal at danger. Nothing awed them so much as the terrifying thought that they might be about to plough into the rear of a train in front of them or be rammed by one following behind.

By far the worst aspect was the weariness, for fog meant delays, and delays led inevitably to engine crews having to spend long hours at the controls. During the Steam Age, fifteen, twenty and even thirty hours at a stretch were not uncommon. And so, in conditions where alertness was vital to the safety of all who travelled on the Iron Road, the reactions of the men on the footplate were at their most sluggish.

The freight train manned by Eddie and his driver had crawled south from Carlisle at a snail's pace. Throughout the wearisome journey their heads had protruded from the cab of the engine like a couple of worn-out battery hens, their eyes streaming tears with the strain of peering into the murk to catch sight of the signals.

After clattering to a standstill at almost every signal along the line, five miles through Preston and five hours behind schedule, they craned their necks even further for yet another. With no detonator to announce its approach, the signal slid halfway past the engine before the driver realised that he was upon it. Acting at once, he slammed on the brakes and, as the train jarred to a standstill, the metallic staccato of colliding buffers rippled through the night.

Eddie peered through lead-laden eyelids for the signal light. Alas, this one was no different from the others they had stopped at. A few feet above the engine the signal post disappeared from sight in the dense fog. Cursing quietly to himself, he raised his tired body from his seat, climbed wearily from the engine and started to ascend the ladder of the signal post to see whether it was showing red or green.

It was an unpleasant task. Not only were the rungs of the ladder moist and cold to the touch, with each panting breath he inhaled the reeking fumes of the fog. The atmosphere was so heavily laden with the smoke of the surrounding factories and the engine below that he had to make his way right to the lampman's platform to make out the colour of the signal. Finding it against them, he descended the ladder carefully and returned to the engine to inform his driver. The driver received the information with resignation and, with Eddie's assurance that he would periodically climbed the ladder if he failed to hear the sound of the signal wire being drawn through the pulleys, he closed his eyes for a welcome catnap.

Eddie had hardly commenced his vigil when his eyelids began to droop involuntarily and he had to shake his head to dispel an overwhelming desire to nod off. It was as he did this that the idea came into his head. It was a brilliant idea! Indeed, it seemed so good that he became slightly suspicious of it, wondering why nobody had thought of it before. The signal was of the old-fashioned type that dropped to the lower quadrant when it changed to the clear position. If he climbed to the top of the signal post and placed the steel bucket every engine carried over the arm of the signal, the moment the signalman pulled the lever to lower it, the bucket would crash to the ballast to alert even the soundest sleeper!

Turning the idea over in his mind, he probed it from every angle for weaknesses without detecting a single flaw. Elated with it, he decided to awaken his driver to get his approval. Responding slowly to the gentle shaking of his arm, his driver emerged from his doze with a hint of bewilderment on his face. Then, as he focused his eyes on the eager face of his fireman, he started to fill his pipe, his eyes continuing to search the lad's face for a possible explanation for his being awakened.

Taking several quick puffs on his pipe he listened patiently as Eddie expounded his idea, considering every word with the mein of a Greek scholar. Hang the bucket on the signal? Why, he had never heard such a thing! And yet, the more he thought of it, the more the idea appealed to him. When Eddie finished his explanation his driver remained silent for almost a minute, his pipe poised a foot from his mouth and his eyes fixed on the roof of the cab in deep contemplation. Finally, he gave his verdict.

'D'yer know, Eddie, that sounds a good idea, lad – a very good idea. Go on, hang the bucket on the signal!'

Encouraged by his driver's approval, Eddie took hold of the bucket, climbed from the engine and started to ascend the ladder again. In addition to the moisture on the steel rungs, the burden of the bucket meant that he had to proceed with care. Slowly searching for each rung with the toes of his steel-studded boots, he climbed higher and higher towards the lampman's platform. Pausing halfway up the ladder, it occurred to him that if he were to insert his arm through the bucket handle so that it rested in the crook, he would be able to pull himself up with both hands. This done, he was about to resume his climb when he happened to glance down at the ballast.

He could see nothing. Even the glare from the firebox of the engine was obliterated by the fog. It was the same when he looked up; five rungs above his head the steel ladder disappeared without any visible means of support. It was eerie. For all he could see he might have been ten thousand feet up, suspended in a chill smoke cloud that muffled every sound from the world below.

As he hesitated, the doubts he had lightly entertained a short time before began to invade his thoughts again. After all, the idea had come into his head so suddenly. Yet wasn't that how inspiration worked – a sudden flash – an inexplicable vision? But surely, after more than a hundred years of accumulated railway experience, someone must have considered the idea before? His nostrils twitched as they caught a whiff of the acrid sulphur fumes from the invisible engine below and he was shaken by a violent bout of sneezing. Gripping the ladder with all his strength to prevent himself from falling, he recovered his composure and, driving all doubt from his mind, resumed the ascent. At last the lampman's platform loomed from the fog; five more rungs and he was there, swaying from side to side in complete isolation sixty feet above the invisible engine.

The bucket hung nicely on the signal. At the end of the arm there was a steel band that might have been put there to stop it sliding off prematurely. After hanging the bucket and taking a final glance at his handiwork, he backed to the edge of the lampman's platform, felt for the first rung of the ladder with the toe of his right boot and started on the descent.

Unhindered by the bucket he came down the ladder in half the time. He was so pleased with the way things had gone that had it not been for the fog he would have straddled the ladder and slid to the bottom. His driver was bound to tell others of his idea, and when news of it spread he could see others doing it. He would be an innovator – a pioneer! It was another glorious example of man's ingenuity in his struggle against adversity! Why, with the bucket on the signal they could both get their heads down, confident that when it fell to the ballast even a deaf man would know the signal had changed!

It worked like a charm. The moment he reached the ground and left go of the ladder, the signalman pulled the lever and the bucket fell to the ballast – bouncing off Eddie's head en route. Had the signalman pulled the lever two or three minutes later the idea might have been adopted by every fireman on the railway, with Eddie keeping the name on his birth certificate to the end of his days.

After a visit to the hospital and a few days' absence from work, the disenchanted fireman resumed his duties at the Junction to continue his career on the footplate for another forty years.

Many years ago they buried him at the age of seventy-five, his coffin borne by six husky firemen. But it wasn't Eddie Price they buried, it was 'Bucket Ed'.

20
John Willie Rule-Book

*D*uring the Steam Age there was more to a railway than just track, locomotives and rolling-stock. For one thing one had to have a Rule Book, a small red volume crammed from cover to cover with more than two hundred rules and regulations, each one blessed with the unique virtue of cloying the whole damned system to a standstill whenever the men took it into their heads to apply it to the letter.

Of course the precise wording of the Rule Book varied according to which country one lived in or the company one worked for, but, just as it is impossible to get to heaven except via font, altar and a hole in consecrated ground, it was impossible to be a railwayman without one.

To most of the men at the Junction the Rule Book was a necessary evil consulted to pass examinations on their way up the ladder of promotion and to refresh their knowledge of the more important clauses whenever they needed to apply them. To John Willie, however, the Rule Book became an obsession, transforming his brain into a porous clinker crawling with rule-regs of every shape and size, each one waiting to trigger a spasm of deadly devotion in every cell of his five-foot-five by eight-stone-six frame.

Like the rest of the men at the Junction, John Willie was entrusted with the clause-ridden volume (to be returned with the rest of the company's gear on dismissal or retirement) the day he passed his fireman's examination. It was pushed over the counter of the stores on top of his allocation of clothing consisting of overalls, serge jacket, overcoat, raincoat and cap.

His fanatical dedication to the closely printed pages commenced the moment he opened the book at its title page, and, within three months, news of his terrible conversion began to spread along the lines in all directions. After ten years on the shovel and thirty as a driver, his reputation as being the most dedicated Rule Book fanatic was known from the East Coast to the West Coast, as far north as Perth and South to Camden goods yard.

How any locoman could harden into the impervious stuff of a High Court Judge is difficult to understand. After all, life on the Iron Road wasn't all sweat and grime; there were the lonely moors of Yorkshire seen through a Bronte-grey mist at daybreak and the limestone shoulders of the Derbyshire hills gleaming white through dark green forests. There were the lonely farmsteads of Cumberland and Westmorland nestling in the gorgeous curves of the hills that became more rugged with each mile northwards. Every city had a smell of its own depending on its manufactures; even the water tasted different. When, after booking into a company barracks on a double trip, one went out to sample the local beer and yarn with the locals, one felt humanity's warmth, even though they talked like foreigners.

To John Willie, as he sped through it all reciting his precious rules and regulations to the rhythm of the wheels on the rail joints, pausing only to observe his fireman to make sure he wasn't breaking any, it all meant nothing. The Rule Book became his Bible, to which he gave his entire devotion both at work and at home. He continually tested himself by choosing a rule number at random and reciting it from beginning to end. When his memory failed him and he found himself hesitating, he would reach feverishly into his pocket for the precious red book for reassurance.

Everyone at the Junction knew that coal burns at its most efficient in small pieces, ideally as big as one's fist, but towards the end of the Steam Age some egghead in the 'Brains' department refined the theory to the point of absurdity. An instruction was issued that no matter how hard the engine was blasting at the chimney-top, the correct way to feed the beast was for the fireman to shovel the coal round the firebox every two minutes. On a Scotch express that took six hours to get to Glasgow, the fireman was expected to get down to the shovel a hundred and eighty times with the precision of a mechanical navvy.

When John Willie read the new instruction he rejoiced at the possibilities and, like a disciple responding to an edict from on high, leapt into the centre of the footplate after counting the seconds to command his fireman to commence shovelling. Aggravating at the best of times, he now became unbearable, terrorising every fireman who had the ill-luck to find himself on the same footplate. When this misfortune befell young Butch Johnson, a fireman who prided himself on his physical powers, a tremendous explosion occurred in their relationship, as when an irresistible force meets an immoveable object.

It wasn't that young Butch was lazy, it was simply that when that huge cob rolled down the tender to the shovelling plate, he saw it as a challenge. About four feet in length, it weighed about a hundredweight. Eyeing the monster cob like an adversary, he set himself, grasped the top end of it with his right hand and the bottom with his left and, lifting it bodily, made to swing it through the firehole with all the power of his mighty shoulders. Another second and the huge cob would have disappeared into the firebox to be pounced upon by the flames, but, at that moment, John Willie took his eyes off the signals just in time to catch his brawny fireman about to violate the new instruction. Instead of the flames pouncing on the cob it was John Willie who pounced on the unfortunate Butch.

'Break it up! As big as y'fist – d'yer hear me? Break it up!'

Screeching like a scalded parrot John Willie leapt from his corner pointing accusingly at the gigantic cob of coal. So startled was the young fireman that he forgot to leave hold of the cob in time and was carried forward by the momentum of his mighty swing onto the hot plates of the faceplate casing. Recovering his balance with difficulty, he let the cob fall to the footplate then, glaring hard at the pious little engine driver, unleashed a stream of invective as black as the inside of a smokebox.

Had Butch left it at that and proceeded to crack the cob into a hundred pieces with his coal hammer, the fracas would have ended there. Unfortunately, after exhausting his stock of profanities and coining one or two shades of invective entirely new to the English language, he took hold of the cob again and slung it into the firebox with such a defiant swing of his shoulders that it was quite evident he cared not a toss for the rules and regulations, and even less for John Willie Rule-Book!

In his report to the Superintendent, John Willie left nothing to his imagination. The last paragraph read:

'... and on my instruction to break up the cob as big as his fist, fireman Johnson replied: "If you don't shut your trap I'll ram it right up your b..."

Your obedient servant, Driver Walsh. No 78.'

Completely unrepentant even after being suspended for two days without pay, when Butch Johnson returned to duty he related the incident to his mates as though his punishment had been well worth while.

It might easily be assumed that because John Willie was despised by his workmates for his fanatical insistence on applying the rules and regulations to the minutest detail, he would have been the darling of those in authority. After all, those same rules and regulations formed the very basis for their authority. And yet, paradoxically, he was a severe pain in the neck to them also.

The main occupation of the men in bowler hats and gold braid was to see to it that the rules and regulations were adhered to. This was what they were paid for. If every Tom, Dick or Harry in any grade took it upon himself to be the guardian of the rules and regulations, what price their authority? They were their rules and regulations, not John Willie's! And they could never forgive him for his presumption.

For forty years John Willie had things entirely his own way, emerging the victor from countless rule-slinging confrontations in the Superintendent's office, storming from the mat with an air of unassailable righteousness as he left behind a speechless group of officials stupefied by his magical manipulation of rules and clauses of which they had never heard. He delighted in answering the mountains of paperwork he received demanding explanations as to why his train was late arriving at its destination or why he refused to leave a sidings with a freight train loaded with two ounces more than the loading schedule stipulated.

On one occasion the awkward little devil refused to leave a main-line station with an express passenger train because the guard happened to be wearing a cloth cap instead of the uniform headgear issued by the railway company. In his report explaining the delay he made great play of the fact that the guard was improperly dressed and that, for all he knew, it could have been an ordinary member of the public that was waving the green flag. I ask you, by what strange coincidence would a member of the public find himself in the vicinity of a guard's van in possession of a green flag?

Making the most of his opportunity, he went so far as to say that if the company chose to countenance such behaviour they too were violating the rules and regulations. The brazen hypocrisy of the procrastinating little so and so was made glaringly evident by the fact that the guard of the train that day was none other than Bert Bowser, a man with a half-hundredweight beer paunch carried on short fat legs that splayed outwards under the weight of it. John Willie and everyone else at the Junction would have recognised Bert half a mile away with a bucket on his head!

For forty years John Willie strutted about the shed like a bantam cock quoting the rule, the clause in the rule and the line in the clause in the rule, and every permutation of these relating to every point he was asked to explain. But forty years is a long time to ride the crest of a wave of infallibility. There had always been those who prophesied his downfall, and although they got fewer as his infamy spread further abroad, one still heard one of them remark occasionally, 'Aye, it's all right. He'll come a cropper yet, you mark my words!'

By this time there wasn't a single man at the Junction who didn't yearn for his downfall. From the Superintendent down to the most menial labourer, they had all suffered at one time or another the indignity of having to bow to his superior knowledge of the Rule Book. Indeed, so many hours of honest endeavour had been ruined by his destructive pilgrimage that it was nothing short of a miracle that he avoided a punch on the nose!

And then, almost at the end of his time on the Iron Road, John Willie's immaculate edifice of inviolable rules and regulations collapsed about his head with startling unexpectedness. Surprisingly, the event that led to his downfall didn't involve one of the more important rules in the book; it turned out to be a simple matter of negligence as ludicrous as a steeplejack breaking his neck falling from a doorstep!

When Wally Philpot, the shed Superintendent, heard the news the next morning, he threw his bowler hat in the air in a wild display of unrestrained gratification. Over the years both he and his foremen had set so many unsprung traps for John Willie that they had come to believe he was destined to establish a legend of rule perfection unsurpassed throughout the long history of railways. For days afterwards jubilation reigned throughout the great engine shed at the news, with one of the few remaining optimists remarking with a self-satisfied look on his face, 'Told yer, didn't I? Didn't I tell yer he'd come a cropper?'

Looking back on the tragedy I often wonder why I found it difficult to share the elation at John Willie's downfall. As a raw fireman I had worked with him on two or three occasions when every mile had been purgatory but, for me, witnessing the humiliation of anyone has always been a sad experience.

That Tuesday night, John Willie left home at eleven o'clock, shutting the door of his little terraced house behind him carefully so as not to disturb his wife who had gone to bed half an hour earlier. As he stepped into the street he found it deserted, for Tuesday was a quiet night in the pubs and cinemas, with most of the folk who inhabited the soot-grimed terraced houses already indoors. At the end of the street where it joined the main road he palmed his watch from his pocket under a street lamp to check it with the church clock. Confirming with great satisfaction that the church clock was three minutes fast, he returned the watch to his pocket and stepped out again on his half-mile walk to the engine shed, his thoughts already beginning to focus on the likely rules and regulations he would be obliged to apply to the letter on his forthcoming journey through the night.

In the drama that he was approaching with every step he took, there were two factors that sealed his fate inexorably. Had he been able to meet them separately on successive days he might have stood a chance, but together they formed a formidable adversary. For one thing, the foreman on duty that night was none other than old Redneck, a heartless disciplinarian who wielded his power like a local Napoleon. Had it been the amiable, jocular King Hal or the blustering, excitable Spit'n'speak, either of the other two shed foremen, his reputation might have remained intact to the day he retired, but old Redneck had dreamed for years of taking John Willie down a peg and, given half a chance, neither pity, propriety nor persuasion would deter him from striking.

The other factor in the deadly equation of destiny awaiting the unwary John Willie was that the train he was to work that night was none other than the 'Ghost Train', and no one trifled with this. The 'Ghost Train' had run for longer than anyone at the Junction could remember. Long before the London & North Western and the Lancashire & Yorkshire railways were absorbed in the London Midland & Scottish, the two had fought a bitter contest to win the contract offered by the newspaper trade to transport their sheets to Leeds and Newcastle. The old L&Y had won the contract by a smokebox length, and, ever since, the train had left at thirty-three minutes past twelve every night on its mad dash over the Pennines.

There were many perishables carried by rail in those days, freight such as milk, fish, meat and fruit, but the freight that perished quicker than any of these was news. It wasn't for nothing that the newspaper proprietors inserted a 'Running late' clause in the original contract, threatening the railway company with forfeiting a portion of the fee they charged whenever the train arrived late at its destination; for this reason everyone connected with the 'Ghost Train' was expected to be on their toes to see that it arrived on time. Although successive mergers removed the competition for its revenue, the tradition persisted, with the challenge of the 'Ghost Train' pervading the crew of the locomotive the moment they stepped on board.

Dead on ten minutes past eleven, old Redneck glanced at the clock on the wall of his office. Although he had only been on duty since ten o'clock, the next twenty minutes would be his most anxious of the night. Only when the engine for the 'Ghost Train' left the shed would he allow himself to relax. Like the crew who manned it and the signalmen who would ensure that it would be given a clear road, he too had a vital part to play in getting the train to Leeds on time by ensuring that the engine left the shed promptly. Normally engine crews were allowed an hour to prepare an express engine for the journey, but in the case of the 'Ghost Train' and similar 'flyers' the preparation was done beforehand by a spare set of men to avoid late starts.

Fifty-five forty-six stood ready on number five pit. A spare set of men had prepared it for the road two hours previously, and immediately old

Redneck had arrived on duty he had sent a second set round it just to make certain. Learning the identity of the driver of the most important train of the night just after he arrived, Redneck was taking no chances. He knew from long experience that the only way to deal with John Willie Rule-Book was to keep two or three moves ahead of him.

Every bearing of the engine's mechanism was bathed in oil and the pointer on the steam gauge indicated two hundred and forty pounds per square inch. The fire was damped down, the footplate swept clean and a warm, pungent smell of oil pervaded the cab.

Back in the foreman's office, Redneck's involuntary anxiety contaminated his assistants. The old time clerk who sat at the same large desk next to the foreman raised his grey head and glanced at the clock, secretly praying that the following twenty minutes would pass uneventfully to allow him to get on with his rosters without suffering one of Redneck's agonising tantrums. Joe, the telegraphist, listened with strained tension for his call-bell, and the junior, whose job it was to hand each driver his time-card as he called out his number and to report to the foreman if he was a minute late, sat at his tray, his fingers holding number seventy-six ready to flick it out the moment John Willie made his appearance.

Five minutes before he was due, John Willie breezed through the door of the signing-on hall and approached the communicating window where the junior stood waiting. Before he could open his mouth to shout his number, the junior slapped his time-card on the desk outside the open window and John Willie reached for a pen. Old Redneck peered through the small glass panes of the petition over the top of his wire-rimmed spectacles, observing every feature of the little engine driver's face for signs of awkwardness. After signing on duty, John Willie moved along the partition to the open window facing the foreman and, looking straight at old Redneck, shouted across the office.

'Driver Walsh reporting for the "Ghost Train", foreman! What engine am I taking?'

By the manner in which the two men dealt with each other it was difficult to imagine that they had known each other for most of their lives, but neither John Willie nor old Redneck was prepared to give any quarter in the way of formality. John Willie always addressed officials by their proper titles; that way they never had cause to pounce first. Old Redneck arrived at the same philosophy from the opposite direction; a driver was a driver, a fireman was a fireman and a shed foreman was God Almighty!

Still seated, old Redneck stared across the office at the driver at the window for a few moments, then, slowly rising from his chair, he walked across the floor to face him, intent on conveying the impression that he was about to instruct just another driver of the many over whom he wielded power. Pushing his bowler to the back of his head and adjusting his spectacles, he leaned on the desk that ran the whole length of the partition and gave the engine number.

'Your engine is fifty-five forty-six, driver! You'll find her all ready for leaving on number five!'

With the foreman's stare piercing his back, John Willie strode from the window to disappear from sight through the archway leading to the pits, and, a second or two later, a fireman rushed into the signing-on hall. It was Charlie Spinks, at the last minute as usual. Signing his time-card hurriedly, he threw it back at the junior then, moving along the partition to the window facing the foreman, bawled for the number of his engine.

'What's on the "Ghost", Dad?'

Redneck bristled at the familiarity. 'I'll have less of the "Dad", sonny!'

Glowering over the top of his spectacles he stared at the young fireman. 'You're taking fifty-five forty-six on number five, laddy! Your own driver's not coming tonight, he's cried off sick.'

Charlie was surprised to hear this. His driver appeared to be perfectly all right when they had signed off duty the previous morning.

'Sick?'

Redneck glared at him even more fiercely. 'That's what I said, laddy, S-I-C-K, sick! Don't you understand the King's English?'

Undeterred, Charlie Spinks brazened him out.

'Well he was all right when we signed off yesterday mornin'! Who've I got then?'

Charlie's question brought to Redneck's face the expression of satanic pleasure for which he was renowned.

'You've got Driver John Willie Walsh for your mate tonight, laddy, so you'd better look sharp and get to your engine!'

Utterly crestfallen, his body sagging quite visibly at Redneck's announcement, the dejected fireman disappeared through the archway to meet his fate.

The moment the fireman of the 'Ghost Train' left to board his engine, things started to happen in quick succession. After being on duty for only an hour, during which time they had shunted a couple of engines about the shed on Redneck's instructions, Sam Harding and his fireman reported for further duties. After telling them to hang about, Redneck addressed Joe, the telegraphist: 'Get me the outlet, Joe!'

Giving the call sign of the signal box at the outlet from the shed, Joe received a reply at once and held out the earpiece to the foreman.

'The Bobby's on the line now.'

Taking the receiver, Redneck straddled the high stool vacated by Joe and began to speak like a conspirator into the mouthpiece fixed to the wall.

'That you, Tommy? Look, I've a right awkward devil on the "Ghost" tonight – I want you to let me know the moment he rings out. Will you do that, Tommy? That's the lad. What time d'yer make it?' He took his watch from his pocket. 'That's right. He's got nine minutes. Yes, that's right – good lad!'

Handing the receiver back to Joe, he went back to the partition, nervously humming to himself. Staring through the open window as though pre-occupied, the presence of Sam Harding registered with him again and, as an afterthought, he addressed him.

'Don't go away, Sam – I might be needing you shortly!'

With this, he turned away from the window and, taking out his watch again, looked at it, then at the clock on the wall and sighed quite loudly. At this point he intended to sit in his chair next to the old time clerk to await the phone call from the signalman at the outlet, but so frayed were his nerves that he returned to the window and, as he glanced at the clock once more, sighed loudly again. With a bit of luck, in five minutes his anxiety would be over.

When John Willie Rule-Book reappeared at the window, old Redneck stiffened like a standing corpse. As he struggled to muster his vocal chords his mouth dried up. At last the words he marshalled screamed from his mouth.

'What the hell are you doing here?'

Like a child about to recite his five times table, John Willie began to reply.

'I'll take that engine off the shed, foreman, when you arrange to send me a fireman to get some steam in her!'

Redneck began to splutter. 'W-W-What are you talking about, man? Your fireman left here ten minutes ago!'

As though he hadn't heard a word, John Willie resumed his recitation.

'The company pays you a very good salary to run this shed, foreman! If you can't see to it that my engine has a full head of steam and a fireman to keep it that way, you shouldn't be wearin' that billy-pot! The company expects me to run my train to time an' answer for any delays, an' I can't do that if there's no steam in the engine an' no fireman to make any!'

Before Redneck could find the words to reply, John Willie vanished from the window to return to his engine.

The foreman was seething with anger. His blood pressure was evident at the best of times, but now his face and neck had turned a deep purple. Suddenly Joe the telegraphist and the old time clerk at the desk winced as Redneck screamed through the window, 'Driver Harding!'

As Sam appeared at the window, the outraged foreman addressed him.

'Get to fifty-five forty-six on five and work the "Ghost" – come on, Sam, you've only got three minutes! She's fully prepared and ready to go!'

Rushing out of the signing-on hall towards the pits, Sammy got as far as the stores before stopping in his tracks as he heard Redneck shouting to him again from behind.

'If you see that bloody Philadelphia lawyer on your way, send him back to me!'

Back in his office Redneck paced the floor, muttering to himself and constantly glancing at the clock as Joe the telegraphist and the grey-haired old time clerk bowed their heads in a vain effort to escape the tension that was beginning to electrify the place.

'You'll have to answer for all the delay, foreman!'

It was John Willie at the window again. Spinning round to face him, old Redneck opened his mouth to reply but dried up completely. He appeared to freeze, his face and neck almost black with rage as John Willie Rule-Book droned on. 'I can't work a train wi' no steam in the engine an' no fireman to make any! I shall report the matter, foreman! I'll be puttin' pen to paper!'

John Willie's final threat echoed and re-echoed in Redneck's brain like the reverberations of a bomb explosion. During his many years as shed foreman he had heard the awkward little engine driver on the other side of the partition use the threat so often that he now wanted to grip him by the throat and strangle him.

'I shall report the matter' – 'I shall report the matter' – as the threat sounded again and again in his tormented brain his rage increased until he found himself rushing to the glass partition to confront again the cause of his anguish.

'What's your game, Walsh? What's your bloody game?'

Thrusting his head through the communicating window so abruptly that he dislodged his bowler hat, he placed his distorted face within an inch of John Willie's and screamed, 'I'll tell you this, Walsh! If the "Ghost Train" is late leaving tonight I'll make you sit up! You mark my words!'

With startling abruptness a bell jangled at the switchboard giving the call sign of the engine shed. Hastily inserting the plug to connect the call, Joe acknowledge it, then held out the earpiece to old Redneck.

'It's the signalman at the outlet for you!'

As Redneck grabbed the phone, Joe vacated his tall stool to allow him to speak into the fixed mouthpiece.

'Hello – hello – yes, Tom. Oh, that's fine! That's fine, Tom! Good lad! Thanks for lettin' me know!'

Handing the earpiece back to Joe, Redneck glanced at the clock on the wall then fixed his eyes in a fierce stare at the pious Rule Book fanatic of an engine driver who was just about to commence another weary recitation on the other side of the partition. Deep in his consciousness he heard again John Willie's stock threat – 'I'll report the matter, foreman' – 'I'll report the matter, foreman' – '… paper!' – and with elation beginning to infuse every cell of his being, his neck and face slowly began to shed the deep purple hue of his anger. At last! After decades of fruitless endeavour, he had the procrastinating little engine driver ensnared, and the long wait only added to the sweetness of it.

Quickly striding to the window, he confronted his victim before the latter could resume his diatribe. Savouring every moment, Redneck began quietly.

'And where d'yer think you've been for the past fifteen minutes, Driver Walsh? Eh? Where have you been?'

For a moment John Willie looked puzzled.

'You know very well where I've been, foreman! I've been on fifty-five forty-five on six like you told me when I signed on duty – an engine wi' no steam in her an' no fireman to make any!'

With victory shining in his eyes, Redneck stared harder at John Willie, determined to delay the coup de grâce as long as possible.

'Oh, so you've been on fifty-five forty-five on six, Driver Walsh? An engine wi' no steam in her and no fireman to make it!'

It was here that his resolve to prolong his revenge wilted. He had waited too long for this moment.

'Well now, you've gone and done it this time all right, haven't you, Driver Walsh?' His voice was rising now. 'I tell you to take fifty-five forty-six on five and you take it into your head you'll take fifty-five forty-five on six! No wonder she had no steam in her! Fifty-five forty-five isn't due off the shed till six o'clock in the mornin'! No wonder you couldn't find your flamin' fireman, eh, Driver Walsh? While you were fartin' about on the wrong engine he was on the right one, the one I told you to take twenty minutes ago!'

Maintaining his piercing stare, Redneck paused to savour the expression of disbelief on John Willie's face.

'You weren't paying attention to my instructions, were you, Driver Walsh? You were so concerned with making sure everyone else was keeping to the rules and regulations, your mind wasn't on your own responsibilities. You got on the wrong engine, Driver Walsh! For your information, fifty-five forty-six is halfway to the station by this time with Driver Harding at the controls! Furthermore, your fireman's on board with him! He didn't find her short o' steam! Now then, Driver Walsh, whose goin' to report who? Tell me that, Driver Walsh! Whose goin' to report who?'

As John Willie struggled in vain to find the words to reply, Redneck pressed home his long-awaited victory with biting sarcasm.

'Now, I'm going to tell you something else, Driver Walsh – you can go home now – there's no further duties for you tonight!

Going over to the time-card tray, Redneck took out number seventy-six, unscrewed his fountain pen with a flourish and, shouting each word, commenced to write.

'Re-fused du-ty for not giv-ing due care and atten-tion to in-struc-tions in gross vi-o-la-tion of the com-pany's rules and reg-u-la-tions!'

Returning the card to the tray, he clipped his fountain pen back in his top pocket and returned to the open window where, for several long minutes, he and the dejected John Willie stared at each other in silence. Then, assuming what he believed to be his most commanding posture, he shouted, 'Goodnight, Driver Walsh! What are you standin' there for?'

With Redneck watching him every step of the way, John Willie turned away from the window and slowly made his way to the door. He was close to tears. He was about to grip the handle of the door when, timed to perfection, Redneck crowned his victory by shouting in a loud, sarcastic voice, 'I shall be reporting the matter, Driver Walsh – I say, I shall be reporting the matter! I'll be puttin' pen to paper!'

When the door closed behind him, an utterly dejected John Willie made his way home completely unmindful that what he had just experienced he had inflicted on countless others over the years. He learned no lessons from his humiliation, and, as he strode homeward through the deserted streets, he found no consolation in the darkness.

21
Perishin' Bob Jackson's
Gigantic Timepiece

*L*ike that of most engine drivers at Clanky Junction, Perishin' Bob Jackson's waistcoat boasted a gleaming watch-chain. On the business end of Bob's, however, was attached the largest timepiece one had ever set eyes on. Handed down from father to son over three generations, the waistcoat pocket destined to house it had to be enlarged on each inheritance. More a formidable example of heavy engineering than a delicate creation of the venerated art of horology, several firemen at the Junction claimed to have heard it ticking above the clamour of the engine at full blast.

On the question of its accuracy Perishin' Bob gave no quarter, swearing that he adjusted it just once a year – at midnight on New Year's Eve. He claimed that the adjustment was so small, no more than a second or two on each occasion, that he took the trouble to do this only because it was a family tradition to be adhered to meticulously by the one in possession of it at the time.

Bob had no need of a watch really; for that matter, neither did any other driver at the Junction. Anyone who believes otherwise is the victim of a long-standing fallacy. With the men on the Iron Road time became an instinct. From the cab of a locomotive speeding through the landscape one witnessed so many time-controlled sequences of human behaviour that a watch was quite unnecessary. Rounding a curve a bus stop would come into view; running towards it struggling into his jacket would be the same man who ran for the bus every morning. At the head of the queue one would observe the man in the fawn raincoat and trilby – the man who always headed the queue. At night one would look for the last bus winding its way up the hill as it always did when the train thundered past.

Of course you might say, 'Ah yes, but suppose the bus was nowhere in sight, how would the driver of the engine know then whether or not he was running to time?' Ah, but you see, as the train pounded along the same line, a mile ahead the driver would look for the pub, its doors closed and the three philosophers arguing it out on the pavement. It was startling to learn with what regularity people cling to their habits. With the sun as its main-spring, the entire world was your timepiece.

Unknown to all but the most discerning, it was the secret ambition of every engine driver to beat his watch at its own game. When one asked an engine driver the time it was certainly true that he took his watch from his waistcoat pocket with the solemnity of a vicar selecting the communion wafer, but if one observed him closely, one would notice that he would volunteer the time a second before he glanced at it. Then, having proved once again that he didn't really need a watch at all, he would square himself up, and, with haughty conceit, walk away reassured.

Proof of this presented itself when a driver I was working with suddenly crossed the footplate looking bewildered. He knew beyond question that we were running to time, for he had seen the milkman exchanging two full bottles for two empties at the second house in the terrace alongside the line, and the old man opening the gate of his henpen situated near the home signal. Providing that we were running to time we witnessed these scenes every morning on passing Wentworth. We couldn't be anything else but on time! Yet there he was standing in front of me, pointing at his watch as though he had witnessed something incredible!

'Hey, just look at this mate!'

Sure enough, his watch showed us to be seven minutes late! Then, his expression changing from one of bewilderment to one of contempt, he exclaimed 'Bloody contraption!' and flung the watch from the speeding train.

No one would have expected Perishin' Bob to throw away his gigantic timepiece if it stopped. His was a watch of superior pedigree – a watch to shame all watches. Even so, one day, when he pressed the knurled winder to lower the front of the heavily embossed case like the ramp of a landing craft, his face clouded in disbelief. There was no doubt about it – the huge timepiece had stopped!

For a few seconds he stared at the still watch in stunned silence, unable to accept the evidence in front of his own eyes. Shaking the watch violently, he held it to his ear then looked at it again, only to observe that the second counter at the bottom of the dial remained quite still. Staring at his fireman as though at a stranger he bellowed, 'The perishin' thing's stopped!'

Startled by his driver's dramatic announcement, Andy Smith stopped shovelling to look at him.

'Did you say summat, Bob?'

The stupefied engine driver held out the watch.

'Me watch! The perishin' thing's stopped!'

The next thing he did was so drastic that it was clear he was suffering from trauma. Unfastening the watch from the equally formidable chain, he hammered twice with it on the steel plates of the cab, then placed it to his ear again. Then, like a doctor who has just felt the final pulse of a patient's heart, he shook his head disconsolately and, more in frustration than hope, hammered with it again. Placing it to his ear again, he declared, 'It's stopped! I say, the perishin' thing's stopped!'

If Perishin' Bob's fireman displayed elation rather than empathy at his driver's ordeal, it was due to a conflict of interest rather than malice. The expiration of Bob's gigantic timepiece was an event he had often dreamed about in moments of wild fantasy. About two years previously Andy Smith had made the remarkable discovery that of all the watches that stopped ticking, a large proportion of them did so because they needed nothing more than cleaning. Possessing an ambitious nature, he decided to join that exclusive band of men at the engine shed who, for the price of a couple of pints, took it upon themselves to restore a watch to life whenever they were given the opportunity.

The day that he was marked on the roster to be Perishin' Bob's regular fireman, Andy found himself staring at the driver's huge timepiece whenever it was exposed to view like a butcher eyeing the carcase of a prize pig. Blinded by ambition, the fact that his knowledge of watch-repairing was meagre in the extreme did nothing to restrain his enthusiasm to get his hands on it. If Bob could be persuaded to part with the watch he was convinced that a thorough soaking in alcohol and a few spots of fine oil would have it ticking merrily again in no time. More important still, when it became known that he had been the one to repair the famous timepiece, his ensuing fame would have engine drivers from all over the railway clamouring for his services.

As Andy watched his driver staring stupidly at his enormous watch each time he withdrew his head from glancing at the signals, his ambition to be the one to get it going again intensified. At that moment he wanted nothing more than to get at its innards. After a bout of shovelling as the train approached Hinty bank, he found he could hold out no longer. Striding across the cab as his driver stared at the watch in bewilderment, he made to take hold of it.

'Let's have it, Bob. I'll fix it for yer. I'll have it back as good as new tomorrer!'

But Perishin' Bob wasn't having any of it. He didn't care for the bold grab his fireman made for it. Clutching the watch to his chest he exclaimed, 'Gerroff the perishin' thing! What makes yer think I'd let you have it?'

Andy appealed to him. 'I tell yer, I'll fix it! Ask Bill Downey an' Jimmy Tittle – they'll tell yer! They've had no trouble since I fixed theirs! I've read all the books, y'know! I know what I'm doin'!'

Perishin' Bob scoffed. 'Bill Downey an' Jimmy Tittle! Them's not watches! Bits o' perishin' tin, them! You don't know what y'sayin', lad. Me father had this watch – an' his father afore him! Here, feel it.'

Placing the gigantic watch in Andy's eager hands, he snatched it back before his fingers could close on it.

'See what I mean? Solid silver. That's yer difference, lad!'

Pausing to stare at his fireman with a superior look on his face, he finally clipped the watch back on its chain and placed it in his waistcoat pocket. Then, after glancing at the signals again, 'Bill Downey – Jimmy Tittle – ugh!'

Diverting his attention to the road ahead as the train began to take the strain of the gradient, nothing more was said for a short while, then, confident that he had the engine striding easily up the bank, Bob addressed his fireman again. Patting the large bulge in the pocket of his waistcoat that housed the watch, he shouted above the blasts of the engine, 'There's a movement in there as you've never set eyes on, lad! I'll tell yer! A cylinder movement! That's yer difference, lad – that's yer difference!'

This was true. Cylinder movements disappeared with Queen Victoria, but the fact that Andy had never seen such a mechanism in his life dampened his enthusiasm not one iota! He started lying like a promiscuous vicar.

'Oh, Bob – cylinder movements? Why, there's nothin' to 'em when y'know what you're doin'! I tell yer, I've read all the books! I've had correspondence courses! I know what I'm doin'! Why d'yer think Bill Downey and Jimmy Tittle trusted me wi' theirs? As a matter o' fact, Jimmy Tittle approached me to repair his watch on Bill Downey's recommendation. Now then – what about that?'

Perishin' Bob still remained unimpressed. 'Bill Downey an' Jimmy Tittle! Haven't I told yer them's not watches! They bought 'em out of a catalogue, that's what they did! A shillin' down an' a bob a week until they were paid for. Bill Downey an' Jimmy Tittle wouldn't recognise a good watch if they saw one!'

By this time Andy was getting desperate. Determined to pursue his cause he made to approach his driver again, but before he could utter a word Perishin' Bob ended the dialogue by indicating the steam gauge.

'Hey, come on, lad – look at that pointer!. The way you're goin' on we'll never get up the bank! Come on, let's have some coal in the box!'

Doing as he was told, Andy got down to the shovel again and the train pounded further towards the summit of the gradient.

During the rest of the trip Andy gave Bob no peace, pleading to be allowed to repair the aristocrat of a watch at every sidings and signal they stopped at.

'Why don't you trust me, Bob? How long have you 'n' me worked together, eh, Bob? Have I ever let you down?'

Then, later: 'Y'know Bob, what you're short of's a little faith. I'd handle that watch as though it were me own. Why don't yer give us a chance to prove it? If you take it to a watch repairer he'll rob yer hand over fist! Y'know I wouldn't rob yer, don't yer – me own mate?'

Although Perishin' Bob resisted bravely, nine hours later Andy's persistent assault wore him down and, as they left their engine on the disposal pit upon returning to the Junction, he finally wilted.

'Here y'are, then, take it. But if anythin' goes wrong with the perishin' thing you an' me are going to fall out! D'yer hear me? That watch is worth a lot – bin in the family fer generations!'

Confident to the end, Andy replied, 'Nothin'll go wrong with it, Bob. I tell yer, I'll have it back as new tomorrer an' when you see it you'll be sorry you showed doubt in the first place.'

With this, he took the watch from Bob's hesitant hands and the two of them made their separate ways home.

It was one o'clock in the morning when Andy arrived home, his wife fast asleep upstairs. Eager to get at the gigantic timepiece, he quickly brewed himself a pot of tea, sat at the kitchen table and, brimming with curiosity, got to work on it at once.

Pressing the knurled winder, he opened the back of the watch, then, inserting a finger nail behind an inner flap, exposed the unusual movement and gazed at it in wonder. It was certainly one he hadn't encountered before. Almost at once his wonder changed to an immense feeling of gratification as he observed every piece of its mechanism congealed in a coagulated paste consisting of coal dust and sweat. Along with its proud owner, the magnificent timepiece had probed the motions of countless locomotives, delved into the dark, ash-laden interiors of their smokeboxes and been subjected to clouds of swirling coal dust on wind-swept stretches of railway lines. But whereas its owner had washed himself free of the pollution every day, it had penetrated the tiny apertures of the casing for more than half a lifetime until, in a mighty thrombosis, its gallant heart had finally succumbed.

Preparing two baths of alcohol, Andy placed them side by side on the table, then, freeing the movement completely from the case, immersed it in one of them and began to moving it about gently until the cloying paste of coal dust and sweat dissolved. When the last of it fell away, he immersed the movement in the clean alcohol of the second bath and, within seconds, it was shining like new. Finally removing it from the bath, he held it until the alcohol had completely evaporated, then, dipping a darning needle into a small bottle of highly refined oil, he held it over each tiny bearing to allow a few drops to fall on it. This done, his face tense with anticipation, he shook the movement and, to his great delight, the gigantic timepiece returned to life! It was a miracle that never failed to impress the ambitious fireman. It was so simple! Anyone could do it!

Rendered bold by his success, he gazed lovingly at the innards of the gigantic timepiece as though hypnotised, and, as he recalled Perishin' Bob's reluctance in entrusting the watch to him, he smiled smugly. As he wallowed in pride, both his confidence and curiosity began to overwhelm his caution and, taking hold of the darning needle again, he started probing the intricate mechanism as it continued to measure the time. Intrigued by a particularly strange arrangement of the machinery, he was carefully exploring it with the point of the darning needle when, with a suddenness that startled him, a minute part sprang from the watch and, as he stared at the gigantic timepiece in disbelief, all movement ceased as it expired again.

For a second he was too dazed to move. Then, in the vain hope that the flying piece of mechanism had nothing to do with the main function of the watch, he began to shake it again and again, but the movement remained quite unmoved. Turning his head, he looked in the direction in which he thought he had seen the renegade piece of mechanism fly, in an attempt to divine its trajectory, but it had happened so quickly that he couldn't be sure. Placing the movement on the kitchen table, he got up from the chair and began searching for the missing part.

Believing it to be shaped like a tiny triangle with a minute spindle protruding from one corner, he searched everywhere. At first he proceeded carefully, but after two hours he was throwing the furniture about like a bailiff on piecework. Awakened by the din, his wife ventured downstairs just as he was prising the skirting board away from the wall in the hope that it had disappeared through a hole in the plaster. However, seeing the wild, desperate look on his face, she fled back upstairs without a word. Finding nothing behind the skirting board, Andy paused in his search and sat on his haunches to give the matter more thought, but fresh inspiration was slow in coming to him.

After considering the problem of the missing link for ten minutes or so, Andy conceived an idea that seemed to have great possibilities. If he were to toss something approaching the same size as the missing part in the direction he believed it to have taken, its trajectory might lead him to it! Going to the table, he rummaged in his tool box until he spied a small ball-bearing. Taking hold of it, he sat exactly where he had been working on the watch and lobbed it towards the window. Alas, after bouncing once on the window sill it dropped straight down the plughole of the kitchen sink. Collapsing despairingly in a fireside chair, he glanced in every direction round the kitchen hoping for a flash of inspiration, but none came, and when the sun rose he was slouched in the chair completely exhausted.

The next few days were the most agonising of Andy's life. Until he found that triangular piece of metal with the minute spindle protruding from one corner he would know no peace. The day following the catastrophe he boarded the engine determined to play for time – to forestall Perishin' Bob's questions by getting in first.

'What a beautiful movement, Bob! D'yer know, I've never seen anythin' like it!'

It worked like a charm. Grinning conceitedly, Bob said, 'I told yer, didn't I? Didn't I tell yer? You an' yer Bill Downey an' Jimmy Tittle! Didn't I tell yer they don't know what a real watch looks like?'

Andy hastened to exploit his mate's good humour.

'It's a real beauty, Bob. 'Course, I'm not gonna rush it. I'm gonna make a proper job of it!'

His driver responded perfectly. 'That's alright lad! Tomorrer'll do!'

Returning home in the early hours of the next morning, Andy found his troubled thoughts focusing on how the ball-bearing had disappeared down the plughole of the kitchen sink after he had tossed it in his attempt to divine the trajectory of the missing part. The moment he entered the kitchen, he took a torchlight and went into the backyard to dredge the drain. Delving as deep as his arm permitted he continued searching until all the dogs of the neighbourhood were barking in chorus and the head of his next door neighbour appeared at the bedroom window demanding to know what he was up to. After making a lame excuse he quickly retreated back into the kitchen where, with increasing desperation, he began to ransack the place from floor to ceiling.

But it was all to no avail. Utterly defeated, he sank into a fireside chair silently cursing in self-recrimination. Why had he probed with the darning needle? Why hadn't he left well alone? For a fleeting moment he re-lived his joy at seeing the gigantic timepiece return to life after he had immersed it in the alcohol, but his joy was short-lived as he plunged back into despondency at the agonising plight in which he found himself.

Arriving at the engine the following day he applied more delaying tactics.

'Hey, d'yer know, Bob, I was working on that watch o' yours this mornin' when a mate o' mine came in. D'yer know what he said? He said he'd give me ten quid for it as it stood! He did! I said ten quid? I said he couldn't have it for fifty! The cheeky devil!'

Noticing the expression of disappointment on his driver's face, he continued, 'Anyway, with a bit o' luck you'll have it back tomorrer!'

Bob replied simply, 'Aye, I hope I do – I mean – it's time isn't it?'

Returning home the following night, in sheer desperation Andy set to again, and, taking every stick of furniture from the kitchen, he stacked it in the back yard and searched every inch of the floor on his hands and knees like a sleuth. When he failed to locate the elusive piece of mechanism on the floor he began to feel along every ledge and shelf and peer into every crevice until, once again, weary with the worry of it, he sank to the floor and fretted.

The following day Perishin' Bob pounced on the miserable fireman the moment he stepped through the handrails of the engine cab.

'Have you gorrit?'

With strained innocence, Andy replied, 'Did you say summat, Bob?'

Scowling fiercely, the deeply suspicious driver repeated the question. 'Me perishin' watch! The one I let you have in good faith on your promise to fetch it back the next day! Have you got the perishin' thing?'

Andy stalled further. 'Hey, hold on a minute, Bob! You want a proper job making of it, don'cher? I told yer I wasn't gonna rush it, didn't I? I mean, let's be fair!'

Perishin' Bob became almost threatening. 'Be fair? What d'yer mean – let's be fair? You said you'd have it back the next day! God's truth, you've had time to make a brand new watch, let alone repair it! Now, you listen to me, lad – good job or bad, I want me watch back tomorrer! I want no more buggerin' about! If I don't gerrit back tomorrer you an' me are gonna fall out good an' proper!'

With this he lunged on the regulator and, as though in complete sympathy with the man at the controls, the engine went into a wheel-slipping tantrum. Quickly closing the regulator, he allowed the engine to regain its feet, opened it again in a more rational manner, and, for the rest of the journey, remained completely silent.

In utter desperation, arriving home in the early hours of the next morning Andy almost demolished the house in a frantic, last search. Coming downstairs to find her kitchen resembling a junk-shop, his wife screamed at him in anguish. With the neighbours hammering on the walls in protest she pummelled her husband's back with her fists as he roughly dragged the pieces of furniture across the room in a manic bid to locate the wayward piece of mechanism. Finally, after a mighty tussle, she managed to bring him to his senses, and together they climbed the stairs to bed. With his reputation as a watch-repairer on the brink of disaster and his relationship with Perishin' Bob Jackson in ruins, Andy's future appeared as bleak as a gale-swept beach in winter. For the rest of the night he lay on his back staring with red-rimmed eyes at the ceiling in a state of abject demoralisation.

The next day Perishin' Bob feared the worst.

'I'll take legal advice, that's what I'll do! All that talk about readin' all the books an' doin' a proper job! Where's me perishin' watch? Eh? Where is it?'

For mile after mile Perishin' Bob continued to rant, waving his arms in the air and shouting threats at the top of his voice. When they stopped at Bradley sidings he exclaimed, 'I wouldn't mind betting you've sold the perishin' thing!' Then, as an afterthought, 'Hey, you haven't have you? You haven't sold it?'

When Andy didn't answer Bob stared hard at him. Then, with venom, he threatened, 'If I thought you'd sold it I'd swing for yer! I would! I'd bloody well swing for yer!'

When, fifteen minutes later, the engine came to rest in number five road at Bradley Sidings to allow the two enginemen to take their meal-break, the atmosphere in the cab was charged with the deep distrust of Perishin' Bob on the one hand and the dismal hopelessness of his fireman on the other. Fervently regretting he had probed the innards of the famous watch with the darning needle, Andy was so mad with himself, when he opened his food parcel he took out the first sandwich and bit on it savagely. Suddenly, as though to compound his misery, a searing pain shot through his head. Freezing, he remained quite still until the pain subsided, then, the moment it eased, began probing the food with his tongue to identify the nature of the object that had inflicted such excruciating pain upon him. Slowly, as he continued to probe warily with his tongue, a remarkable transformation occurred in his demeanour. Unable to believe what his tongue was trying to tell him, he probed even more sensitively, but there was no doubt about it! There it was – a tiny triangular piece of metal with a minute spindle protruding from one of the angles! His sense of relief was so overwhelming, the thought of how it had found its way into his sandwiches never entered his mind. Instead, almost inebriated with jubilation, he turned his back on his driver, slyly removed the piece of mechanism from his mouth and, taking his wallet from the inside pocket of his overall jacket, put it safely away. Then, in an attitude of deeply injured self-righteousness, he immediately turned on his unsuspecting driver to launch into a devastating counter-attack.

'Right, Bob – you'll have your flamin' watch back tomorrer! You're an ungrateful devil, that's what you are, Bob Jackson – a bloody ungrateful sod! I offer to fix it – spend the best part of a week of nights getting it perfect – and all you can do's accuse me of sellin' it! Why, I've treated that watch like one of the crown jewels! Well you can have it tomorrer – and good riddance to it! I wouldn't waste another minute on it if you offered me a hundred pounds!'

Overcome by his fireman's unexpected boldness, Perishin' Bob became unsure of himself.

'Hey, now then, Andy – I-I-I didn't mean it like that!'

Andy scorned him. 'After what you said – you didn't mean it? Don't give me that, Bob! You meant it all right! Anyway, I don't want to hear another word about the damn thing – you'll have it back tomorrer an that'll be the end of it!'

As Perishin' Bob made to plead with him, again his ebullient fireman cut him short.

'I've told yer, Bob – I don't want to hear any more about it! You'll have it back tomorrer an' that'll be the end of it!'

When he signed off duty in the early hours of the morning, the triumphant fireman made his way home quietly singing. There was one moment when his cockiness briefly faltered as, assailed by doubt, he thrust his hand into his inside pocket. When he eventually felt the tiny metal triangle through the thin leather of his wallet, however, his panic subsided and, with his reputation as a watch-repairer untarnished and the owner of the most famous watch at the Junction beholden to him, he laughed in the darkness.

22
The Runaway Train Went Over the Hill

*T*he night that the two o'clock Eccleston goods crashed at Warby, Henry Cartwright was the driver and I was the fireman. Hardly anything went right that night. From the moment I arrived at the engine shed to sign on duty, an atmosphere of doom seemed to hover over the place.

If there was such a thing as a discernible respite in the constant activity of Clanky Junction, it was between ten o'clock on Sunday night and four o'clock on Monday morning. It was then, with only the last of the engines of long-distance trains arriving back on the shed after completing their journeys, that every one of it's twenty-five roads was crammed with motionless locomotives waiting to be boarded in the darkness to start another week of hectic running.

To intensify the depressing atmosphere of the shed, the silent pits gurgled under a heavy deluge. I thought enviously of the rest of the city's populace sleeping off their weekend pleasures in warm, cosy beds, and, arriving at the engine, I expressed my discontent by throwing my tools and shovel on board resentfully.

Despite the shed roads being crammed with locomotives of every shape and size, we were allocated a Lancashire & Yorkshire relic built long before the turn of the century. The design of the class to which it belonged afforded hardly any shelter from wind, rain or snow, and so, in desperate haste, I started at once to rig a tarpaulin sheet over the footplate. I was almost at the end of this task when Henry made his appearance.

Henry's cheerfulness was irrepressible. No matter how tough the going or how long the journey, he could make you feel on top of the world by uttering a few simple words. In my experience he was the first man to acquire a gimmick. In those days a hillbilly band used to broadcast on the radio. The band leader's name was Big Bill Campbell and, every Sunday, he led his band in lively Western music. One of his most devoted fans, Henry cultivated the ability to imitate him in a remarkably life-like manner. On boarding the engine he greeted me with, 'Howdy, pardner – I guess you could do with a helpin' hand wi' that little task!'

On hearing this, the gloom of that wretched night seemed to vanish.

After we had fixed the weather sheet, Henry filled his oil can and, jumping down into the pit, reached into the Joy's motion to lubricate the bearings. Meanwhile, having spread the fire evenly over the firebars, I put several shovelsful of coal into the firebox to keep the old girl simmering, then left to replenish the sanders. By the time Henry climbed back on to the footplate I had a bucketful of hot water ready in the centre of the swept cab and, with my irrepressible hillbilly driver singing 'The Wheel of the Wagon is Broken' at the top of his voice, we washed our hands and arms vigorously. It was then that Henry informed me that he wasn't conversant with the line past Warby and that he was going to the foreman's office.

'I guess I ain't been down the trail beyond Warby in all my born days, pardner! I'll have to go and fix m'self a guide!'

With this he gripped the handrails and, swinging himself from the engine, disappeared on his way to the foreman's office to arrange by telegraph for a conductor to meet us on our arrival at Warby.

There was a disappointment awaiting us when we arrived at the departure sidings – a full load for our ancient locomotive on that stretch of railway was twenty-nine fully loaded wagons, and this was exactly the number we coupled up to. Had there been one more wagon we would have been permitted to call for a bank engine to assist us up the stiff gradient from Freeland to Habton, a challenging climb at the best of times. To get up the gradient with a full load on wet rails meant that our L&Y relic would have to be in the best of fettle. When I heard the guard shout details of the loading to Henry my spirits sagged at the prospect ahead of us, but, once again, my indomitable driver came to my rescue with another of his hillbilly homilies.

'Don't you worry, pardner! We'll get them thar wagons a rustlin', have no fear!'

And so, at two o'clock on that fateful morning, in a deluge that showed no sign of abating and with a locomotive built long before the Boer War, we started our forty-mile journey to Warby. To get the heavy train moving Henry had to reverse time and time again, easing the couplings and snatching at the wagons until we finally got under way. The old relic slipped and snorted in protest, exploding into a fit of tantrums after each determined stride to send a shower of red-hot cinders into the miserable night sky. When her plates threatened to part from the rivets that held them, Henry closed the regulator until she quietened down, then opened up again until slowly, yard by yard, we dragged the heavy train from the sidings and finally got into our stride on the main line.

With the rain falling incessantly and streaming through the tiniest rents in the tarpaulin weather sheet in miniature waterfalls, we blasted through the black night with sparks spewing from the chimney. In another two or three hours the railway would be swarming with trains, but now we seemed to be the only one running. With the pointer on the steam gauge clinging to the red mark our decrepit locomotive tackled the gradient with surprising vigour, shattering the early morning peace with gushes of excess steam from her safety valve as though in celebration. Henry welcomed the sound each time by bellowing across the footplate.

'Mighty fine! Mighty fine, pardner! Keep her rollin', cowboy, keep her rollin'!'

As he encouraged me in his imitation Western drawl I began to wonder if there was any trial or discomfort in the entire gamut of life's experience that could dampen Henry's spirits.

Alas, the elements were against us. Within a quarter of a mile of the summit of the gradient the game engine betrayed Henry's confidence by slipping madly on the wet rails.

'Some sand, pardner! Give her some sand!'

With Henry yelling at the top of his voice I began to jerk the sander lever backwards and forwards and, as the engine regained her feet, he yelled again, 'Mighty fine, cowboy! Mighty fine!'

But she slipped again.

'More sand, pardner! More sand!'

As I worked the sander lever vigorously backwards and forwards again she gripped the rails momentarily but slipped again the moment I paused. It was quite clear by this time that the saturated atmosphere had penetrated the sand. Had she been fitted with the more modern steam sanders the steam would have forced the sand through the delivery pipes, but with the air as sodden as a wet sponge, the only hope of delivering sand to the rails immediately in front of the wheels was to pull and push the sander lever vigorously in an attempt to shake it free. As each dribble of sand fell on the line she regained her feet, but as it clogged again she slipped like an elephant on an ice rink. Henry started coaxing her as though the engine was a horse.

'Come on, old gal – that's it – you can do it – whoa there, steady now…!'

Proceeding in fits and starts we struggled towards the summit of the gradient until, finally, almost on her last gasp, our ancient locomotive dragged the heavy load over the crest and, to our immense relief, we slowly began to coast down the other side. Henry patted the firebox casing as though it were the rump of his favourite nag.

'Mighty fine, old gal – mighty fine!'

Then, as he closed the regulator for the last time and began to apply the brake to check the heavy load down the incline, the gloom of that wretched, rain-sodden night was suddenly dispelled as he burst into song again.

'Home, home on the range, where the deer and the antelope play. Where seldom is heard a discouraging word and the skies are not cloudy all day...!'

Coming to rest at Warby's home signal, Henry gave a final 'Whoa there' and applied the brakes. Here there were two signals on a small gantry; the taller of the two permitted a train to proceed along the main line into the station platform, while the lower one to its left gave trains access to the loop that ran behind the station into the sidings. It was the signal for the loop that we required, for we were scheduled to put off and pick up in the goods yard. Henry was familiar with the main line as far as the station, but he had never steamed along the loop that flanked the sidings and it was for this reason that he had wired for a conductor to meet us at the signal.

Looking first over his side of the engine, then mine, he returned to his seat and sat down to await events. Suddenly the signal for the loop clattered to the lower quadrant for us to proceed. Henry looked puzzled. Then, after looking for the conductor again, he remarked, 'Well, wad'yer know, pardner! Ain't no conductor an' he wants us to go!'

Henry was behaving quite correctly in refusing to pass the signal. To be at the controls of a locomotive on a stretch of line with which one wasn't familiar without the assistance of a conductor was a serious misdemeanour in the world of railways. If a driver took a chance and found himself on the wrong line he couldn't turn round as with a truck or an aeroplane. Furthermore, we were loaded to the limit and, with the sanders on the point of packing up altogether, if the loop descended steeply we could slide to kingdom come!

Impatient at Henry's refusal to proceed, the signalman began to wag the signal up and down, but my hillbilly engine driver made no attempt to move.

'No siree, I ain't amovin', cowboy!'

Then, just as I was putting on my raincoat to carry out Henry's instruction to walk to the signal box to inform the signalman of our need for a conductor, the Inspector from the sidings appeared at the foot of the engine steps dripping like a statue in a fountain. He shouted up to Henry.

'D'yer intend stayin' here all night, driver? The signal's been showin' green for God knows how long!'

With a stranger, Henry abandoned his western drawl.

'I can see it's green, me old flower, but I've never been down that loop in me life! I wired for a conductor to meet us here!'

On hearing this the Inspector traipsed wearily back to the sidings to make some enquiries.

Past the signal the main line continued through the station to run into a tunnel three hundred yards beyond it. Unfamiliar to Henry, the loop ran behind the station on a steeply falling gradient. Thirty yards from the tunnel a train could be switched back to the main line or allowed to continue ahead to a stout set of buffers situated right up against the tunnel wall.

Ten minutes later the Inspector reappeared at the bottom of the engine steps, his raincoat and cap dripping profusely.

'There's no conductor here for you, driver! Just take your train down the loop as far as the signal that takes you back on the main line an' I'll get the pilot to come behind you to exchange the wagons. You can wait in the loop until your conductor arrives.'

Henry expressed doubt at this suggestion. 'But I haven't been down there before in me life, me old flower! What's it like past the signal?'

Anxious to deal with the train so that he could return to his cabin out of the deluge, the Inspector made light of it.

'Oh, there's nothin' to it, driver – nothin' to it! Past the signal it runs downhill a bit, that's all. Anyway, I'll come on board and conduct you as far as the signal that takes you back on the main line – it'll be a damn sight better than bein' soaked to the skin out here!'

With this the Inspector climbed on board and, releasing the brakes, Henry gave a little nudge to the regulator and we began to move forward slowly.

Looking back on the event, this was where Henry made his fatal mistake. The regulations firmly laid down that when a driver was unfamiliar with a stretch of line he should be conducted by another driver who knew it intimately. He didn't know the road past the signal and that ought to have been the end of the matter. But, you see, Henry wasn't the kind of man to make a mountain out of a molehill. There wasn't a grain of awkwardness in him. He would do anything rather than make a nuisance of himself. Overlooking completely that ours was the first train to enter the loop for many hours, he replied, 'Alright, me old flower – I'll go as far as the signal for the main line and wait there.'

The trap was set. Because of the lack of traffic over the weekend and the deluge that had continued unabated throughout the whole time, the rails were coated with a film of rusty slime – a hazard even to a driver who knew the line like the back of his hand.

Cheerful as always, as we passed the signal Henry started singing 'Wagon Wheels': 'Roll on mule, there's a steamer at the landin' – waitin' for the cotton to load…!'

Forgetful of the Inspector standing near the tender dodging the water streaming through the rents in the weather sheet, Henry shouted across to me in his hillbilly drawl.

'Won't be long now, pardner! We'll soon be at the end of the trail!'

My irrepressible driver was still singing as we veered off the main line on to the loop twenty yards past the signal.

'…wagon wheels, carry me ho-ho-ho-home – wagon wheels carry me home!' At that moment my hillbilly engine driver was the happiest man alive.

The first sign that something was wrong came as the line started to dip. As Henry touched the brake to check an almost imperceptible increase in the speed of the train, I felt the engine slide forward in a sudden spurt. Releasing the brake to allow the wheels to rotate, he applied it again, but it was to no avail. She picked up her wheels again to slide menacingly forward. Henry was already yelling across at me.

'Sand, pardner! Give her some sand!'

I was operating the sander lever before he finished yelling, pulling and pushing it frantically for all I was worth. But again it was to no avail. The sand simply wasn't running. Quick to see the danger, the Inspector, making an excuse of the water streaming through the rents in the weather sheet, made for the handrails and jumped from the engine, shouting, 'I'll see you at the end of the loop, driver!' Before Henry could protest he had vanished.

Responding to Henry's urgent shouts for more sand, I began to pull and push the sander lever as though my life depended on it, but, dampened by the saturated atmosphere of that foul night, the sand remained clogged in the valves. Each time the cast iron brake blocks gripped the wheels the engine slid forward as though on a ski-slope. Now, with the heavy load running away with the engine, we had little hope of stopping, and for the first time since leaving the shed Henry showed concern.

'Jump for it, kid! Go on, jump! Take your brake-stick and try to pin some brakes down!'

I didn't need telling twice. Grabbing the brake-stick I leapt from the careering train to land full length on the ballast. Quickly getting to my feet I reached out to grab the brake lever on the first wagon to pass me, but it was travelling so fast that I achieved nothing but a cracked wrist. Unable to do anything to slow the train, I could only stand there helplessly watching as it sped past me heading directly for the solid stone wall at the end of the loop!

After what seemed an age, there was an impact that shook the whole of Warby, and right in front my eyes the wagons started to climb to the sky, one on top of the other as though in a slow motion film. The very marrow in my bones seemed to freeze as I watched the wagons disintegrating no more than six feet in front of me. Higher and higher they climbed until, when I thought it would go on for ever, they started to fall back to earth with the sickening sound of tortured steel and splintering timber. Running a safe distance from the line I continued to watch until everything stopped moving. Then, as a deathly silence fell on the scene, my mind was invaded by frightening thoughts of Henry.

My thoughts were gruesome. Propelled at something like fifty miles an hour by the unstoppable load into that massive stone wall, the engine would come to an abrupt halt; continuing to move at the same speed, my hillbilly engine driver with the cheerful disposition would slam into the projecting controls of the cab breaking every bone in his body, his flesh reduced to a bloody pulp! A tortured cry of anguish escaped from my mouth in the darkness.

'Henry-y-y!'

As the sound of my cry died I shouted again.

'Henry-y-y-y!'

The effort of shouting transformed my trauma into action and I found myself scrambling over the debris towards the engine to recover Henry's mangled body. Perspiring more with fright than effort, after two or three urgent strides I stumbled over a piece of wreckage to go sprawling to the ballast again. As I paused to regain my breath I heard footsteps crunching the ballast ahead of me and, peering into the darkness, I saw the outline of someone approaching. Assistance was coming! Then, just as was about to shout, from the darkness I heard, 'Mighty fine! Mighty fine! That sure was some ambush, eh, pardner?'

23
Moody's Cow

*T*here were times when Clanky Junction was threatened with being buried under a gigantic mountain of printed paper. Somewhere, on one printed page or another, the locomotives that glided from under its soot-grimed roof, the men who manned them, alterations to the permanent way and the amendments to the rules and regulations were all given due reference in a style reminiscent of military documents.

Hardly a month went by without the engine drivers being called to the hut where the stuff was distributed. There, after signing their names as many times as the number of publications issued to them, they would tie them into a bundle, grip the string under the knot and trudge homeward like pilgrims bearing a penance. Once inside their houses, they would toss their bundles of printed paper on the pile already lying there and sigh.

Although the time books, permanent way instructions and Rule Book were the weightiest weapons in the armoury of Clanky Junction's paper control, they were by no means the most harassing. Like an iceberg, these formed only the portion one could see. Beneath the surface there existed a morass of chitties, forms and dockets, appendices, statements and cards that niggled and nagged the men of the Iron Road from the beginning of their service to the end. It wasn't a bit of use trying to fight the system, for it was akin to getting involved with the law or the medical profession; once in its clutches it was loth to let you go.

Paradoxically the most innocuous-looking pieces of paper could be the most formidable. Among these were the ones the drivers found pinned to their time-cards when signing on or off a trip, demanding an explanation as to why they had run late or forgotten or violated some other pettifogging regulation. If the driver answered these in lengthy detail he would find himself corresponding on the same matter for months on end. By far the best way was to close one's eyes, count to ten, then write the first thing that came into one's head as briefly as possible.

Long before the last wisp of steam evaporated from the Junction forever, there was a glorious moment when Jimmy Moody thought he had the system licked. He was in a blazing temper at the time. Signing on duty one day, he found one of these innocent-looking bits of paper pinned to his time-card. It read:

'DRIVER MOODY. 385.
RE: DELAY TO THE 8/40 PM BOAT TRAIN.
It is reported that on Monday Jan 3rd, the train of which you had charge – the 6/5 pm Bickleton-Eltondale goods – lost eleven minutes between Bickleton Colliery and Tarnton sidings, causing delay to the 5/40 pm Boat train. PLEASE EXPLAIN.
                                        SIGNED: W. C. Philpot.
                            District Locomotive Superintendent.'

It wasn't surprising that Jimmy Moody blew off when he read the memo, for on the third of January his engine had ploughed through deep snow in one of the worst fogs in living memory. On reading the memo he was so outraged that he was severely tempted to tear it to pieces in front of the shed foreman. When he expressed his feelings to his fireman on boarding his locomotive, he was shaking with suppressed anger. Holding the offending memo at arm's length as though it was the rotting corpse of a dead rat, he scrambled up the steps of the engine, strode wildly across the footplate and brandished it in front of Charlie Brown's face.

'Eh, just read this, Charlie!'

Charlie looked at him bewildered.

'Go on, read it! Just read what it sez!'

Taking the memo from Jimmy's trembling hand, his fireman began to read it, but before he had taken in the first line, Jimmy's frustration broke through again.

'What about that then, Charlie, eh, what about that?'

Jimmy's wild interruptions made it impossible for Charlie to concentrate.

'Calm down, Jimmy, calm down! I'm tryin' to read it – just give me time!'

Impatiently accepting the rebuke, Jimmy restrained his anger while Charlie focused his eyes once more on the memo. Then, the moment he looked up to indicate that he had digested every word, his driver set off ranting again.

'You remember, don't yer, Charlie? A week last Monday? Bloody snow up to the axles an' fog so thick we could hardly see each other across the footplate! Eh? D'yer remember? "Please explain"? Huh, I'll explain alright, you see if I don't!'

His fireman expressed complete agreement. 'I'll say I remember! A week last Monday was the day we worked round the clock! We ran out o' tea an' sugar an' fags! I remember all right. But what's he goin' on about? I'll bet there wasn't a single train ran to time a week last Monday!'

Charlie's recollection triggered Jimmy's tantrum again.

''Course, it's alright for 'im, isn't it? Sat there behind his bloody great mahogany desk with nothin' to do but hand out silly bits o' paper like this!'

After flourishing the memo under Charlie's nose again, he turned about with every intention of retreating to his own side of the cab, only to whirl round suddenly to confront him again.

'What does he know about drivin' a locomotive, eh, Charlie? Go on, tell me! What the bloody 'ell does he know about it? You know how mister Wally Cecil Philpot got his job, don't yer? He's a premium man! That's what he is! His bloody father bought 'im the job – that's what they did in them days – paid the railway company three hundred quid so's their sons could play at trains! "Please explain"! I'll explain all right, just see if I don't! I'll need two pens, a bottle of ink and a whole roll o' paper to say what I'm gonna say. "Please explain"! I'll show 'im!'

With this, he glanced at the offending memo once more then scrambled down the steps of the engine to make his way to the signing-on hall to make out his report. When he arrived there, his rage had increased.

Going straight to the broad shelf fixed to the partition that served as a desk for the engine crews, he grabbed a report form from the rack and took hold of a pen. Without a pause in his movements, and with a distinct flourish, he dipped the nib of the pen in the inkwell and stabbed it so hard on the paper that the nib splayed. Irritably grabbing another pen, he dipped it in the inkwell and started writing at once.

'What the bloody hell did you expect me to do...'

Pausing here to look at what he had written, he decided that this was a little too strong, and, grabbing another report form, he started again.

'Are you aware that on Monday the 3rd January...'

No, this wouldn't do either. Give the man a bit of respect – after all, he was the Superintendent! He tried again.

'Sir, With regard to the very pertinent question as to why my train was late...' Here Jimmy paused again. His indignation had subsided quite a bit by this time. When he thought of his fireman's words to the effect that on the day in question not a single train would have run to time in the conditions prevailing, he began to feel vindicated, a feeling that quickly changed into one of self-righteousness and, as he considered the matter further, he was gripped by a powerful desire to be sarcastic.

It was then that Jimmy experienced one of those rare moments of sublime inspiration that accompany all great and noble decisions. Slowly screwing up his third report form, he threw it in the waste paper basket, then, in the space below the Superintendent's signature on the original memo, he wrote simply, 'Cow on line'.

This done, he folded the memo carefully, dropped it in the correspondence box and, with the bearing of a man highly satisfied with himself, strode back to his engine.

When his feelings returned to normal as he got his train under way an hour later, Jimmy began to have misgivings about the report. To tell a white lie was one thing; to reply with a sarcastic fabrication entirely another. He did his best to clear his mind of the incident, but no matter how he tried, he couldn't dispel the feeling that he and the Superintendent were headed on a collision course.

When he signed on duty the following day he fully expected to find a piece of paper a yard long pinned to his time-card, but there was nothing. The next day he was certain he'd find one, but again there was nothing. When a whole week passed without a further word on the matter, he came to the conclusion that the Superintendent must have accepted his explanation. After all, he consoled himself, it wasn't beyond the realm of possibility for a stray cow to hold up a train!

Months later, as he swayed with the lumbering motion of his locomotive coupled to a heavy freight train with his head over the side of the cab, thoughts of the report entered his thoughts again. This time he saw it from a different angle entirely. Suppose – just suppose – that those report forms were never read! Suppose they were a mere formality – a ruse designed by Wally Philpot himself to keep the drivers on their toes! On the other hand, had he stumbled across the perfect explanation with which to answer all such pieces of paper? If either of these suppositions were true, the discovery would be as important to those who laboured on the Iron Road as Newton's Law of Gravity to the draymen who lowered the barrels into beerhouse cellars!

When Jimmy found another piece of paper pinned to his time-card three months later, he was somewhat puzzled.

'DRIVER MOODY. 385.
It is reported that on Friday the 5th March, despite all signals being set clear, you stopped your train between Haresby and Trimpton Junction for a period of nine minutes.
PLEASE EXPLAIN.

Signed: W. C. Philpot.
District Locomotive Superintendent'

The line from Trimpton Junction to Haresby was a short spur laid at the turn of the century to supply raw cotton to several mills and transport coal from a small colliery. When Clumpy Jennings, a retired engine driver himself, decided to set up in business on his smallholding he knew what he was doing. With a good number of chickens and a couple of pigs, the profit he earned from selling free range eggs, chickens for the table and the cuts of pork from the pig he had killed just before Christmas augmented his pension very nicely. He erected a sign at the side of the line:

'CHICKENS.
From the pen to the pot – 4/6d.
Free range eggs – 1/6d per doz.'

After four years of trading, Clumpy established a regular clientele for his produce, and many of the engine drivers and firemen who steamed that way, along with the three signalmen who manned the signal box at Trimpton Junction on alternate shifts, were among his most valued customers. Indeed, Clumpy's enterprise was granted most favoured treatment by the signalman at Trimpton. To allow the men of the train crews time to make a purchase at the smallholding without harassment, they delayed obtaining a clear road through the junction to the main line until the trains came to a stand at the home signal. This amicable arrangement not only benefited Clumpy and allowed the train crews to make their purchases without exposing themselves to a charge of delaying trains over the junction, but it also earned the signalmen a small discount on their purchases.

One couldn't purchase a fresher chicken anywhere. When, after giving a subdued cock-a-doodle-do on the whistle, a driver or his fireman approached Clumpy's smallholding, he would be waiting for them at the gate. Accompanying him to where the chickens scratched, he'd ask them to point out the one they fancied, then, pulling its neck, he would hand it over still kicking in exchange for the money. The entire transaction took only a few minutes.

Unfortunately, on the day that Jimmy asked his fireman to get him a chicken as he applied the brake, two factors combined to dislocate the long-established arrangement. The first was that when Jimmy's fireman entered the pen, Clumpy was acting as midwife to his sow, a circumstance that led to a prolonged transaction. This by itself wouldn't have mattered in the slightest, for the signalmen at Trimpton, eager participants in the arrangement, were extremely accommodating. Sadly, however, on the day in question the signal box at Trimpton was manned by an ambitious young relief signalman with his sights set on promotion. The moment Jimmy's train was offered to him as it left Haresby, he was offering it to the next main-line box at once. Obtaining a clear road for it, he had lowered his home and starting signals before Jimmy braked his train to a standstill and, after observing the fireman leave the engine, the eager young signalman fumed with impatience for so long that he was already making out his report when the train eventually passed his signal box.

Completely unaware of this, when Jimmy read the memo pinned to his time-card he didn't turn a hair. Flourishing his pen like a benefactor signing a cheque, in the space between the Superintendent's signature and the bottom of the memo, he wrote boldly, 'COW ON LINE'. Then, folding it, he dropped it in the correspondence box with the nonchalance of a millionaire posting his telephone account, and walked away whistling.

When he heard nothing more about the matter after three days, he was more convinced than ever that he had stumbled upon a magical formula for answering memos concerning all pettifogging breaches of the regulations, and a remarkable change came over him.

Jimmy became cocky. When he noticed Alf Smith, his bosom mate, scratching his head in the signing-on hall as he struggled to answer a similar memo, he felt honour-bound to enlighten him. Placing an arm round his shoulders, he said, 'You don't wanna bother to much wi' that, Alf lad!'

Leading his friend away from the rest of the assembled enginemen he continued, 'Just put "Cow on line" there, under his signature, an' you'll 'ear no more about it.'

For a moment Alf thought Jimmy had gone completely off his head, but, as he stared at Jimmy completely nonplussed, his friend continued, 'It's right! I've done it twice an' never heard a word! He never reads the flippin' things! I'm tellin' yer – you put "Cow on line" there like I tell yer an' you'll hear no more about it!'

More out of curiosity than conviction, after a little more encouragement Alf did as his pal advised and, to his astonishment, after four days he hadn't heard a word about the matter.

Whatever anyone said about Wally Philpot, premium man or not, he knew his railways. A man of conflicting attitudes, he wasn't averse to turning a blind eye to the little peccadilloes of those under him, but when anyone attempted to exploit his humane approach to matters managerial, he was capable of pouncing like a raging beast. With almost two hundred and fifty locomotives and a thousand drivers, firemen and cleaners to manage, not to mention five subsidiary sheds, his job was no picnic, but, being a wise man, he contrived with all his railway nous to ensure that things ran smoothly.

Major incidents such as passing signals at danger, derailments and running the boiler dry, he would deal with urgently, charging the driver concerned on the regulation Form 1 and instituting an official enquiry at once. With minor infringements like running a few minutes behind schedule, arriving late for duty or emitting black smoke, he would simply memo the culprits for an explanation. Ninety-five times out of a hundred the explanations appeared so reasonable that sometimes, as when he himself was being harassed by those in the higher echelons of the managerial hierarchy, he would go through them with a cursory spot-check and, if nothing raised his hackles, file them away to let them lie while continuing to memo the men just to show them that nothing escaped his attention.

Quite fortuitously, this had been the situation when Jimmy Moody first used 'Cow on line' to explain his late running, and, had he been content at getting away with it once, nothing further would have been said about the matter. Like most mortals on to a good thing, however, he couldn't resist the temptation to exploit his good fortune to the limit. Moreover, keen to bask in the glory of his discovery, he had boasted of it to Alf Smith who, being of the same ilk, did likewise, and before a week was out it seemed that every cow in the land had become partial to the grass that grew alongside the tracks.

When, in one of those rare moments when he found himself at peace with the world, Wally Philpot decided to check the explanations meticulously, and found that five out of seven drivers used 'Cow on line' as their excuse for late running, he reacted in a most uncharacteristic manner. Beginning slowly, he started to shake as a tremendous spasm of uncontrollable laughter took hold of him. Rising to a tempestuous crescendo, this involuntary explosion of mirth threatened to dislodge him from his chair. Gripping the arm rests, he pulled himself upright to prevent himself sliding to the floor of his office and, with a great deal of willpower, adopted an attitude more befitting a District Locomotive Superintendent. When his managerial demeanour was finally restored, he dived to his files and, after perusing the reports for the previous two months, found beyond dispute that the first driver to be delayed by a cow had been Jimmy Moody.

When Jimmy stood on the mat in front of Wally's huge mahogany desk nervously holding his cap in his hands, he feared the worst, but it turned out worse than he bargained for.

The Superintendent started quietly enough. Looking at Jimmy, he said, 'This 'ere cow, Moody – not only does it appear to have developed a strong affection for you – it appears that you hire her out on contract!'

Realising at once that he had been rumbled, Jimmy shifted his weight from one foot to the other without replying.

'What's her name, Moody – Bluebell? Buttercup?'

Of course this was only Wally's customary preamble. Gradually, word by word, his voice increased in volume until he could be heard bawling above the noise of the locomotives thirty yards from his office, and when Jimmy finally emerged after his grilling, he appeared as though he had just tumbled from a hair-raising roller-coaster.

The following day a notice appeared on the driver's notice board in the signing-on hall. With a thick, black border round the edges, it read:

'TO WHOM IT MAY CONCERN.
It is with deep regret that I have to inform you that Moody's cow is dead and buried. For the sake of everybody – especially yours – may she rest in peace.

Signed: W. C. Philpot.
District Locomotive Superintendent'

Needless to say, when the identity of the initiator of the magic formula became known throughout the engine shed and beyond, the nickname-coiners got to work and, within weeks of his grilling, Jimmy Moody became known as 'Cow-on-Line' for the rest of his time on the Iron Road.

24
Saul the Silent

*A*s the best textbooks on 'Man Management' make clear, the efficiency of any workforce depends to a large degree on getting your human relationships right. One can have the most up-to-date machinery in existence backed up by plans worked out by the best brains available, and yet, if the lads on the shop floor bicker like spinsters over a Christening cake, one might as well pack up.

Oddly enough, the fewer people involved, the more acute the problem becomes. If there are two men in a balloon and one wants to go up and the other wants to go down, the flight plan is no more significant than a pub without beer. On the other hand, when there are three men in the balloon, the problem can be solved by chucking the odd one out, so to speak.

With electrification the railways found the perfect solution to the problem, for, with only one man at the controls, the need for amicable human relationships disappeared entirely. After all, those cases where drivers of electric locomotives have been overheard arguing with the dead man's handle are completely unrelated to the problem.

In the days when Clanky Junction knew nothing but steam locomotives, however, it took two to make 'em roll. Then, when an engine driver and his fireman could be together for more than a year at a time, the relationship that existed between them was as crucial to a smooth journey as the signals themselves. Put an agnostic with a local preacher, a teetotaller with a beer-swilling swashbuckler, or a gluttonous carnivore with an evangelising vegetarian, and boy, how the sparks would fly! Such conflicts were known to have caused many a train to arrive late at its destination. Indeed, when a complete history of the Steam Age is written, I suspect that they will find that for this very reason, more than one train never arrived at all!

This is not to say that fractious relationships were all that common on the footplate. Oh no – why, there were many partnerships that seemed blessed with the sweet balm of harmony right from the moment the driver and fireman found themselves together on the same engine, the most idyllic of all being that of little Tommy Trot and Charlie Harper, already described. After all, what could an engine driver blessed with a beautiful tenor voice desire more than being allocated a fireman with a baritone as rich as treacle? Apart from a severe breach of faith on Tommy's part which they overcame by virtue of Charlie's superior vision, these two remained together on the same footplate for years.

Then there was Jud Spence and his fireman who, in a sublime example of co-operation, became watch repairers to Clanky Junction's locomotive fraternity; the moment they found themselves in a porter's room at a remote station as they waited to relieve the crew of another train, out would come their little canvas satchels and eyeglasses. Give them your lifeless watch at the start of a trip and you'd have it back ticking its heart out when you signed on for the next.

Those who stood the best chance of a trouble-free relationship were the first-aid men. In the days of steam the St John's Ambulance Brigade was a thriving institution on the railways, the Clanky Junction contingent being one of the most dedicated on the London Midland & Scottish. If you happened to be a member of this organisation and discovered that your mate was a member also, every trip would be a golden excursion. These dedicated souls would discuss the human anatomy at every opportunity with every bone identified and every nerve, muscle, vein and organ verbally dissected with the enthusiasm of a couple of gourmets recalling a favourite meal. So eager were they to demonstrate their prowess in bringing the dead back to life that many an unsuspecting youth was enticed on board their engines on the pretext of a 'Ride down the line' only to find himself bound head to foot in splints before the engine got moving!

If you happened to be a young fireman on your first day with a new driver, the best approach was one of cautious exploration; refraining from hastily declaring one's own beliefs and enthusiasms in case one established one's colours prematurely. After being relieved on a journey, suggest a call at the nearest pub to a driver who preached total abstinence, or insist wiring for relief after ten hours on the footplate with a driver dedicated to making a fortune by grabbing all the overtime he could lay his hands on, and your relationship would be doomed from the start. With a driver who could make your time on the footplate purgatory, there was nothing like compromise. Then, if in due course you found a common interest, your time with your new mate would be golden.

But what could a young fireman do in the way of establishing a friendly, working relationship with a driver who never uttered a word? Despite all the diplomacy and tact he had accumulated getting on good terms with his first two drivers, young Tich Goodwin was coming to believe he would never succeed in making a mate of Saul Pepper. Beyond the slightest doubt his new mate was the oddest engine driver he had ever encountered! Trip after trip, from signing on to signing off duty, he voiced not a syllable! As Tich complained to his colleagues when they enquired: 'It's like working with an animated corpse!'

Tich recognised only too well that his new mate hadn't been nicknamed 'Saul the Silent' for nothing, but he never imagined anyone capable of maintaining silence so completely! No matter what happened along the line, he gave not a grunt, not a sigh, not a murmur of response. The only sound he seemed capable of producing was an ecstatic sucking noise as he consumed his aniseed balls. Saul got through half a pound of these on every trip, sucking each one until the last minute particle dissolved on his tongue.

His appearance did nothing to relieve the morbidness of the man. With his deep chest, his short thin legs and his oversized feet, he looked like something from Toad Hall. His face, despite his fifty-odd years, was round and youthful, but what might have been a pleasing countenance was spoiled by its inability to break into a smile. His eyes watered constantly, and as he looked at you with lowered head, he seemed to experience difficulty focusing his eyes.

When Saul arrived at the engine on their first trip together, Tich, determined to make an effort to get off on the right foot, had already been to the stores to collect a supply of oil so that his new driver could start at once to oil the bearings and slides of the engine, and had the two cans warming gently on the warming plate above the firehole. As Saul began to discard his overcoat, Tich greeted him in the friendliest manner.

'Good morning, Saul!'

Pausing with his overcoat half removed, the uncommunicative engine driver stared at his new fireman through watery eyes, his head lowered as though trying to ascertain what kind of creature had addressed him, and, with a long, squelching suck on his aniseed ball, resumed the removal of his coat without a word.

Undismayed, Tich climbed from the engine and left to collect a couple of sand buckets to replenish the sanders from the bin situated at the top of the pit. Saul Pepper wasn't the only queer old devil he had had to cope with; he had found a way round old Jim Pomfret, hadn't he? And that was no easy task. Jim Pomfret could burn a ton of coal more than any other driver at the Junction on any train worked from there.

It doesn't sound much when you say it quickly, but if you're the one who's doing the shovelling it is no laughing matter.

The trouble with Jim was that he was hard of hearing; unless the regulator was wide open with the engine blasting at the chimney-top like a piece of heavy artillery he didn't feel he was moving. As fast as you shovelled the coal into the firebox it was shooting from the chimney like red-hot golf balls. Whenever a cornfield burst into flames as a steam train roared by, you could bet your life the man at the controls was Jimmy Pomfret. Whenever Jimmy got carried away by his enthusiasm, Tich learned to cross the footplate, place his mouth to his mate's ear and bawl, 'Hey, ease up Jimmy – they can hear us coming an hour before we get there!'

Jimmy seemed to welcome the interruption. He had a sense of humour, you see. Turning his head, his vacant stare would melt into a grin as he eased the throttle.

Recalling his experience with Jimmy, Tich searched for a clue that might help him with his new mate, but, try as he might, he found nothing. After three hours on the same footplate he suddenly realised how inappropriately his driver had been christened; had the Saul of biblical fame been as tight-lipped, he wouldn't have got a mention!

Sadly, Saul's demoralising silence was only the half of it. Before the end of their first trip together he revealed that he could communicate without words. When he thought it was time for Tich to get down to the shovel he drew his head inside the cab, glowered with lowered head at the unfortunate fireman until he had his attention, then, quickly tracing an imaginary circle with his forefinger, he jabbed two fingers through it and stuck his head over the cabside again. It was the same when he wanted Tich to look out for a distant signal coming up on his blind side; crossing the footplate, he'd thrust his face to within inches of his mate's and, looking straight at him, drag down the lower lid of his right eye with his finger to reveal a large expanse of waterlogged eyeball. Satisfied his fireman had got the message, he'd release his eyelid, from which a giant teardrop splashed on to the boards of the footplate, then dart back to his own side of the engine to stick his head over the side again.

These strange antics began to annoy Tich. They made him feel like a monkey in a cage with someone pulling faces and gesticulating at him through the bars. In an attempt to compel his driver to communicate by word of mouth, he decided to ignore him completely, but it was to no avail. A mile along the line, as he stood swaying with the roll of the locomotive with his head through the cab window, he turned to glance at the steam gauge when, from the corner of his eye, he saw Saul leap from his seat to the centre of the footplate intent on giving another of his infuriating signs. Determined to force him to open his mouth, Tich immediately turned his back on him and, thrusting his head through the window again, waited to be addressed. Instead of speaking, however, Saul began prodding him between the shoulder blades to compel him to turn round. When, unable to bear the discomfort of his prodding, Tich turned to face him – there it was again – an imaginary circle swiftly traced with his forefinger and – phut – two fingers through the centre!

After a week with his new driver Tich was utterly fed up. He made his feelings known in no uncertain terms when he was hailed by a colleague of his own age as he signed off duty one day.

'Hiya, Tich! How a'yer gerrin on with old Blabbermouth?'

Down in the dumps, he replied, 'Terrible, Joe! He's persecutin' me, that's what he's doin' – persecutin' me with silence! Y'know what I'm gonna do, though, Joe? Eh? D'yer know what I'm gonna do? If he doesn't open his mouth soon I'm gonna sort out the biggest cob o' coal I can find and drop it right on his toes! That should make him say summat!'

And then, just when Tich was thinking seriously of carrying out his threat to misdirect the largest cob he could find and send it sliding from his shovel on to his driver's toes in the hope of activating his vocal chords, something quite remarkable occurred.

As the inarticulate engine driver withdrew his head into the cab to open the regulator after getting the 'right away' from the guard at Derrydale station, Tich noticed faint signs of agitation in his driver's movements. At every station along the line his agitation increased, as though he couldn't wait to get his head inside the cab. Furthermore, for three stations he had allowed Tich to shovel the coal and look out for the signals on his blind side without his infuriating deaf and dumb signs! A little further along the line the puzzled fireman observed that whenever Saul pulled his head inside the cab, his gaze seemed to become transfixed on a point high up on the fireman's side of the cab. Following the direction of his gaze, Tich looked up towards where his own jacket hung on the side of the cab.

Searching for the object that seemed to be hypnotising his strange driver, he could see nothing unusual. Looking closer he noted his union badge in his lapel of his jacket and the fountain pen in his top pocket next to the fishing float he had purchased on his way to the shed, but nothing that he could imagine might stimulate the curiosity of Saul. Shrugging his shoulders and whistling in relief at being spared his driver's maddening sign language, he dismissed the matter completely from his mind and dived for the shovel once more.

Tich was no wiser as to the object of Saul's curiosity when their train finally lurched to a standstill at the terminal station of the line. Jumping to the platform he disappeared from sight between the buffers where he uncoupled the engine preparatory to running round the coaches for the return trip. When he climbed back on board the engine he got the surprise of his life! Saul's watery eyes were actually smiling! Furthermore, wonder upon wonder – he spoke – and with such eloquence too!

Holding out the yellow fishing float he had taken from Tich's pocket during the latter's brief absence, Saul said, 'You never said you were converted to the art piscatorial, son!'

Tich could hardly believe his ears. 'What's that, Saul? The what?'

Still holding out the fishing float, Saul continued, 'The art piscatorial! Fishin', lad – fishin'!'

Taken completely by surprise by Saul's uncharacteristic verbosity, Tich faltered as he replied.

'Oh, yeah – fishin'. That's my float you've got there, isn't it? Yeah, I go fishin' every time I get a day off.'

By this time Saul's eyes were glazed with tears of deep emotion.

'Well why didn't you say so? You've been workin' on the same footplate with me for trip after trip without a word for the cat – an' now you tell me! You an' me have a lot to talk about, lad! Sit yoursel' down!'

Needless to say, from that day forth Saul the Silent and young Tich Goodwin became bosom mates. Together, taking advantage of the concessionary fares to which they were entitled by reason of their being company servants, they fished every river, pool and mere within a hundred-mile radius of Clanky Junction whenever they found themselves with a day off. Before long Tich's pals were remarking on how he was becoming more like his strange driver with every week that passed. Certainly, whenever they asked him how he was getting on with the notorious, self-afflicted mute, he just traced an imaginary circle with his forefinger, jabbed two fingers through the centre of it and walked away grinning.

25
Between Trips

O ne of the inevitable tribulations suffered by the men of the Iron
Road during the Steam Age was that they often found themselves
at home when their wives were in the throes of the housework, an
unfortunate experience that can only be described as an occupational
hazard.

It was all due to a conflict of enthusiasms. The women could never
find anything to get excited about in back pressure valves, eccentric
motions, cut-off settings and big ends. Likewise, their husbands never
came round to understanding that to achieve a full line of dry washing
by teatime on Monday was, to their wives, tantamount to reaching
Shap Summit on time with the 'Scot'. During the daytime the women
just didn't appear to care whether their husbands were rolled up in the
carpets or thrown out with the refuse.

Since the dawn of time, women have tackled their housework during
the hours of daylight – if you happened to be an engine driver on nights
it was just hard luck. Oblivious to anything that got in their way, the
moment they took hold of their dusters or started gathering the sheets
for the wash, they moved about the house in a relentless fury. It wasn't
a bit of use settling down in your favourite armchair with a newspaper
in front of your face – if you did this you were liable to be shunted to
and fro across the room as your demon spouse pursued that equally
determined dust that would appear again the very next day.

Early in his career on the railway Eli Jenkins, an engine driver since
the days of the Lancashire & Yorkshire Railway, made the fatal mistake
of concluding that perhaps the best way to end the agony of being at
home during the day would be to assist his wife with the chores. With
the hopefulness of a reasonable man he calculated that his effort in
sharing the work would result in it being finished in half the time. No
man miscalculated so disastrously! Instead of the work being completed

in half the time, it was done twice as thoroughly. To make matters worse, Eli's back yard flanked the branch line; when drivers of passing trains spied their colleague with a pinafore over his overalls they broadcast their discovery, and in no time at all they were calling him 'Sarah' – a name that stuck to him to the end of his days on the Iron Road.

The dilemma of the engine driver on night shift coming downstairs to find his wife battling with the household chattels had been with the men of Clanky Junction for well over a century, since the first engine steamed to the outlet signal. It soon became obvious that what the situation called for was a legitimate, manly retreat to which they could escape until the house became safe to enter again. It had to be near enough to enable them to sneak into the kitchen for a cup of tea when the coast was clear, yet far enough away to be out of their wives' minds as they wrestled with the domestic chores.

And so over the years the men of Clanky Junction developed a remarkable tendency for getting close to nature. There were more gardeners, poultry-keepers and bird-fanciers at the engine shed than one would encounter in half a dozen factories put together.

By far the most popular hobby with the engine drivers was gardening. The devotees of the herbaceous border and the vegetable plot could do no wrong, for not only did the larder benefit from their devotions, whenever they appeared at the door bearing a large bunch of freshly picked flowers their wives didn't even notice the clay on their boots. The Clanky Junction Horticultural Society thrived from one generation to the next, the annual show being one of the highlights in the shed calendar.

The king of the gardening fraternity was old Josh Singleton, of whom it was said that he could grow roses on concrete. Josh's appearance was as untidy as his garden was immaculate. Whenever one set eyes on him at the engine shed he would have clogs on his feet and bicycle clips round the bottom of his overall trouser legs. He supplied half the men of Clanky Junction with their potatoes and cabbages and, whether arriving for work or returning home, he seemed always to be embracing a forest of shrubs or wrestling with a bag of fertiliser. When he applied for a council house he insisted on being allocated the one with the largest garden on the estate, but even this wasn't big enough to satisfy his passion. In addition to the garden surrounding his house, he rented an allotment almost as large as the municipal park.

Josh was the most contented engine driver I ever encountered at the Junction, and, considering that he had a wife and six daughters to please, this is saying a great deal. On one occasion, after assisting him in carrying home a large bale of peat after we had signed off duty, I saw him received into his home like an eastern potentate into his harem! From all sides he was approached by his wife and daughters – one to take his jacket, another bearing his slippers and the rest to usher him into the kitchen where they prepared the table as he washed himself at the sink. It is often said that the way to a man's heart lies through his stomach, and Josh Singleton proved to me that day that a woman's heart is more than susceptible to a bunch of flowers and a regular supply of fresh vegetables. Indeed, when two of his daughters ushered me to the door as I left, I gained the impression that they were anxious to return to him to pursue their pampering further!

While most of the engine drivers at Clanky Junction found contentment in their diversionary pursuits, poor Bill Badger found nothing but misery. No one had been surprised when, years before, he had taken to building model locomotives, for Bill wasn't a railwayman just between the hours of signing on and off duty; he thought of nothing else every minute of his waking hours. The secretary of the Mutual Improvement Society at the Junction, the organisation through which the enginemen taught themselves the intricacies of the steam engine, Bill Badger knew more about locomotives and the operating of railways than many of those in positions of management.

Although his first efforts in model engineering were praiseworthy, good enough to evoke the admiration of all who saw them, they continued to display an amateurishness largely due to his inadequate tools. Undaunted, as each model was completed his enthusiasm increased until he was finally overwhelmed by a burning ambition. He was always singing the praises of the 'Dreadnought', the four-cylinder premier express engine of the old Lancashire & Yorkshire Railway. When I started work at the Junction I had the good fortune to work on one of the last of these, but Bill remembered them in their full glory. Slowly he became obsessed by a desire to build an exact, working scale model of a 'Dreadnought' in the all-black livery of the old L&Y, thinly lined with red. When it was completed he would present it to the Mutual Improvement Society at the Junction where, resplendent in all its glory, it would be displayed in a glass case on the lecturer's table long after he himself had died.

Completely obsessed by his dream, when he came downstairs one morning to find the carpets rolled up and the furniture pushed to one side, he did no more than put on his cap and jacket and leave the house to buy a small lathe; from that day forth he spent every spare minute in the shed at the bottom of his garden. For six years he laboured, lovingly turning and shaping the many parts of his beloved 'Dreadnought', determined to complete the model perfect in every detail even if it took him the rest of his life.

Had his wife not been equally obsessed by her need to have everything within her domain spick and span and in its place, there is no doubt that Bill Badger would have achieved his ambition, but, alas, she was the kind of woman who would come downstairs in the middle of the night to make sure the vases hadn't strayed half an inch along the sideboard.

Going into the garden one day when Bill was lodging away on a trip to Carlisle, she noticed the door of his workshop slightly ajar. Taking hold of the door-handle with the intention of closing it, she hesitated as her curiosity got the better of her, and peered inside. What she saw struck horror into her tidy soul! Dust lay everywhere and, in every crevice of the roof and shelves, cobwebs shivered in the draught from the open door. Unable to deny her passion to have everything shipshape and tidy, she returned to the house to don her headscarf and pinafore, then entered the shed to set about the place as though it were the parlour itself.

When Bill returned from the Carlisle trip in the early hours of the next morning he went to bed and slept into the afternoon. On waking, he went downstairs and, after hurriedly devouring his breakfast, retreated to his workshop for further devotion to his beloved 'Dreadnought'. When he looked round the shed he found that it wasn't only the dust and cobwebs that had disappeared; the delicate pieces of mechanism that he had left on his bench wrapped in oil-soaked rags were nowhere to be seen. When his wife readily confessed what she had done, he rushed at once to the dustbin, only to find that it had been emptied while he slept.

That was the day when, apart from questions like 'When are you going to change that shirt so's I can wash it?' on her part, and 'What's for dinner?' on his, Bill Badger and his wife virtually stopped talking to each other. Furthermore, so deeply had his pride been wounded that he lost all interest in steam engines, resigned from the Mutual Improvement Society and went on the beer.

Without question, the driver who dealt most successfully with being at home when his wife was in the throes of her housework was Peter Perkins. Peter was a rotund little engine driver with red cheeks and a twinkle in his eye. I can see him now, his merry face suddenly becoming serious when, so many years ago, I announced my intention to get married. Considering the news in silence for several minutes, he finally shut the brake steam valve to permit a silence to descend, crossed the footplate and, with a seriousness that I had never seen his features express before, began to address me like Moses from the mountain.

'Getting married? My word, that's a big step to take, lad! Are you sure you've thought hard about it? I mean, once you've done it you're with her for life, y'know!'

Slightly disquieted by the pessimistic tone of his voice, I replied, 'Oh, I don't know, Peter – I've been engaged for two years – don't you think that's long enough to get to know someone?'

He looked at me astonished. 'Two years? Long enough to get to know her? Eh lad, you never get to know 'em! Any road up, if you've made up your mind I don't suppose anythin' I say'll make you change it – but don't go into it believing you know her!'

After looking at me incredulously for a few seconds, he returned to his seat and retreated into a thoughtful silence. Then, after looking over the cabside to see if the sidings Inspector was ready to resume shunting after our meal break, he declared, 'I tell you what I am going to do, though – I'm going to give you some advice – something a driver told me long before you were born! Now look at me when I'm talking to yer, an' you'll learn something!'

Settling himself on his seat, he went on.

'Now listen to me! Never refuse to do anythin' your wife asks you to do! Whatever she asks you to do, give her a big smile and jump to it like a slave. If she asks you to do a bit o' decorating – go and get the wallpaper right away – d'yer see?'

Nodding uncertainly, I waited for him to continue.

'Now, the thing is – now listen to what I'm sayin' – when you put the paper on the walls, make sure you put one or two lengths on upside down!'

Here he looked at me quizzically with his head on one side, as though he wasn't quite sure that I was getting the message.

'D'yer see what I'm getting at? It's the same when she asks you to do a bit o' washin' up! Don't object – say "Certainly, love, certainly", and leap to the sink like a good 'un! Let her see you're keen! Then, when you're wipin' em – drop a couple o' cups on the kitchen floor – d'yer get me? You've got to start right away! It's no good delayin'! You've got to start the way you mean to go on!'

Here he wagged a stern finger at me, then, 'Now you do as I tell yer, lad, an' you'll be as contented as I am. Ha ha ha, d'yer know, my wife wouldn't trust me to feed the cat! She wouldn't! She tells everyone I'm hopeless!'

As he dissolved into a fit of uncontrollable laughter, the Inspector shouted to indicate that our twenty-minute meal break was over. Pulling himself together, Peter opened the brake valve and, reversing into the sidings to be coupled to another raft of wagons, left me dwelling further on the cunning advice he had given me.

26
A Most Eventful Trip

*T*he three twenty early morning West Coast newspaper train was a joy to work. With a sleek three-cylinder 'Jubilee' locomotive capable of hauling a much heavier train, it sped through the pre-dawn darkness like the wind. With its light, rapid staccato exhaust emitting from its chimney-top all the way, the fireman could commence the journey with an incandescent fire no thicker than six inches spread evenly over the firebars, and, as he proceeded to feed it with eight lightly loaded shovels of coal every two or three minutes throughout the fifty-mile journey, he couldn't help but find the experience exhilarating.

The only drawback to that wonderful race through the night was dragging oneself from bed at one thirty in the morning to get to the engine shed at two thirty, a penance made worse if the wind howled or the rain fell incessantly. Once on board the locomotive, however, one's spirits soared in anticipation of the prospect ahead.

When, that Monday morning, after coupling to the four vans in Victoria station, Bill Middleton stepped from the footplate for an exploratory stroll along the platform, he did what any other driver would have done in the circumstances. One of the perks of working a newspaper train was that the driver had only to poke his head into a van where the newspapers were being sorted to be handed a copy of every title by an assistant working there. In this way the men who manned the engines that hauled the newspaper trains became privy to the latest news long before the rest of the populace were out of their beds.

It was therefore no surprise when Bill returned to the engine with a large bundle of newspapers under his arm. Sorting one out, he offered it to me and placed the others in his locker. Then, as I placed the one he handed to me in my locker, he made a remark that certainly aroused my interest.

'There's a Yankee GI on the platform – wants a ride on the footplate?'

Although his remark was a plain statement, he intoned it as a question deliberately. It was strictly against the rules and regulations for an unauthorised person to travel on the footplate, and if Bill was going to accede to the Yank's request, he would have to get my tacit agreement not to split on him. As I considered his remark, he continued to look at me, trying to judge my reaction.

Before I could reply, he said, 'Well?'

Anxious to put him at ease, I replied, 'Well, you're the boss, Bill. If you want to let him ride on the footplate it's all right by me as long as he keeps out of my way.'

It was then that I became aware of the GI standing on the platform observing us through the handrails of the cab. Unlike a British soldier he carried a large valise instead of a kitbag. Assured of my co-operation, Bill stepped off the engine again and spoke to him. I heard every word.

'Aye, it's all right son, but don't get on the engine yet. Keep your eye on the guard. The moment you see his head disappear inside the van after he blows his whistle and gives us a green light, jump on the engine smartish.'

The Yank was clearly grateful. 'Gee, that's mighty good of you, sir. Thanks a lot.'

It occurred to me that this must have been the first time in his life that Bill had been addressed as 'Sir', but before I could consider the matter further, I was thinking of how I was going to park the Yank and his huge valise on the footplate to avoid them getting in the way of my shovelling.

A minute later the guard's whistle shrilled and Bill's hand snaked out to take hold of the regulator. Opening it a little, the engine began to move forward slowly and, a second later, the valise came hurtling through the handrails followed immediately by the eager Yank. As I grabbed the valise, the young American soldier went sprawling on the footplate with the unfamiliar movement of the engine and, after quickly stowing his valise on top of my locker on the tender, I helped him to his feet. Hustling him to my side of the cab, I sat him on my seat, saying to him, 'If you sit there with your legs held in, I'll have plenty of room to do my work.'

Responding at once, he sat down, pulled in his legs and took hold of the steel frame of the sliding window.

By this time, threading its way through the web of tracks leading from the station, the engine was gathering speed as it ploughed through points and diamond crossings towards the main line. Quickly opening the firehole door I dived for the shovel and expertly swung eight lightly loaded shovelsful into the firebox. The fire was an incandescent white over the entire area of the firebars, and in the blinding glare that filled the cab I caught sight of the American's face.

His mouth hung open in a childlike expression of wonder and, as I swung my fourth shovelful of coal into the firebox, I distinctly heard him exclaim, 'Gee!'

Completing my stint, I threw the shovel into the tender well and, half closing the firehole door, darted to the cabside to catch a distant signal coming up on Bill's blind side. It showed green, so I bellowed across the cab to my driver, 'Right away!' Then, grasping the injector valve, I opened it a little until it began to sing, then opened it fully to feed water into the boiler. Darting to the cabside again I glanced at the chimney-top to observe that the smoke trace had completely disappeared, and closed the firehole door fully. Again, as I brushed past the American, he exclaimed, 'Gee!'.

Having cleared the maze of tracks of the station by this time, with the regulator wide open and the valve gear wound up fine, we sped along the main line. The 'Jubilee' was beginning to roll with our ever-increasing momentum, the exhaust at the chimney-top sounding as sharp as a pneumatic road drill and, as the smoke trace disappeared from the exhaust again, I flung open the firehole door and dived for the shovel once more. This time, so help me, very much aware I had a spectator, I swung the shovel with panache, moving with exaggerated precision and feeling the smug pride of a novice ballerina receiving her first encore as our American friend exclaimed again, 'Gee!'.

Catching sight of Bill palming his watch from his waistcoat pocket, I stepped across the undulating footplate and shouted in his ear, 'How're we doing, Bill?'

He shouted back at once. 'We're well in front, cock – well in front!'

Satisfied, I turned about and fully closed the firehole door to see the American GI warily returning to his seat with a carton in his hand. Taking advantage of my brief exchange with the driver he had clearly retrieved the carton from his valise. As he sat down again, drawing in his legs as I had asked him to do when he boarded the locomotive, I darted behind him to glance at the chimney-top again and, observing that the exhaust was white as virgin snow, I immediately opened the firehole door and dived for the shovel again. After swinging eight shovelfuls of coal into the blinding maw of the firebox and half closing the door, I turned to see our guest holding something out to me. As I looked questioningly at him, he said, 'Here y'are, buddy.'

I could hardly believe my eyes. In his hand he was holding two packets of Chesterfield cigarettes! It must be remembered that this was between the end of the war in Europe and the end of the war with Japan, when cigarettes were handed over the counter like contraband.

For the sake of appearances I made a half-hearted attempt to decline the offer, saying, 'Oh, it's all right, mate. There's no need for you to give your fags away.'

But he persisted. 'Nah, you're welcome, buddy!'

Thrusting them towards me, he continued, 'G'arn, take 'em – I've plen'y more!'

Taking the cigarettes, I thanked him very much. With characteristic American nonchalance, he responded, 'Aw shucks, you're welcome!'

With this, I stowed the cigarettes in my locker and dived for the shovel. After this there was no restraining the generosity of the American GI. As the locomotive got into her stride as we left the city behind to speed unrestricted through the night, his wide-eyed wonder intensified. With the engine rolling and swaying with its momentum he stuck his head through the cab window to savour more the exhilaration of speed, pulling it inside again to exclaim, 'Gee!'. Likewise, when his attention was grabbed by the sudden glare from the firebox as I opened the firehole door to commence shovelling or he was suddenly startled as Bill sounded a blast on the whistle, he would exclaim 'Gee!' again and offer me another packet of Chesterfields.

When Bill finally braked the train to a standstill at Preston, our only stop on the journey, the American GI reluctantly took hold of his valise and made to step from the engine. After shaking hands with us both and showering us with thanks, he handed me the last two packets of Chesterfields remaining in the carton and stepped down to the platform. As Bill and I watched him from the footplate he retreated from the engine along the platform walking backwards, never taking his eyes from the engine and, if my lip-reading was reliable, exclaiming 'Gee!' every few yards. Lingering on the platform until the guard gave us the 'right away', he gave us a final wave and, after acknowledging it with a wave of our own, Bill opened the regulator to start the second leg of our journey.

Feeling no little pride in the fact that we had impressed one of our American cousins, I handed Bill five packets of Chesterfields, half of my hoard, saying, 'He was a nice feller, Bill, don't yer think?'

Placing the fags in his locker as the train began to gather speed, he replied, 'He was a nice feller, cock – a very nice feller.'

Arriving at our destination a minute before time, we waited until the newspapers were unloaded. Then, after the station pilot drew the vans off us, Bill whistled for the signal that would take us to the north shed where we would turn the engine and replenish the tender with water. This accomplished, I turned the points to lead Bill on to a quite road and, after screwing on the handbrake, we commenced our scoff. Strangely, as I ate my sandwiches I felt the absence of my admiring spectator, and, still finding it incredible that a man not much older than myself from 'God's own country' could be so impressed by a ride on the footplate of a British locomotive, I broached the subject with Bill.

'Don't you think it's strange that an American should be so impressed by a ride on our engine, Bill?'

Stopping a sandwich halfway to his mouth, he replied, 'Oh no, son, not all Yankees come from New York an' Chicago, y'know, lad! I mean it's a vast country. There's more 'n two hundred million folk live there.'

As he bit into his sandwich I responded, 'Yes, but they have some fine locomotives over there, don't they? You wouldn't think he'd be impressed with ours, would you?'

Waiting until he had swallowed his mouthful of food, he replied, 'Oh aye, I'll give you that, but they're not like ours, son. Compared to our greyhounds their's are like bloody elephants! Bloody great big lumbering hulks designed to pull trains a mile long over the Rockies. They're not built for speed.' Then, with a challenge in his eyes, 'Who has the world record for steam traction, eh, lad?'

Before I could answer him he replied, 'Aye, we have. That's yer difference, lad – that's yer difference!'

Here Bill retreated into a thoughtful mood as he finished the rest of his sandwiches. Then, wiping his mouth on a huge red handkerchief and taking a deep draught from his tea bottle, he recommenced speculating on the American.

'D'yer know, son, I wouldn't mind betting he was from the sticks. I wouldn't. I know they all look like film stars in their natty uniforms, but I wouldn't mind betting he's a bloody cowboy from the wilds of Oklahoma or Nebraska like yer Tom Mix an' yer Roy Rogers!'

Laughing at the very idea, I asked, 'D'yer reckon, Bill?'

Looking at me with a hint of a smile, he answered, 'It's not impossible, y'know! Didn't yer notice his bowed legs?'

An hour later we ran back to the station and coupled to the eleven gleaming coaches of the seven-thirty club train on which, in half an hour's time, hundreds of bowler-hatted businessmen would be transported to their offices in the industrial city. With three times the load of the newspaper train, our return journey would test the 'Jubilee' to its limit and, with the fire in the firebox needing to be substantial enough to withstand the powerful drag of the blasting exhaust, I started to build it.

On the dot of seven thirty, the whistle shrilled, the doors stopped slamming and, with a heave on the regulator from Bill, the 'Jubilee' blasted from the station. With a white-hot fire two feet thick spread evenly over the firebars, I waited until we cleared the platform, then got down to shovel, little realising that our return trip would be even more remarkable than the trip out.

Coupled to three times the load of the newspaper train, the exhaust from the chimney-top of the locomotive now sounded more like a continuous cannonade of howitzers than a pneumatic road drill. To maintain a sturdy fire to prevent it from being ripped to bits by the devastating blasts of air being dragged through the firebars, I loaded the shovel to the limit with coal on every swing. With the water in the boiler being converted to steam in an instant, the injector sang constantly, and, as I got down to the shovel every two or three minutes, the exhilaration of speed and power, as always, began to intoxicate the whole of my being.

It was broad daylight now, and the sensation of speed was intensified by the fleeting glimpse of the signals and station buildings rushing past us, and, as we continued to speed with furious urgency towards Preston, the elder and the alder alongside the line bent eagerly in a frantic attempt to follow in our wake.

With no signal checks or permanent way restrictions to slow our progress, we pulled into Preston two minutes before time. Giving the fire a closer examination I found that I had succeeded in maintaining a thick, sturdy bed of white-hot coals spread evenly over the firebars, and, with the injector still singing as the water in the gauge glass bobbed up and down half an inch from the top, I waited anxiously for the sound of the guard's whistle before getting down to the shovel again.

It was here, as I surveyed the footplate undecided whether or not to spray it with the degging pipe to keep down the coal dust, that I inadvertently noticed something odd about the way my driver was behaving. Bill was a solidly built man about five feet eleven inches tall with a belly and posterior of generous proportions. Firm in the belief that they kept one's feet warm in winter and cool in summer, he always wore clogs on the footplate. Now, as I viewed him from his rear as he stood with his head through the cab window watching for the guard's signal, he seemed to be switching his weight from one foot to the other in a faintly anxious manner. However, before I could fathom the possible significance of this, the guard's whistle shrilled and, as Bill withdrew from the window to grasp the regulator, further consideration of the matter abandoned my thoughts as I closed the injector valve and dived for the shovel.

Increasing momentum with every revolution of the wheels, we tore through Farington station platform so fast that the buildings flashed passed the train in a blur. Jumping from my seat for another stint with the shovel I saw Bill looking at me with a rather pained expression on his face. Now, instead of merely switching his weight from one foot to the other, he was almost performing a dance! Suddenly he spoke.

'I'll have to go in the tender, lad!'

For a moment I was puzzled. 'Go in the tender, Bill? Why go in the tender?'

Now he was moving his feet in a most uncomfortable manner.

'It's that bloody beer I had last night – I thought there was something wrong with it! If I don't relieve meself soon, I'll do it in me pants! Will you be able to manage on yer own?'

As the full implication of Bill's gastric torment dawned on me in all it's stark reality, I rallied to the occasion at once. Quickly grabbing the coal hammer, I struck the clasp holding shut the tender doors and held them open for him.

'Right, come on, Bill, crouch on the left-hand side of the tender to do what you have to do and I'll shovel on the right to miss you.'

Grabbing a newspaper from a pocket of his jacket hanging on the side of the cab, he squeezed his buttocks mightily, tiptoed warily across the bucking footplate and stooped to enter the tender. As he disappeared inside, he addressed me again.

'Shut the doors behind me! I don't want a bloody spectator watching what I have to do!' So the moment he cleared the doors I closed them and tapped the clasp to secure them.

With Bill out of the way, his modesty duly satisfied, I crossed the footplate of the thundering locomotive to observe the signals. With the distant for Leyland in the clear position I left the controls, whipped open the injector then dived for the shovel to swing eight more heavily loaded shovelfuls into the firebox, making sure to slide the blade to the right of the tender as I did so. This accomplished, I darted back to the driver's side as we thundered through Leyland platform and, after getting a clear distant for Euxton, heard Bill bellowing from the tender.

'Ease her up, lad! You've got Euxton curve coming up!'

A little disappointed that he thought it necessary to advise me, I eased back the regulator to reduce speed to take the severe curve that would take us off the West Coast main line for Chorley, and, glancing at the steam gauge to observe the pointer hovering on the red mark, reassured myself that the engine would require no further coal until I opened her up again after negotiating the curve.

From time to time during the Steam Age, once they felt able to trust their firemen, engine drivers allowed them to take the controls for short periods, but this was usually in sidings or when hauling a lowly freight train. Now, in the clear knowledge that Bill's enforced absence from the footplate had left me in complete charge of one of Clanky Junction's most powerful locomotives at the head of one of its most prestigious trains, my exuberance knew no bounds. Moreover, the undoubted fact that the situation had been brought about by what can only be described as an emergency, made me determined to discharge my unexpected but nonetheless exciting responsibility to the very best of my ability.

Easing the regulator as we approached Euxton Junction, the train slowed until we started to round the curve. Maintaining this momentum until we were back on a straight track again, I opened up the regulator to regain speed, then dived to the shovel again. With the engine blasting powerfully at the chimney-top, I opened the firehole door once more and drove the blade of the shovel deep into the coal on the right-hand side of the tender to avoid my indisposed mate. Instantly I was startled by a high-pitched howl of anguish and, a fraction of a second later, propelled by a sudden avalanche of coal, Bill's clogs abruptly appeared under the steel doors of the tender draped in his overalls, trousers and long johns!

To increase my horror, the condition of his long johns bore indisputable testimony that his attempt to relieve himself had gone terribly wrong! Spurred into action, I released the shovel and, grabbing the coal pick, struck at the clasp to release the tender doors. Grabbing his hand the moment he came into full view, I yanked him to his feet on the lurching footplate and stared at him incredulously. With his shirt-lap covering his embarrassment but the varicose veins of his legs exposed to full view, he looked a sorry sight. The expected expletive came at once as he stared down at his stained long johns.

'Just look at the bloody mess I'm in! You'll have to manage on your own till I clean meself up, lad! I can't drive the bloody engine in this state!'

His announcement cheered me up no end – I couldn't wait to get my hands on the regulator! Feeling honour-bound to show some empathy with him in his unfortunate predicament, however, I shouted some words of comfort above the noise of the speeding train.

'I'll manage, Bill! You take off your things and clean yourself up. You can wash your underpants in the bucket.'

To assist him further, as the engine pounded up the incline to Chorley I hustled him into the corner on the fireman's side of the cab, emptied the tools and detonator canister from the bucket, and, after handing him the degging pipe, darted back to the driver's side to satisfy myself that the signals were clear for us as far as I could see along the line. Then, as Bill began prising off his clogs to free himself of his underwear, I got down to the shovel again.

By the time I had shovelled another round of coal into the firebox, Bill, exacting all the privacy he could from a series of painful contortions, was fully occupied with washing his person in a bucket of steaming water using the clean white rag issued to him by the stores earlier that morning. Taking full advantage of the situation, I grasped the regulator and stuck my head over the side in complete charge of the prestigious train, and my burgeoning exultation banished all further thoughts of him from my mind.

The rare opportunity to take the controls presented by Bill's unfortunate indisposition that day had all the makings of an indelible memory to be recalled with sweet nostalgia for years to come. Alas, though certainly memorable, the occasion was destined to turn out anything but sweet. But as Bill donned his trousers and overalls and re-shod himself in his clogs to commence the more serious task of washing his long johns in the bucket, there was yet no inkling of what was to come.

In a state bordering on euphoria, as the locomotive responded instantly to every nudge I gave the regulator, I began to look forward to passing Blackrod where the tracks began a long descent for the remaining sixteen miles of the journey. There, after attaining an exhilarating speed of something approaching eighty miles an hour, I would shut the regulator for the last time, give her full valve travel and go like a tornado. Slyly glancing at Bill sitting over the bucket of scalding water stirring his long johns with the brake-stick, I silently prayed that he would leave me completely alone at the controls until we arrived at our destination. But sadly it wasn't to be, for it was at this point, his self-esteem fully restored by his being re-garbed in his trousers, overalls and clogs, that he started harassing me.

'Have we got the distant signal for Adlington?'

Then, as I bent to the shovel again for the last mile of the gradient, 'Come on lad, get the injector on! She's showin' a bit low in the glass!'

From here on he had me darting backwards and forwards between the controls and the firebox like a shuttle on a loom. As the track started to descend on passing Blackrod, I allowed the engine to accelerate, then, shutting the regulator for the last time, gave her full valve travel so that by the time we approached Lostock Junction we were fairly flying. It was here that Bill interfered again.

'Ease up, for Christ's sake! What're tryin' to do – beat the *Mallard*?'

And so he went on throughout the remainder of my time at the controls.

As we sped through Clifton Junction Bill finally got to his feet and began to wring out his long johns over the side of the swaying locomotive. Then, reaching up, he proceeded to tie the ankle of one leg to the driver's side of the whistle rod. This done, he tucked the crutch of his underpants neatly under the regulator gland, tied the ankle of the other leg to the whistle rod on the fireman's side and, after draping the waist over the hot faceplate so that they hung down almost to the warming plate just above the firehole, he stood back to admire his handiwork. Grunting with satisfaction, he then confronted me, saying, 'Right y'are, lad, let's be 'avin' yer!'

With this he hustled me from the driver's side of the cab, thrust his head through the window to catch the signals for Pendleton just three miles from the end of our eventful journey, and my hour of glory came to an end.

As we braked to a standstill in number fourteen platform at Victoria station exactly on time, the doors along the train opened almost in unison to disgorge hundreds of city gents in their bowler hats and smart suits, each hugging a folded newspaper under his arm and brandishing a rolled umbrella. Some of these gents, along with not a few vicars, doctors and judges still faithful to their childhood dreams, often imagined themselves at the controls of a steam engine. As though to reassure themselves that their childhood dreams were not being betrayed, from time to time such men liked to check up on those who actually manned the locomotives, and so it was no surprise to me when one approached the engine and stood directly under the cab window to address Bill.

'That was an excellent run, driver! An excellent run!'

After Bill replied to the effect that it was all in a day's work, the city gent, hearing the clatter of the tools and detonator canister as I threw them back into the bucket that Bill had abandoned on my side of the cab, took a step backwards to get a better view of me through the handrails.

'Good work, fireman!'

His face fairly beamed with pleasure as, thinking how little he knew of how hard I had worked on the trip, I smiled back at him. Then, quite abruptly, as though drawn by a powerful magnet, his gaze became riveted on the bizarre spectacle of Bill's long johns draped in magnificent splendour over the controls. Instantly his beaming countenance changed to a deep frown and, turning away, his childhood dream tarnished for ever, he retreated back along the platform hunched deep in thought.

27
Requiem

*A*s he always did on Thursdays when the weather was fine, the old man walked along the pavement towards the bridge that carried the road over the railway cutting. He was a tall man with a slight stoop to his shoulders, but despite his seventy-five years it was clear from the freshness of his wrinkled face that he was a proud man. His wasn't the aimless stroll of senility, he was going somewhere. His eyes were alert to all they saw and his steps were deliberate and purposeful. His cloth cap sat squarely on his grey-fringed head and the collar of his overcoat was turned up to warm the delicate lobes of his parchment ears, for it was late in November and winter had its feelers out.

Amos was older than most of the things around him. He could remember the time when the land where the council houses stood was a lush meadow grazed by cows, and the asphalt road was nothing more than a cobbled cart track. He could remember the start of the first bus service and how, where the road encountered the railway again two miles further on, they had to enlarge a span of the viaduct to let the first of them through.

At the last of the council houses the old man turned off the pavement to step on to the path that led to the disused railway station. Not long ago the path had been bald with the incessant tread of weavers and miners on shifts, but the cotton mills became silent, the miners redundant, and Beeching had closed the station. From the council house gardens on his right to the fence of the railway cutting on his left the grass had crept forward to reclaim its own, so that now the path appeared nothing more than a trickle of earth through a meadow, and the old man's tread did nothing to stop the invasion.

Thirty yards along the path, Amos stopped and leaned on the fence alongside the cutting. He always came to the same section of the fence, not merely from habit, but because there, half concealed in the grass at the foot of a fencepost, was a large boulder. He had discovered the boulder on his first visit to the cutting on the second day of his retirement ten years before. By resting his foot on it he found that he could stand watching the trains go by without getting the stiffness in his legs.

With his foot on the boulder and his chin resting on dovetailed hands, Amos gazed down into the cutting where the lines glinted in the bright, autumn sunlight. From where he stood he could see a good half-mile of track. Focusing his eyes on the road bridge to his left, he could turn his head to follow the lines with his gaze as they passed through the abandoned station, on past the signal box and the platelayer's hut to where they curved out of sight just beyond the signal post. Nothing had changed since the last time he was there. The same signal box with the paint peeling from warped boards, the yellow distant signal on the down line, the sleepers, the rails, the ballast, the points – everything was exactly the same. But then, only a week had gone by since his last visit.

Old Amos knew the railway line better than he knew the way to the post office where he collected his pension every week. For sixty of his seventy-five years he had worked on the railway, forty of them as an engine driver. He would have gone on working until he had dropped dead at the controls, but even the union insisted on drivers leaving the service at the age of sixty-five, to say nothing of the senior firemen who were only too eager to leap across the footplate at the earliest opportunity to occupy a vacated driver's stool. When they had given him his clock on his presentation night they had shouted 'Good health Amos' and 'All the best!' They had made pretty speeches too, as though turning one's back on a job one had done for a lifetime was something to celebrate.

It wouldn't have been so bad had Edith lived to share his uselessness, but she died the year before he retired. It's true that there was his son Joe and his daughter Christine, but they were parents themselves now, both absorbed in the wearying process of cramming into their lives as many washing machines, televisions and motor cars as their time would allow. Now and again there was a half-hearted suggestion, by post, that he should go and live with one or the other of them, but he knew his children well enough to know that these were no more than salves to conscience.

As it always did at this time of the day, down in the cutting a three-coach diesel train slipped into view round the curve of the up line and an expression of disgust clouded the old man's face as it sped by, emitting its metallic chatter as it passed over the rail joints. He started muttering to himself.

'Glorified buses! Glorified buses, that's all they are! If them things were meant to run on rails I was meant to walk on water!'

As quickly as it appeared, the diesel sped out of sight under the road bridge and the cutting became quiet again. The yellow distant signal, raised to the upper quadrant for the passage of the train, fell with a clatter and the silence returned to the cutting deeper than before.

Slowly, the old man's awareness of the familiar features of the railway cutting began to fade. As though hypnotised by the glint of the autumn sunlight reflecting from the steel tracks, his consciousness began to shimmer in an ocean of confused memories, probing with invisible antennae for a single experience to bring to the surface. The ocean was vast. It was all there in a lifetime on the Iron Road. Gradients – sweat coursing in rivulets down a fireman's face, dripping in trembling drops from his forehead. Lights, red, green and yellow, reflecting from the glass-like surface of wet rails in the night. Buildings, stations, houses, farmsteads. Children waving. Night, black night, the shadowy outline of rolling hills, jagged lightning tearing the sky through a mane of smoke.

Then, vaguely at first, a youth dwarfed by the giant wheels of a locomotive pulled himself up to the footplate. A youth, heart pounding, climbed through sixty years of memories and boarded an engine in the darkness as, from the depths of an old man's mind, a single experience surfaced through the thought-store of a lifetime to take possession of his senses again.

Amos no longer saw the cutting. He recalled the memory of his first trip on the main line so vividly that he felt again the heat from the firebox of the 'Dreadnought' and relived the terror he felt when, more than half a century before, he gazed with youthful eyes round the enormous cab of the locomotive with its mass of steampipes and valves illuminated by the light from its gaping firehole.

Everything had happened so quickly. One moment he was waiting for his driver to appear, when they would go to relieve the men on North End shunt, the next he was being bawled at by an excited foreman through the window of the signing-on hall. 'Hey, laddy – yes, you! Get to number three pit – the Mail. Come on, put a spurt in it! The fireman's not turned up!'

At seventeen years of age and with only three weeks' experience on the shovel to his credit, young Amos had fired on nothing larger than a saddle tank, seesawing up and down a local goods siding at a snail's pace listening to the stories of the Iron Road from a driver whose eyesight was failing. In his youthfulness, landing a shovelful of coal at the far end of the firebox of a saddle tank was still something of a miracle; the cavernous firebox of a 'Dreadnought' was three times the length. He started to protest.

'But I've only fired on shunting engines! I've never...'

The harassed foreman was in no mood to listen. Why couldn't the lad understand that if the Mail was late the Superintendent would be down on him like a ton of bricks? Couldn't he see that he was the only fireman available in his moment of need? He jumped on the youth again.

'Well now's the time to learn! Come on, get a move on! Get to number three pit before I put me foot behind you!'

As Amos ran to the waiting 'Dreadnought' he tried desperately to recall all he had been told about handling the shovel on a main-line express, and he arrived at the engine as confused as a cat with three mice to chase.

As he stepped on board the driver paid no attention to him. With his head and shoulders through the sliding window of the cab and his hand ready on the regulator, he stood in the shadows peering into the darkness of the shed yard. Then, just when Amos was about to confront him to confess his woeful inexperience, he withdrew his head from the window and barked, 'Handbrake!'

Like a timid bird Amos leapt to the large wheel fixed to the tender and started to turn it frantically anti-clockwise, and the moment the cast iron brake blocks eased their grip of the wheels, the driver slid the regulator through the guides and the 'Dreadnought' began to move out of the pale light of the shed roads to be swallowed by the night.

It was too late now for the lad to protest; five miles away, waiting for the engine to arrive in number three platform at Central station, the loading of the Mail train was nearing completion. In twenty minutes' time, when the engine coupled up to it and the last door was slammed, it would blast from the station on its non-stop journey of over a hundred miles.

Even as the engine left the shed, minds were getting anxious. The driver, needled by the late arrival of his fireman, palmed his watch from his pocket to count the minutes he had left to get to the station. Signalmen along the line watched warily the passing of slow-moving goods trains, urging them on to the next loop to clear the main line. An air of expectancy prevailed. The drivers of trains held back in the sidings along the line pulled out their pipes and relaxed in the darkness as they waited for the roar of the Mail to signal that they could get moving again. Coal, cotton, fish and fruit, machinery, molasses, livestock and jute – the sustenance of several counties was brought momentarily to a standstill as the passing of the Mail drew near. And this night its passing depended on the guts of a young lad whose heart pounded in his chest so hard that it felt as though it would burst at any second.

From the shed to the station the railway ran four-tracked downhill, curving and twisting through the tunnels under the slum-congested city. The engine ran tender-first so that, on coupling to the train, it would be the right way for the journey. With all the signals showing green, the driver made up for lost time and a violent lurch of the engine flung Amos across the cab. In the nick of time he grabbed hold of a steam valve and hung on with the tenacity of fear. Beneath the soles of his heavily studded boots the floorboards of the footplate jumped and jerked every time the engine crashed through a junction or hit a straight length of line after squealing round a curve. The 'Dreadnought' seemed to be boring its way to the centre of the earth as in a Jules Verne fantasy, and young Amos waited anxiously for the clamour to subside. He knew now that a locomotive at speed wasn't the smooth-functioning leviathan that it appeared at a distance, but a rolling, lurching, clamouring mass of steel that threatened to hurtle off the rails at any moment.

At last the engine started to slow down as the driver gently applied the brakes and, seizing his chance, Amos darted across the cab and stuck his head and shoulders through the cab window. There he found he could wedge himself in the steel frame and sway with the engine without being thrown off balance, and for the first time since climbing aboard, he could look along the line in the direction that they were travelling.

A quarter of a mile ahead, an island of light in a black desert, he saw the station. A mass of red, green and yellow signals winked as the smoke from many beetle-like engines drifted past them. As they got nearer, the island of light became brighter and the platforms began to materialise. Squealing like a pig in pain, the 'Dreadnought' threaded its way through a myriad points until, with a final check of the brakes, it clanked into number three platform and pinged against the buffers of the awaiting Mail train.

Completely oblivious to the scene around him, old Amos continued to daydream of his main-line baptism. He saw nothing of the town-tyke of a rabbit that poked its head from a clump of twitch grass on the far side of the cutting. Looking first one way then the other, like a child trained in kerb drill, it suddenly darted from cover and bounded from sleeper to sleeper along the down line. It arrived at the dilapidated signal box just as the signalman jerked open an ill-fitting window to empty the slops from his teapot, and, startled by the noise, it bolted from the track to disappear again in the tall grass of the embankment. A crazy furrow betrayed its evasive flight as it scampered unseen to safety, and, as the signalman slammed shut the window, the cutting became still again.

Old Amos heard nothing. Years back in thought, he was shovelling coal for all he was worth into the huge firebox of the 'Dreadnought'. The driver was on the platform exchanging a few last-minute words with the guard. Making the most of his absence, Amos swung the shovel as best he knew to land the coal at the far end of the firebox. Betraying his pitiful lack of experience with every swing, he could tell that it was falling short, but it wasn't the strength he lacked, it was the knack. With the blower fully open, air was rushing through the firebars, blasting the coal to a white heat. Beads of sweat formed on Amos's forehead, dropping like rain to the footplate, and he felt his vest sticking to his skin beneath his shirt. In his naivety he reasoned that coal equated steam, and in a blind desire to succeed he resolved to cram as much as he could into the firebox before the driver returned.

Pausing briefly in his labour, the desperate young fireman began to regret not having stood his ground with the foreman. Everything seemed too much for him. But it was too late now; he would just have to make the best of it. Wiping the sweat from his forehead with a grimy hand, he started to swing the shovel again with even more determination, but no matter how hard he tried, he still sensed that the coal wasn't reaching the far end of the firebox and, from the little he knew about the technique of stoking a locomotive, he was certain that this boded ill for running the train to time.

Urgent shouts began echoing along the platform punctuated by the slamming of van doors. It was almost time to go. Bustling through the handrails the driver strode briskly across the footplate to his own side of the cab just as the guard's whistle shrilled. As he thrust open the regulator a powerful gasp came from the engine, followed a split second later by a great tremor as the pistons took the strain. Then, with a thunderous noise, the mighty wheels slipped on the rails in a mad frenzy. Shutting the regulator to allow the engine to find her feet, the driver opened up again, and this time the wheels gripped the rails and with giant strides the Mail train left the station with young Amos rushing to his window to get wedged in the frame before they attained speed.

Clinging to the steel plates of the cab with his head through the window, the raw fireman swayed with the pounding 'Dreadnought' as she gathered speed. His throat was as dry as the dust of a tomb, and a blanket of tiredness began to weigh heavily on every muscle of his limbs. He wanted to shut his eyes as the swaying of the locomotive threatened to rock him to sleep. He tried shaking his head vigorously to dispel the feeling, but no sooner did his muscles respond than the tiredness returned heavier than before. Suddenly he sprang to life! His driver was bellowing at him above the tumult of the engine. 'Come on lad – get some rock on!'

Darting from his corner, Amos pounced on his shovel, opened the firehole door and swung his first shovelful. At the same moment the engine lurched, spilling the contents of the shovel all over the footplate. Thrusting the blade of the shovel again into the tender he tried once more. This time he lost his balance completely and had to release the shovel to save himself from falling to the footplate.

Suspicious now, the driver left the controls and crossed the footplate. Glancing at the steam gauge he saw the pointer showing fifty pounds below the red mark. Taking hold of the young fireman's shoulders he turned him round to get a better view of his face in the glare from the firebox. He wasn't pleased with what he saw. As they swayed together with the motion of the thundering 'Dreadnought', the young fireman stared guiltily through a film of sweat at the serious face of the driver and waited for the curses.

'How old are you, sonny?'

With the signals green all the way ahead and with no one at the controls, the 'Dreadnought' blasted up the twisting gradient piercing the black night with a shaft of incandescent light from the firebox. Swallowing hard, Amos confessed, 'Seventeen – the foreman wouldn't listen – I told 'im but he wouldn't listen!'

The driver remained remarkably calm, almost fatherly.

'Wouldn't listen, eh? Well you listen to me, young feller – you're gonna work harder tonight than you've ever worked in your life! We've got a hundred miles to go an' I'm gonna run to time if I break your back an' mine doin' it! D'yer understand?'

Amos nodded in mute compliance.

'Right. Now do as I tell yer an' we'll manage!'

Releasing the youth's shoulders, the driver grabbed hold of the shovel and, shading his eyes with one hand, he inserted the blade with the other and peered along it into the white heat of the furnace.

'I thought as much! You're fallin' short! There's a mountain of coal a yard from the far end of the box!'

So saying, he darted back to his own side of the cab and thrust his head through the window to glance at the signals. Satisfied that they were still coming green, he returned to join the helpless fireman.

'Look, sonny, you'll do no good until you shift that lot. Now listen – keep your eyes on me and when I shout "Right" I want you to climb on the tender and fetch down the dart! You'll have no time to dawdle – if you're not down with the dart before we reach the next bridge you'll be knocked to kingdom come! D'yer understand?'

Amos nodded again.

'Right then, come on, get ready to scramble up that bulkhead the moment I shout.'

Returning to his own side of the engine, he stuck his head outside the cab while Amos, choosing a moment when the engine ran smoothly, darted to the tender like a tightrope walker. With his eyes fixed on his mate, he gripped the top of the tender bulkhead waiting anxiously for the word to go.

The dart, a long fire-iron forged from inch-and-a-half steel, was part of every engine's equipment. As he waited for his driver to yell for him to go, Amos speculated how long it would have to be to reach the far end of the firebox of the 'Dreadnought'. Certainly he knew that it wouldn't be easy to free it from the coal and lower it down to the cab.

As the 'Dreadnought' blasted under a bridge, a cloud of swirling steam filled the cab, embracing Amos and his driver in a warm, clammy caress, and the moment they cleared the bridge the driver sent a high-pitched yell across the cab.

'Right – now!'

With a powerful surge of energy, his boots kicking frantically for toe-holds on the cleats and rivets of the steel plates of the tender, Amos scrambled up the bulkhead. Reaching the top, he balanced himself above the speeding train, took a deep breath and leapt through the night to the coal. His landing caused an avalanche. Before he could steady himself he was sliding down with the coal into the shovelling well. Wincing with pain as jagged edges of the coal tore into his knees, he reached out wildly to save himself. Panting and cursing like a veteran, he pulled himself to the top of the coal and reached out blindly for the handle of the dart. Already the driver was shouting anxiously from the footplate.

'Hurry up, for God's sake – we'll be at the next bridge in a minute!'

As he was about to scuttle back to the safety of the cab without the fire-iron, a signal box rushed by. In the fleeting light from its windows he saw the dart and made a grab for it. On his first pull it didn't budge, but trying again with all his strength he managed to free it from the coal, lifting it high above his head he hurled it like a huge spear through the space between the cab roof and the tender, then, gripped by the fear of being smashed to pulp by the rapidly approaching bridge, he vaulted the bulkhead and dropped to the footplate trembling in every limb, a second before the 'Dreadnought' blasted under it.

As the Mail roared up the gradient Amos watched as the driver plunged the dart into the firebox as easily as handling a domestic poker, driving it with powerful thrusts into the unburnt coal. Satisfied that the coal was spread evenly over the firebars, he withdrew the dart, the lower half of which was now white hot. Lifting it high, he swung it over the tender and rested it on top of the coal with the handle protruding in case they should need it again.

'Right, come on, laddy, have a look at this!'

Placing an arm round the youth's shoulders he hustled him to the cab window where, thrusting his head and shoulders through the opening, he pointed to the chimney-top.

'See that smoke?" As Amos looked towards the chimney he saw thick black smoke belching from it. 'That smoke tells you the coal's burning, but it also tells you we're wasting carbons.' Here the driver pulled his head inside the cab and half-opened the firehole door. He shouted to his fireman again. 'Now d'yer see?'

As Amos looked again at the chimney top he saw that the black smoke had almost disappeared, leaving just a trace in the exhaust. 'It's almost gone!'

The driver confronted him again. 'That's right! That's what you call perfect combustion. D'yer understand? There's no point shovelling carbons into the firebox if we're gonna blast 'em straight up the chimney before they're burnt! Now you keep your eyes on that chimney and shout me when what smoke there is disappears altogether! You understand?'

When Amos nodded, the driver darted back to his own side of the cab and thrust his head through the window. Watching the chimney-top himself, the driver waited until the smoke cleared then looked across at Amos. The moment he did so, Amos pulled his head inside and shouted, 'It's gone!'

The driver grinned. The lad was learning.

'Right, now shut the firehole door and look at the chimney-top again!'

Amos quickly did what he was told, and on thrusting his head through the window again, he shouted, 'She's showing a trace of smoke again!'

Through his perspiration the driver smiled broadly. 'That's fine – perfect combustion! Now shout to me again when it disappears.'

When Amos shouted to him again to inform him the smoke had disappeared, the driver left the controls, opened the firehole door and took hold of the shovel again.

'Right, come on, watch me put some on!'

Driving the blade of the shovel into the coal, he addressed the novice fireman again.

'Don't hold y'self stiff – keep y'self loose – like this!'

Swinging the shovel through the firehole with an easy movement of his shoulders, he turned round and repeated the task twice more. Then, offering the shovel to Amos, he said, 'Now you have a go!'

With renewed confidence the young fireman took hold of the shovel. His driver had made it look so easy. Holding himself as he had been shown, he swung the loaded shovel at the firehole and, as the blade kissed the lip at the end of his swing, the coal left the blade in a tight cluster. Feeling the perfection of his movements he knew at once that it would land at the far end of the firebox and, despite the sweat that began to rain from his forehead again, he smiled in triumph and swung the shovel again and again as though afraid that if he stopped the knack might desert him.

'Hey, hey, hold on a bit! Give it time to burn!'

As the driver restrained his enthusiasm he threw the shovel in the tender and, half closing the firebox door, rushed to the window again to see a faint trace of smoke in the exhaust from the chimney-top. The moment the smoke disappeared, he closed the door fully to see a fresh trace of it in the exhaust and, at that moment, the safety valve blasted off to release the excess steam that he had produced.

With a six-mile level stretch of line ahead of it as it mounted the crest of the gradient, the Mail train began to increase speed. Waiting until it accelerated to about seventy miles an hour, the driver opened the regulator fully and wound back the reversing gear to reduce the valve cut-off, and, with the four cylinders of the 'Dreadnought' exhausting at split-second intervals, the noise from the chimney-top began to sound more like that of an aeroplane than a steam locomotive.

Convinced that his fledgling fireman had now got the hang of things, the driver was able to concentrate on the signals while Amos, exhilarated by the speed at which they were travelling and bursting with pride at having mastered the technique of maintaining a full head of steam on a 'Flyer', dived for the shovel with supreme confidence the moment the smoke trace vanished from the exhaust.

As the old man leaned on the fence of the railway cutting dreaming away, the triumph of his youth showed clearly on his face. All his senses responded to that moment long ago when, for the first time, he experienced the joyous satisfaction in coaxing a machine to its highest level of efficiency. He heard again the pounding of the 'Dreadnought' and saw the pointer of the steam gauge quivering on the red mark; he felt the grain in the wood of the shovel handle as though he held it in his hands that very moment. The hot, oily atmosphere of the cab enveloped him again and he tasted the salt of his own sweat as it ran down his face.

Then, like all dreams, it ended as quickly as it had begun. Down in the cutting a freight train punched its way lazily through a cloud of swirling steam under the road bridge. One of the last few remaining steam engines on the system, it was streaked with rust and spurting steam from every joint. The old man stirred from his reverie as the clamour of the engine shattered the delicate veil that divides dream from reality and, in an instant, the memory of his youth plunged like a stone to the depths of his consciousness.

Recognising the lone spectator leaning on the fence, the driver of the engine waved to him. Waving back, the old man started to count the wagons, registering each one with a childlike nod of his head as it emerged from under the bridge. There were fewer than he had ever seen before and he recalled the time when the same train would have consisted of sixty.

As the freight train finally chuffed out of sight round the curve, he began to mutter to himself.

'God's truth – nine wagons! Huh, if this goes on there'll be no wagons at all soon. Sendin' it all by road, that's what they're doin' – chokin' the roads wi' freight and starvin' the railways. Oh, they'll rue the day, so help me! Aye, when they've choked the roads wi' freight from Land's End to John o' Groats they'll rue the day. Nine bloody wagons!'

Still muttering, the old man took his foot from the boulder and began to square himself up. Then, pulling the collar of his overcoat closer to his ears, he set off back along the path towards the main road. High in the sky the vapour trail of an invisible jet aeroplane traced its progress towards the horizon. Past the opening where the path joined the main road a gaggle of schoolchildren twisted and jerked to the music of a transistor radio. Without so much as a glance at these harbingers of a new age, old Amos thrust his hands deep into the pockets of his overcoat and made his way home.

The end came at last for the Age of Steam,
Dying gasps of Stephenson's dream.
But a second ago in history's time
It thundered and throbbed on a thousand lines.